INTRODUCING THE SOUTHERN CONTINENTS

DAVID CLEE
DAVID JONES

Holt, Rinehart and Winston of Canada, Limited
Toronto

Copyright © 1975
Holt, Rinehart and Winston of Canada, Limited
Toronto

ISBN 0-03-925408-9

The Metric Commission has granted use of the National Symbol for Metric Conversion.

Printed in Canada

4   5   79

TABLE OF CONTENTS

THE SOUTHERN CONTINENTS

1. INTRODUCTION

To study geography effectively, you have to be constantly asking questions. You should find out the causes and effects of certain situations; work out reasons for certain problems and try to find solutions; and relate one situation to another. You must establish similarities or differences between various parts of the world and try to discover reasons for these. You must also find out why people live in certain regions and avoid others, and how people adapt their ways of life to the area in which they live.

As a student of geography, you should constantly ask *why, where, when,* and *how.* The following rhyme by Kipling might sum up the approach you should take:

> "I kept six honest serving men.
> They taught me all I knew.
> Their names were What and Why
>   and When
> And How and Where and Who."

You should learn to use an atlas and resource books, and should also refer to magazine articles, study pictures and photographs, and look at appropriate films. Above all, keen observation is required, whether the location is the local shopping plaza, the neighbouring conservation area, or another area — at home or abroad.

During the study of the southern continents — the region consisting of Australasia, Antarctica, South America, and Africa — you should try to establish where they are located, what types of climate they experience, how these two factors affect the vegetation, and how, in turn, the plants and crops affect the animal life and eventually the lives of the people. You should try to work out comparisons and contrasts and how the various countries fit into the total world picture today. Most of these factors are related to location.

WHERE ARE THE SOUTHERN CONTINENTS?
Latitude and Longitude

To locate a place on the globe or on a map, a series of parallel lines called a grid is used. As the earth is a sphere and rotates on its axis, and as the ends of its axis are the Poles, these two extremities provide definite points from which to make measurements. Midway between the two Poles is a line on a globe or map called the equator which "equates" it into northern and southern halves or hemispheres. Other lines parallel to the equator and circling the globe indicate distances north or south of this midway line. These lines are called parallels or lines of latitude, and, because the earth is round in shape, these distances are measured in degrees. Hence the equator is Latitude 0° and the Poles are 90° North and South respectively.

Another set of lines, running at right angles to the parallels, are known as meridians or lines of longitude. All these lines of longitude extend from the North to the South Poles. Since there is no natural "midway" line like the equator from which to measure longitude, most countries have agreed to use the line that runs through Greenwich, near London, England, for this purpose. This line, Longitude 0°, is known as the *prime meridian.* Longitude is, therefore, defined as the distance in degrees east and west of the prime or central meridian, while latitude is defined as distance in degrees north and south of the equator.

Atlas Exercise

Using a globe or a map of the world answer the following:

1. Name the four continents which are located on or south of the equator. Which is the southernmost continent?
2. Name the important Tropic which crosses three of these continents. Which continent lies well south of this latitude?
3. The prime meridian crosses a part of two of the southern continents. Name these two landmasses.
4. Indicate three continents that are "within the Tropics".
5. Which continent is nearest Canada? Which one is farthest away?
6. Name the "Southern Oceans".
7. Name the respective lines of latitude and longitude which act as a framework for each of the four southern continents.
8. Find the location (latitude and longitude) of each of the following places: your nearest city, Buenos Aires, Cape Town, Sydney, and Auckland.

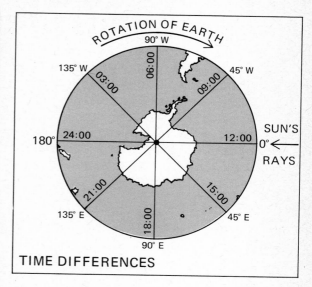

TIME DIFFERENCES

Figure 1.1 Diagram showing local times at certain meridians when it is 12:00 along the prime meridian (Longitude 0°) at Greenwich, near London, England. All meridians to the east of Longitude 0° have sunrise *before* that meridian, and therefore local times along these lines of longitude are *ahead* of Greenwich Time. To the west of the meridian, sunrise is later and therefore local times are *behind* Greenwich Time. Note Longitude 180°. What time is it along this meridian when it is 12:00 at Greenwich? Why is Longitude 180° called the International Date Line? What time changes are necessary when travellers "cross" this meridian?

Longitude and Time

Jet travellers are familiar with the fact that they have to put their watches "forward" or "back" before they land at the end of a long journey. In Canada we realize that a football or hockey match we are watching on television may be being played in some distant part of the country at a different hour from the one at which we are actually viewing it in our homes. For example, when an event is taking place in Vancouver at 15:00, it is 18:00 in Toronto. Furthermore, when it is 08:00 in Halifax, it is 04:00 in Vancouver. This time difference is because Canada stretches across approximately 90° of longitude of the earth's surface.

Time is based on the position of the sun in the sky and it is at its highest at 12:00. Since the sun appears to rise in the east and set in the west, it will reach its highest point in the sky later in places to the west of us and earlier to the east. For example, it will be 12:00 in Halifax before Winnipeg, and in Calgary before Vancouver. However, although the "east-west" places have different times, any place on the same line of longitude has the same time. Lines of longitude are called meridians because meridian means "midday" and all places on the same meridian record 12:00 at the same time.

Although each place has its own "sun time" it would be most confusing if each had its own "clock time". Therefore, in 1884 many countries agreed to establish standard *time zones* from east to west, each zone being approximately 15° of longitude, which is the distance the overhead sun appears to move in 1 h as the earth rotates. Thus large areas work on the same time and we adjust our clocks and watches as we journey through the various zones.

CLIMATE

As the southern continents are studied, a variety of climates will be observed. For example, in the Amazon Basin of South America and in the Congo region of Africa it is hot and wet, while in the continent of

Antarctica temperatures are generally well below -18°C and the precipitation, or the moisture that falls on the earth from the atmosphere, is in the form of snow. Three of the continents have hot deserts and regions with a climate similar to that of the Mediterranean lands or California. These regions will be dealt with later in this chapter. The questions at this point are: *What is climate?* and *Why are there different climates?*

What is Climate?

The planet Earth is surrounded by air, and some consider the land as being at the bottom of an "ocean of air". It is in the lower parts of the atmosphere that the weather originates — the weather that, in part, controls our life patterns. Weather varies from day to day and from place to place. In certain regions of Canada however, we can expect snow in winter and heat waves in summer. Such a variety is part of the climate, for climate is the total of the weather conditions over a long period of time, and changes little over the years. The three most important elements of weather are temperature, precipitation, and wind (strength and direction), because they have the greatest influence on the clothes we wear, the shelter we need, the methods of transportation we use, the crops we grow, and the food we eat.

Why are there Different Climates?

The reasons for the world's different climates are many and are generally due to a combination of factors, including: (a) latitude, (b) air masses, (c) large bodies of water, and (d) mountains.

The Influence of Latitude

Latitude is possibly the most important influence on climate. The nearer the equator, the more direct the sun's rays, and therefore the hotter the climate. Farther north or south, away from the equator, the sun's rays are more slanted and therefore cover a larger area of the earth's surface, resulting in the spreading out of the heat. The sun's direct rays occur only within the tropics, i.e. between 23½° North and 23½° South.

Compare these two pictures. Describe the climate of each area. How will climate influence man's clothing and housing? What are the effects of climate on the vegetation? Estimate the latitudes at which the two pictures were taken.

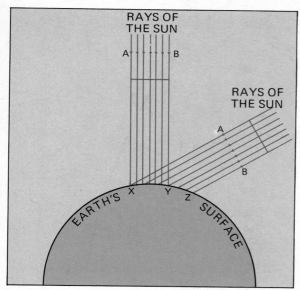

RAYS OF THE SUN

A B

RAYS OF THE SUN

A

B

EARTH'S X Y Z SURFACE

Figure 1.2 Diagram to show the influence of the sun's rays on the earth. When the sun's rays are directly overhead, as they are within the tropics, the heat is concentrated (see area XY). However, when the same rays are slanted towards the higher latitudes (i.e., latitudes away from the tropics and towards the poles), they cover more of the earth's surface area and the heat is less concentrated. (Compare the surface area XY with XZ.)

This is one of the reasons why it is always warm within the tropics and there are no cold winters. As you travel northwards and southwards, the climate is said to be cooler or more temperate and there is a distinct winter season, which increases in duration until you reach the cold polar regions.

Atlas Exercise

1. Which southern continents does the equator cross? Name the rivers in these two equatorial regions.
2. Name the three southern continents which lie partly within the tropics. Which continent is completely outside the tropics?
3. Which continent lies within Latitude 66½°S? What is the name given to this line of latitude?

The Influence of Air Masses

The atmosphere that surrounds the earth is composed of air masses. These cover vast areas of land and water, and may be warm or cold according to their position. An air mass, therefore, has the same conditions of temperature and humidity throughout. Air masses over the polar regions are cold and dry, while those over tropical seas are warm and moist. They reflect the conditions of the region over which they occur.

Air masses are composed of high and low pressure centres. For example, the areas around the equator are low pressure and are known as the Doldrums, while the polar regions are centres of high pressure. Winds blow out of high pressure cells and into centres of low pressure.

Winds are named according to the direction from which they blow, and a wind blowing over an area with more regularity than any other is known as a prevailing wind. The prevailing wind influences the climate of a region by bringing wet or dry conditions, for example, a wind blowing over a large body of water picks up moisture. If the water body is warm, the air temperature is increased and finally warms the land over which the wind blows. Similarly, moisture-laden winds bring rain to a region when they prevail at certain seasons.

Questions
Study the map on page 6 and answer the following:
1. Locate the shaded areas on your atlas map.
2. What have these regions in common regarding latitude, location in relation to landmasses, and prevailing winds?
3. From which direction do the winds blow? During what season of the year do they prevail?
4. Why would these winds bring rain? Give reasons.
5. Describe the winter climate.
6. What state in the United States, between these latitudes, also has this type of climate?
7. Describe the vegetation and crops in all these regions.

Because air masses move at certain seasons of the year and come in contact

Figure 1.3 Mediterranean regions of the world.

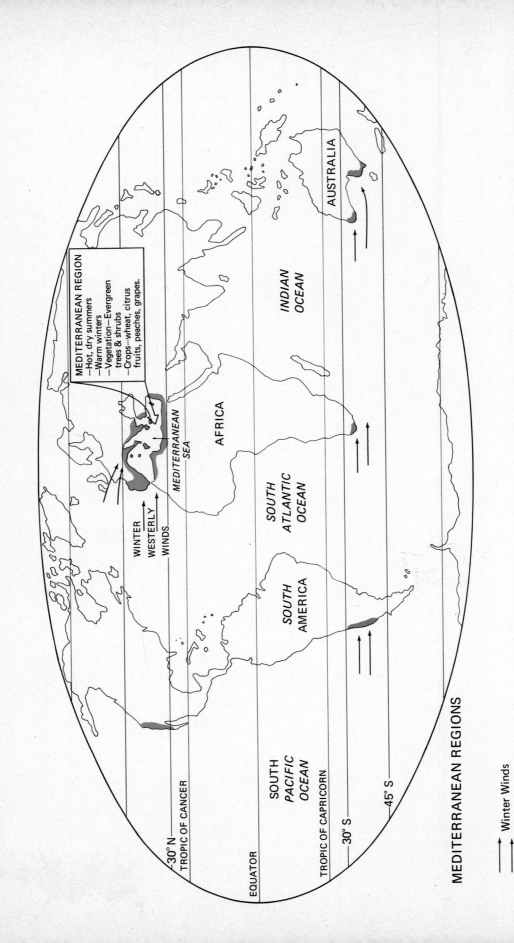

MEDITERRANEAN REGION
—Hot, dry summers
—Warm winters
—Vegetation—Evergreen
   trees & shrubs
—Crops—wheat, citrus
   fruits, peaches, grapes.

30° N
TROPIC OF CANCER

WINTER
WESTERLY
WINDS

MEDITERRANEAN
SEA

AFRICA

INDIAN
OCEAN

AUSTRALIA

EQUATOR

SOUTH
PACIFIC
OCEAN

SOUTH
AMERICA

SOUTH
ATLANTIC
OCEAN

TROPIC OF CAPRICORN

30° S

45° S

MEDITERRANEAN REGIONS

Winter Winds

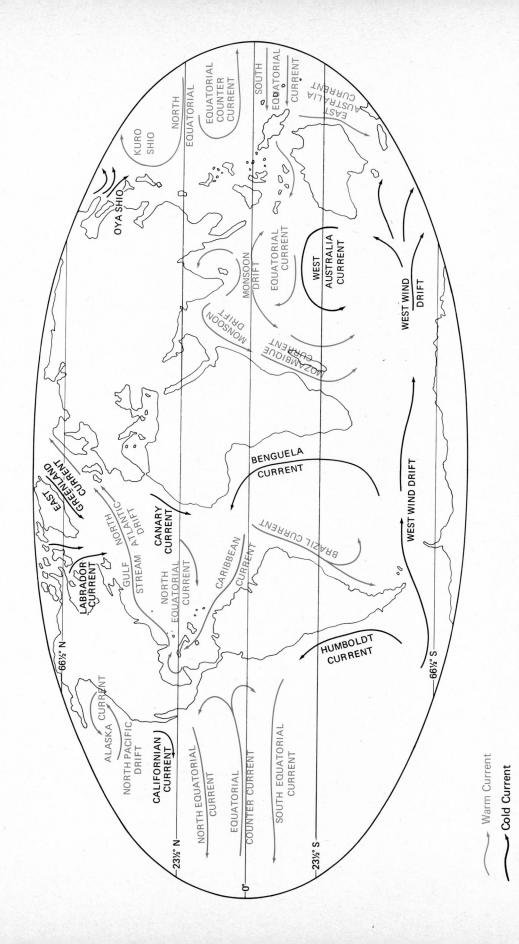

Figure 1.4 Main ocean currents of the world.

— Warm Current
— **Cold Current**

7

with one another, regional storms or winds occur. For example, in North America we experience hurricanes in the fall, and in the China Seas typhoons are a menace in the late summer and early fall. Two interesting conditions in the southern continents are the *willy-willy* of Australia and the *harmattan* of the west African coast. These have been selected because of the harmful and beneficial effects they have on their respective regions.

The willy-willy is a tropical storm which occurs in the Timor Sea in late summer. Its high winds and heavy rains often cause severe damage along the coast. However, having lost much of its force, as it later moves into the interior of the continent it brings welcome rain. The harmattan, on the other hand, is a dry, dusty wind which blows from the hot Sahara Desert towards West Africa. It is so hot and dry that it sometimes splits tree trunks, and is so dusty as to cause thick hazes. However, the wind has the effect of temporarily drying the humid air of the coastal region, thus providing some relief and cooling. In this region it is often known as the "Doctor" wind.

The Influence of Large Bodies of Water

During a hot summer, bathers often have to walk across an unbearably hot stretch of beach to get to the cooling waters of the ocean. During the winter, when the land is snow-covered and icebound, the waters just off the coast are relatively warmer and have wave action. Large bodies of water, such as oceans, seas, and lakes, do not warm up or cool down as quickly as do landmasses. Such bodies of water are generally warmer in winter and cooler in the summer than the land in the same latitude. For this reason, the climate of coastal areas may be modified by the adjoining water. However, for such moderation to occur, the air over the ocean must be blown across the land by winds. Examples are seen in southeast Africa, Australia, and South America.

The influence of oceans on land climate may be complicated by warm and cold ocean currents. Winds blowing over cold currents are generally cooled down and thus do not carry as much moisture. A study of the map on page 7 will establish some of the major ocean currents of the world.

Questions
1. How are the currents similar along the east and west coasts of South America and Africa?
2. Generally, where do warm ocean currents originate, and from what waters do cold currents flow?
3. Note the two currents off the east and west coasts of Australia. Name them and state which would be the warmer. Give reasons.

The Influence of Mountains

Mountains influence climate in two major ways: (a) by altitude and (b) by acting as "rain barriers" to prevailing rain-bearing winds.

Temperatures are cooler on higher land — the higher one ascends the colder it becomes. As a general rule, temperatures drop about 1.7°C for every 300 m increase in altitude. Mountainous regions, even in the tropics, have cooler temperatures than areas at sea level. For example, Quito in South America, situated almost on the equator but high in the Andes, has an average annual temperature of 13°C while Manaus, located just south of the equator in the Amazon lowlands, has an average annual temperature of 27°C. Similarly, temperatures in the highlands of Kenya, Africa, are lower than those in the coastal regions. The highest mountains, even in the lower latitudes (nearer the equator), are snow-covered all year.

The diagram explains how mountains act as rain barriers. Mountains help to create some of the driest and wettest regions in the world.

(Top) Snow-capped Mount Kilimanjaro in Tanzania, latitude approximately three degrees south of the equator.

(Bottom) Figure 1.5 The rain barrier effect of mountains.

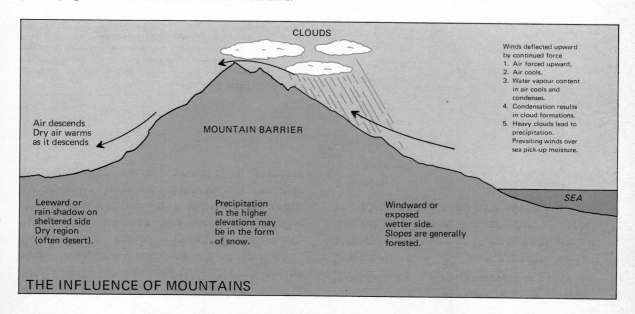

CLOUDS

Winds deflected upward
by continued force
1. Air forced upward,
2. Air cools.
3. Water vapour content
   in air cools and
   condenses.
4. Condensation results
   in cloud formations.
5. Heavy clouds lead to
   precipitation.
   Prevailing winds over
   sea pick-up moisture.

Air descends
Dry air warms
as it descends

MOUNTAIN BARRIER

SEA

Leeward or
rain-shadow on
sheltered side
Dry region
(often desert).

Precipitation
in the higher
elevations may
be in the form
of snow.

Windward or
exposed
wetter side.
Slopes are generally
forested.

THE INFLUENCE OF MOUNTAINS

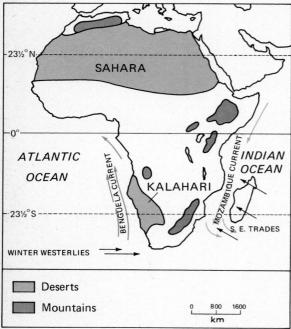

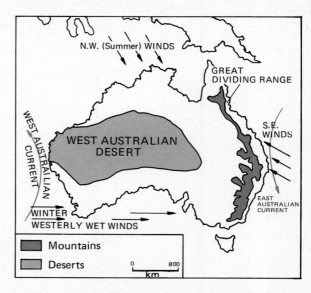

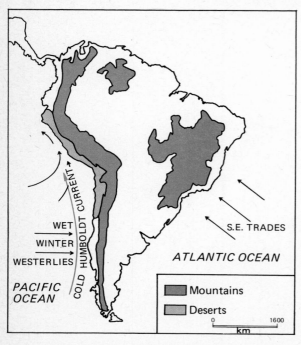

(Top left) Figure 1.6   The Atacama Desert of South America. Situated in Northern Chile, this almost rainless desert extends for some 960 km along the Pacific Coast. What mountains act as a rain barrier to any rain-bearing winds from the east? What type of current is the Humboldt? Why would the winds pick up little moisture? Why would the winds have little or no effect on this region? One centre in the Atacama has not recorded any rainfall in nineteen years!

(Bottom left) Figure 1.7   The two large deserts of Africa — the Sahara and the Kalahari. The Sahara is the largest hot desert in the world. It stretches some 5600 km from east to west and approximately 1600 km from north to south. Like all hot deserts of the world, it supports a minimum of vegetation and, therefore, little animal life. The prevailing winds are mainly from the northeast and, blowing over land, they are dry. As they are also warm winds, they retain the little moisture they carry. The Kalahari Desert is within the rain shadow area of the Drakensberg Range. Compare the winds and ocean current on the west coast with those on the west coast of South America.

(Top right) Figure 1.8   The Great Desert of Australia is sometimes known as the "Desert Heart" of the continent. Name the prevailing winds. What mountain range acts as a rain barrier? Where would the wettest regions be located? Why would the southeast winds pick up a great deal of moisture? This great desert covers about half the area of Australia. It supports very few people.

VEGETATION

Natural vegetation varies according to rainfall, temperature, and soils. Thus, as we move away from a desert towards a wet region, the grass will become longer and trees will gradually appear. Geographers have tried to divide natural vegetation into *zones*, but this is not very meaningful on the ground because one kind of vegetation

Study the maps and note the locations of the hot deserts in the three continents. Relate the locations of the deserts to (a) the mountain barriers and (b) the prevailing winds. Note the locations of the deserts on the western side of each continent.

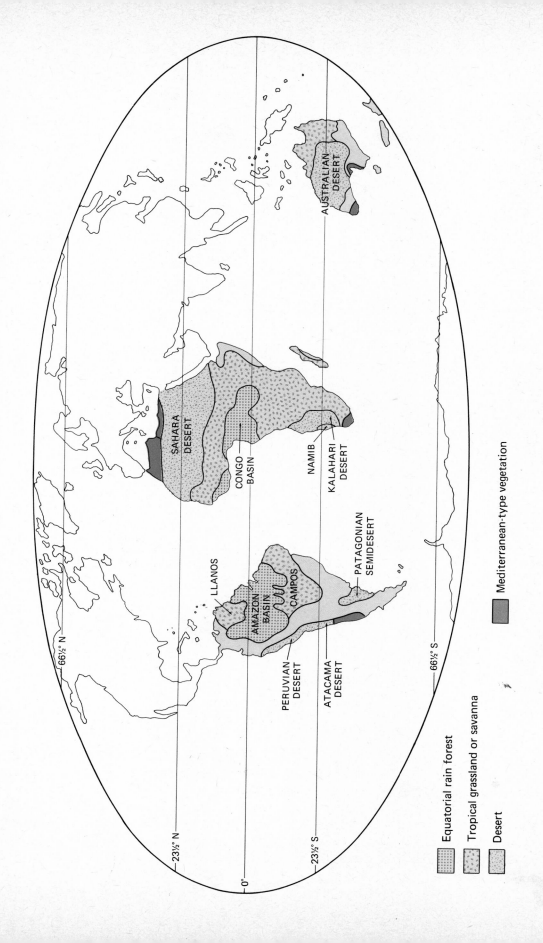

Figure 1.9 A simplified map showing some of the major vegetation regions the southern continents have in common.

Equatorial rain forest

Tropical grassland or savanna

Desert

Mediterranean-type vegetation

AUSTRALIAN DESERT

SAHARA DESERT

CONGO BASIN

NAMIB

KALAHARI DESERT

LLANOS

AMAZON BASIN

CAMPOS

PATAGONIAN SEMIDESERT

PERUVIAN DESERT

ATACAMA DESERT

66½° N

23½° N

0°

23½° S

66½° S

11

pattern grades gently into the next. As with so many natural phenomena, there are no clear dividing lines. However, the idea of zones is useful in that it tells us roughly what kind of vegetation to expect at a given spot, although soil or drainage differences cause wide variations within each zone.

Certain vegetational regions are common to the southern continents. For example, South America, Africa, and Australia have hot, arid deserts, grasslands, and so-called "Mediterranean-type" regions. Africa and South America have vast lowlands of equatorial rain forests. Antarctica is also a desert — a cold, ice desert.

The map on page 11 shows the distribution of some of the major vegetation areas of three of the southern continents.

Questions
1. Locate the equatorial rain forest regions.
2. List the desert areas of the three continents.
3. Locate the Namib Desert — the so-called "waterless desert" of Africa.
4. Which is the largest hot desert in the world?
5. What are the names given to the tropical grasslands or savanna regions of South America?

---

6. The savannas of Africa are also known as Parklands or Big Game Lands. What native animals are found in these African savannas?
7. The Mediterranean-type regions are located in each of the three continents. Why are they so called?

Equatorial Rain Forests

Located some five to ten degrees north and south of the equator in the Amazon and Congo basins and along the west coast of Africa, the equatorial rain forests are regions of great heat and humidity. The forests are thick and gloomy, and viewed from an airplane look like a green carpet. Trees grow to great heights as they struggle for the sunlight. The dense undergrowth of ferns and bushes adds to the profusion of foliage. Vines and creepers (lianas) drape from the overhanging branches and entwine themselves around the tree trunks. The equatorial rain forest has been described as "green monotony". There is no definite period of leaf fall; each species fulfils its own annual cycle.

Valuable hardwood and rubber trees grow in these hot, wet forest regions. There are few large animals, but birds, monkeys, and snakes are common. The forests are thickest

(Left) Eerie mists, mosses, and rare flowers make the high rain forests an unusual, dream-like environment.

(Right) These African grasslands once abounded with wildlife, but today, as in many other countries, man's greed and irresponsible hunting have sadly depleted their numbers. To preserve the native wildlife, vast natural parks have been established.

near the rivers. These forests are the homes of nomadic tribes such as the Pygmies of the Congo Basin and the Boro of Amazonia.

Hot Deserts

The deserts of the world are regions where the rainfall is so scanty or so spasmodic that it will not adequately support vegetation. A desert in which absolutely nothing grows, however, is uncommon; there may be either extremely poor grassland or scanty, stunted vegetation. Deserts may be mainly sand, rock, or stone. The Sahara, for example, has vast areas of sand dunes, but has also equal regions of rocky outcrops. The "gibber" or pebble desert areas of Australia are examples of the stoney desert.

Savannas

The savanna is a region of coarse grassland dotted with clumps of trees. The grasses grow several feet tall and during the dry season they become parched and brown. In Africa these tropical grasslands are known as the Big Game Lands. There is found the home of the impala, the elephant, the lion, the rhinoceros, the hyena, the zebra, and the giraffe.

These grasslands once abounded with wild life, but today, as in many other countries, man's greed and irresponsible hunting have sadly depleted their numbers. To preserve the native wildlife, vast national parks have been established.

Mediterranean-type Vegetation

The natural vegetation of these regions of hot, dry summers and warm, wet winters may be described as "evergreen trees and shrubs". The trees vary from conifers and laurels, to cork oaks and olive trees. The plants have to survive through long, hot, summer periods of drought and so they, like the desert flora, have adapted to their arid environment. Mediterranean plants generally have tough, leathery, waxy leaves to cut

down water loss through transpiration. They also have deep-reaching roots to search for moisture, and thick bark to protect the trunk from the sun's hot rays. The fruits of these regions, such as oranges and lemons, are juicy, providing necessary moisture for the seeds.

SIZE AND POPULATION

Before beginning a more detailed study of each of the four southern continents, you should compare the size and population of each.

(Top) Figure 1.10 A comparison of the area of the continents. Which of the four southern continents is the largest? How does Antarctica compare in size with Africa? Compare this graph with a map of the world.

(Bottom) Figure 1.11 A comparison of the population of the continents. Which of the four southern continents has the largest population? Which the smallest? Account for the almost nil population of Antarctica. Give some possible reasons why Australia's population is comparatively low for her land area.

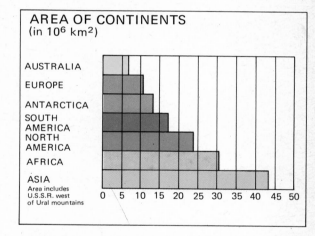

AREA OF CONTINENTS
(in 10^6 km^2)

AUSTRALIA
EUROPE
ANTARCTICA
SOUTH AMERICA
NORTH AMERICA
AFRICA
ASIA
Area includes U.S.S.R. west of Ural mountains

0 5 10 15 20 25 30 35 40 45 50

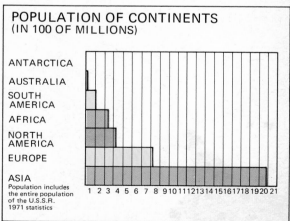

POPULATION OF CONTINENTS
(IN 100 OF MILLIONS)

ANTARCTICA
AUSTRALIA
SOUTH AMERICA
AFRICA
NORTH AMERICA
EUROPE
ASIA
Population includes the entire population of the U.S.S.R. 1971 statistics

1 2 3 4 5 6 7 8 9 10 11 12 13 14 15 16 17 18 19 20 21

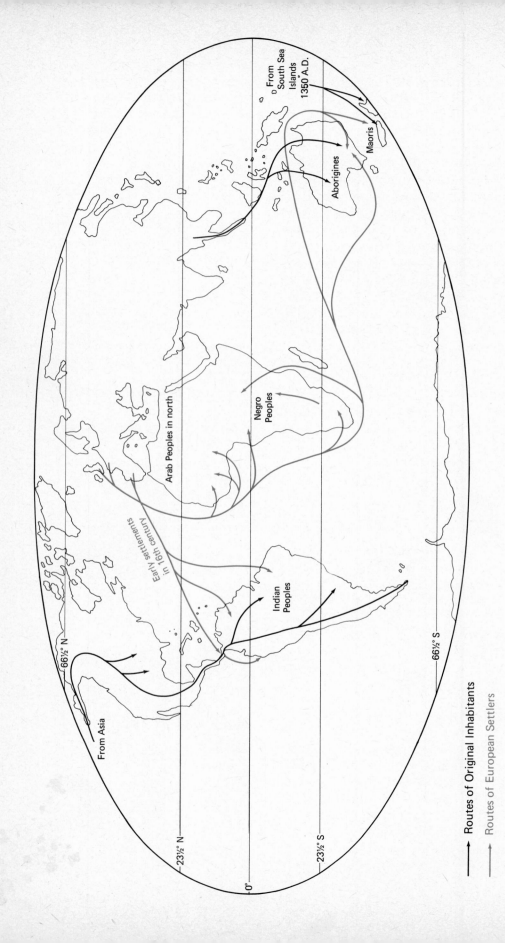

Figure 1.12 A simplified map showing routes of original peoples, and those of the European settlers who arrived in later years.

From South Sea Islands 1350 A.D.

Maoris

Aborigines

Arab Peoples in north

Negro Peoples

Early settlements in 16th century

Indian Peoples

From Asia

66½° N

23½° N

0°

23½° S

66½° S

Routes of Original Inhabitants

Routes of European Settlers

An interesting feature about three of these continents is that they were each settled by Europeans. The map helps to reveal the story of settlement.

Questions

1. From where did the Indians of South America originally come?
2. Where did the Aborigines of Australia originate?
3. Find the original home of the Maoris of New Zealand. How would they have travelled to New Zealand to establish a new homeland?
4. Which two European nations sent explorers to South America and colonized the continent?
5. What two major peoples originally occupied Africa?

SUMMARY

In this introductory chapter, some basic ideas have been presented to help in understanding the geography of the southern continents. Some broad patterns have been established as to location, climate, and settlement. Each of the four continents, however, is unique in its shape, distribution of climatic regions, vegetation, and peoples. Each of these aspects requires individual study.

As a continent, Australia has a simple physical structure and is less complex to study than Africa or South America. Thus we shall start with the study of Australia and its neighbour, New Zealand.

2. AUSTRALIA

INTRODUCTION

Position

Australia, because of its position so far south of the equator, is sometimes known as the "Land Down Under". A glance at a globe bears out this descriptive title.

The continent is almost bisected by the Tropic of Capricorn. Nearly forty percent of the area lies within the tropics; the remainder lies within the temperate zone.

Australia is the driest, least mountainous continent, and it is one of the oldest landmasses in the world.

Although it is the only continent occupied by a single nation, Australia is divided into six federated states and two federal territories. The two territories, administered by the federal government, include the vast North Territory and the small Australian Capital Territory in which Canberra, the seat of government, is located. Australia is responsible for the administration of eight external territories in the Pacific, in the Indian Ocean, and in Antarctica.

Atlas Exercise
1. Locate Australia on a world map.
2. Within which lines of latitude and longitude is the "island-continent" located?
3. Name the surrounding oceans and areas.
4. With the aid of the scale on the map, estimate the breadth of the continent from east to west near the Tropic of Capricorn.
5. List the six states and their capital cities.
6. Which is (a) the largest state, and (b) the smallest?
7. Name the strait that separates the island state from the mainland states.
8. Locate the Barrier Reef and estimate its length.

Australia was the last continent to be developed by Europeans. Even its original inhabitants, the Aborigines, are comparative newcomers.

Discovery, Exploration, and History

During the second century A.D., Ptolemy, the Greek mathematician, geographer, and astronomer, drew a map of the known world of his time. Beyond the coast of Asia he indicated the existence of a vast lake, which we now know as the Pacific Ocean. To the south of this lake he outlined a vast landmass which he labelled *"Terra Incognita"* — the Unknown Land.

Two contrasting scenes. *(Left)* Rainforest in Tasmania and *(Right)* a desert scene in central Australia.

It is known that the early Portuguese and Spanish merchant ships sailed along the coasts of the continent, but made no landings. For example, in 1606, the explorer Torres sailed through the strait which separates Australia from Papua, New Guinea.

The Dutch sailed along and landed on the northern and western coasts, but their reports were so discouraging that little further interest was shown. Some Dutch ships did, however, explore the area, and the continent was once known as New Holland.

The first Englishman to visit the continent was the buccaneer William Dampier, in 1688. After many adventures in the Caribbean and along the South American coast, he landed on a group of islands off the northwest coast of New Holland, which were christened Buccaneer Archipelago. In 1699, he returned in command of a Royal Navy ship, the *Roebuck*, to explore the surrounding coastlands. However, his reports of the barren and inhospitable nature of the land were as discouraging as those written by the Dutch many years earlier, and his discoveries did little to awaken England's interest in this distant land. Had these early explorers discovered the more fertile and attractive east coast, Australia's history as a European-occupied country would have started earlier. Instead, it was not until 1770, more than seventy years after the earlier explorers had visited Australia, that Captain James Cook of the Royal Navy first sighted the east coast of the continent.

Cook had been sent to Tahiti to make certain astronomical observations, but after his mission was completed he sailed south in his ship, the *Endeavour*, and circumnavigated New Zealand. He sailed westward and, after charting much of the eastern coastline of Australia, he landed on April 29, 1770, at Botany Bay (the site of present-day Sydney), which he so named because of the profusion of plant life to be found there. From Botany Bay he sailed northwards along the coast for approximately 2100 km until his ship was severely damaged on a coral reef and he spent two months on repairs before sailing north again. On an island, which he christened Possession Island, some 3 km off Cape York, Cook hoisted the British flag and formally took possession of the eastern parts of the continent.

The first settlers arrived in Botany Bay eighteen years later, in January, 1788. Under the command of a Captain Phillip, eleven ships carrying 1500 people entered Sydney Cove. Of the 1500 passengers, 800 were lawbreakers — men and women who had, for some reason or another, been judged and convicted under the harsh British laws of the time. The flag was raised and the new colony of New South Wales was established. This was the beginning of Australia and this is the occasion which Australians celebrate as Australia Day on January 26 each year.

"The early colonists faced great difficulties. There were few farmers or skilled workers among them and the young settlement was hemmed in on a strip of land between the ocean and the great wall of the Blue Mountains. Sometimes it was months between rains, the soft English wheat died, cattle sickened or escaped into the bush, supply ships were lost or damaged, and the infant colony was on starvation rations before the initial problems were overcome."

From: *A Look at Australia*, Australian News and Information Bureau (20th Edition)

Such were the problems of the early pioneers. However, during the following years settler-explorers crossed the mountains and found great, fertile plains that stretched away to the west. Their reports inspired others, and in their tracks came the cattlemen, sheepmen, and farmers. The introduction of Merino sheep and the experiments with crossbreeds to obtain types suitable to the Australian countryside encouraged further settlement. Settlers with their sheep and cattle took possession of vast tracks of land and established ownership by just occupying the area. They became known as "squatters" and the term, meaning a pastoralist, is still used in Australia today.

In 1851, gold was discovered by a prospector, Edward Hargreaves, at Bathurst, on the western plains of New South Wales. This was followed by incredibly rich finds at Ballarat and Bendigo in Victoria. The news spread around the world and thousands of prospectors hurried to Australia in the hope of "striking it rich". In a ten-year period, Australia's population increased by 700 000.

Year	Population
1788	1 500
1820	3 400
1850	405 000
1860	1 146 000
1870	1 650 000
1920	5 000 000
1945	7 000 000
1963	11 000 000
1968	12 000 000
1973	12 800 000

Figure 2.1 Chart showing the growth of Australia's population from the year of settlement.

Questions

1. Where did the first settlers land in Australia?
2. Describe the composition of the first group of settlers.
3. Account for the slow growth of population during the first seventy years.
4. Account for the rapid increase in population during 1850-60.
5. Australia's population increased rapidly after 1945. What great world event came to an end in 1945? How would this affect population growth?

Another outbreak of gold fever occurred in 1892, when new fields were discovered in Coolgardie in Western Australia, and again in the following year even richer deposits were discovered at Kalgoorlie. So rich were the deposits in Kalgoorlie that the gold was said to be there for the taking because it could be literally broken off the outcropping reefs in lumps. The Kalgoorlie fields today are still the country's greatest producers of gold. Gold really brought the people to Australia and helped to establish the country.

With increasing settlement, agriculture continued to develop, and with development came responsible government. In 1855, the colony of New South Wales gained responsible self-government. Self-government soon spread throughout Australia and eventually each of the six colonies acquired its own parliament. On January 1, 1901, the six self-governing colonies joined together as a federation of states in a single Commonwealth. After the six states had confederated, a special area was set aside for a national capital, called the Australian Capital Territory (A.C.T.).

Australia Today

Australia's present population is approximately 12 800 000. For a country of nearly 7.75×10^6 km², the number is very low. Density of population over the entire continent is approximately 1.7 people per square

The Federal Parliament House in the capital city, Canberra. Located in the Australian Capital Territory (2433 km²), the federal capital boasts of modern buildings and fine parks.

kilometre. This low figure is due to the fact that a third of the country is at present uninhabitable because of hot, desert conditions. This vast, barren desert in the western part of the continent is sometimes known as the "Dead Heart" of Australia. Another third of the continent does not support a large population because of the low rainfall, which is under 250 to 375 mm per year. Hence most Australians live in the more temperate regions of the southwest and southeast where there is adequate rainfall.

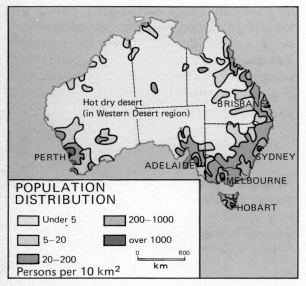

POPULATION DISTRIBUTION

	Under 5		200–1000
	5–20		over 1000
	20–200		

Persons per 10 km²

0   800
km

Continent or Country	Population per km²*
Netherlands	379
Belgium	315
Britain	227
West Germany	234
Europe (excluding U.S.S.R.)	92
Asia (excluding U.S.S.R.)	71
United States	21
U.S.S.R.	11
Canada	2

*Figures for June 30, 1968.

(Top) Figure 2.2   Population distribution map of Australia. Note the large "empty" areas and the regions of population concentration. Why do most of the people live in the south, east and southeastern areas? Compare this map with the map showing the rainfall distribution (page 28).

(Bottom) Figure 2.3   Chart showing the density of population for certain countries. How does Australia compare with these? Which country is very close to Australia? Give reasons why this country also has a low population density.

Australians are the most "citified" people in the world. Approximately fifty-eight percent of the people live in the large cities such as Sydney, Melbourne, Adelaide, Brisbane, Hobart, and Perth; twenty-five percent live in the smaller urban centres; while only seventeen percent inhabit the scattered rural areas. Actually over three-quarters of the population live southeast of a line drawn from Adelaide to Brisbane; the two largest cities, Sydney and Melbourne, between them support a population of over 5 000 000.

There is apparently room in Australia for about three times the present population. Australia's immigration policy is based on national needs, the availability of suitable settlers, and "the country's capacity to harmoniously integrate new arrivals". Australia, like all countries, needs immigrants who are qualified or skilled. The Australian government offers financial help to accepted immigrants. For example, in 1970-71, Australia admitted 180 000

Page 21

(Top)   Sydney (population 2 712 600), with its rich historical background, is the largest and the most famous city in Australia. Over half of the people of New South Wales live in Port Jackson. The city has 257 km of beautiful coast with fine beaches. The harbour is spanned by Sydney Harbour Bridge, over which the city's workers pour from the dormitory suburbs each morning.

(Centre left)   Melbourne (population 2 372 700), capital of Victoria, lies at the head of Port Phillip Bay. It has a fine sheltered harbour. Before the parliament moved to Canberra, this city was the seat of government.

(Top centre right)   Alice Springs, or Alice as the Australians affectionately like to call this town, is located in the desert where rainfall is 250 mm or less per year. Alice, which is a cattle marketing centre, is a modern town and a fine example of how man, by the careful planning of water resources, is learning to live in the dry, inhospitable regions of the world. Before the Second World War, Alice Springs was a small settlement with one general store.

(Bottom centre right)   The warm sunny climate, extensive sandy beaches, and beautiful scenery in vast stretches of open country encourage outdoor activities. Sports include swimming, surfing, cricket, tennis, golf, football, and skiing.

(Bottom left)   Perth (population 752 800), capital of Western Australia, is built on the banks of the Swan River.

(Bottom right)   The Aborigines, the original people of Australia. Once nomadic, they now live in reservations, mission stations, farms, and on city outskirts. Only a few now lead the traditional nomadic way of life.

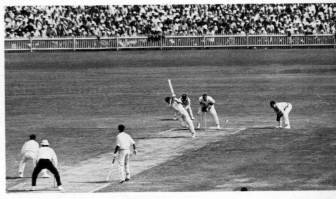

immigrants. Of these, 123 500 were helped financially with their travelling expenses. Migrants were admitted from some sixty countries with Britain heading the list.

Most Australians can trace their ancestry back to the British Isles. However, since World War II many immigrants from European countries have made Australia their home. English is the spoken language.

THE PHYSICAL ENVIRONMENT

Landforms

Australia is the world's smallest and flattest continent. It is often referred to as an "island-continent" because it is very large for an island and rather small for a continent. Australia has an area of approximately 7.75×10^6 km² — about the size of the United States of America excluding Alaska and Hawaii, and a little less than Canada's 9 978 780 km². It is a continent of very old rocks, rising to an average height of only about 305 m above sea level. Even the highest mountain ranges average only 915 m above sea level.

The structure of Australia is very simple. It has three main regions.

Questions
Study the map and answer the following:
1. Name the oceans to the east and west of the continent.
2. Name the large island to the south of the continent. Bass Strait is only 60 m deep. If the sea level fell by this amount, what would happen to the island?
3. Name the three major regions which form the structure of Australia.
4. Locate the major ranges of the Western Plain.

Figure 2.4 The structure of Australia.

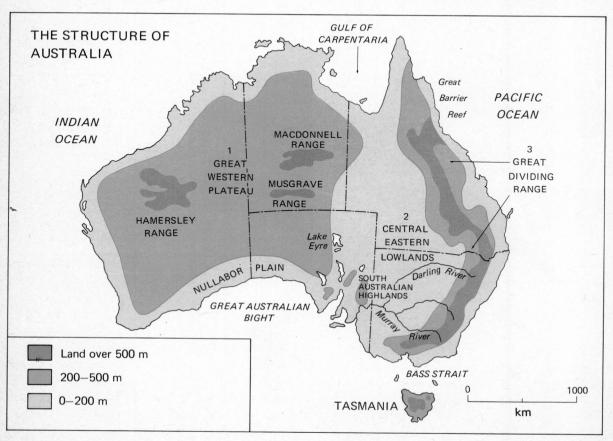

22

All the ranges of the Great Western Desert are composed of lava rocks which have, to some degree, withstood erosion. The most famous is Ayer's Rock. Composed of red sandstone, it stands 335 m above the sandy plain. It is a single rock, some 10 km in circumference, and is sometimes referred to as "the largest pebble in the world". The native peoples of Australia, the Aborigines, once believed that their ancestors rested in this rock. Ayer's Rock is a great tourist attraction and is one of the most photographed places in Australia. The rock, apparently, changes colour with the daily movement of the sun.

The Great Western Plateau

Nearly three-quarters of the landmass is a vast, ancient plateau, its altitude averaging about 305 m above sea level. Formed mostly of very old, hard rocks, the region has been worn down over millions of years to a flat, desert-like plateau with a few mountain ranges breaking the monotony. A great part of this Great Western Plateau is desert — sand ridges, *gibber* plains of pebbles, ("gibber" comes from the Aborigine word meaning "rock"), or barren land with tough, drought-resistant grasses and small, spiky bushes. This region is aptly called the Dead Heart of the continent.

The Central Eastern Lowlands

These lowlands, which cover about one-fifth of the continent and extend from the Gulf of Carpentaria to the southern shores, are the remains of an ancient seabed that once occupied the region. The average elevation of the Central Eastern Lowlands is less than 152 m above sea level, and Lake Eyre is 12 m below sea level.

Many of the rivers of the lowlands drain into Lake Eyre, which, because of the high rate of evaporation, is saline. In very wet periods, Lake Eyre covers a vast area, while during a long season of drought, it dries up to a series of salt marshes and salt sheets. The rivers, too, become a series of shallow water holes. More will be said in a later chapter about these rivers and the Great Artesian Basin, with its underground water reserves, that occupy this lowland area. To the south of the Central Lowlands run Australia's great rivers, the Murray and the Darling and their tributaries, the Murrumbidgee and the Lachlan.

The Eastern Highlands or The Great Dividing Range

This eastern highland rim of the continent extends from Cape York in Queensland to southern Tasmania. Despite their name, the mountains of the Great Divide are relatively low. They rarely exceed 1525 m above sea level in the northern and central regions, although in the rugged southern area, known as the Australian Alps, many peaks exceed 1830 m. This area contains Australia's highest land, including its highest peak, Mount Kosciusko (2229m).

The Coastal Plain

Surrounding the continent is a narrow coastal plain, which varies in width from less than 33 km to approximately 167 km.

The Great Barrier Reef

Of great interest for its structure, scenery, tourist attractions, and present problems, is the Great Barrier Reef of Australia. The Great Barrier Reef is a collection of coral reefs and coral islands which extends down the east coast of the continent for 2083 km, from just north of Brisbane to the island of New Guinea. The inner edge of the reef is 17 km from the coast at its nearest point, and 250 km at its farthest. The reef encloses an island-studded area of about 207 254 km².

How were these coral reefs and islands formed? Each, in fact, is the architecture of millions of minute coral polyps. Coral polyps are minute, primitive animals with tubelike bodies, and mouths surrounded by tentacles which wave back and forth, catching tiny organisms for food. Individual polyps vary in size — from that of a pinhead to that of a pencil eraser — but, living in their millions in closely-knit colonies, they are capable of forming the foundations of large islands. Polyps are soft-bodied animals, and so for support they secrete a substance which, in contact with seawater, forms calcium carbonate. This encases the polyp in a tubular, chalky type of exoskeleton. Polyps multiply by a simple budding process and as each matures it also multiplies. Each polyp develops its own skeleton. Thus one creature, over a period of time, multiplies into thousands of polyps. As the younger corals grow upwards and outwards, only the outside of the colony is alive. The central mass is composed of the dead skeletons of earlier generations.

Reef building corals are very sensitive. They grow only:
(a) in warm tropical or subtropical areas, with a minimum sea temperature of 20°C,
(b) near the water surface where there is light,
(c) where the depth of water is not greater than 46 m,
(d) in clean seawater — fresh or muddy water kills them.

A coral reef growing near a coastline usually has gaps in it which correspond to the river mouths in the neighbouring coastline.

One theory suggests that coral reefs and islands are formed in the following manner:
(a) Because coral polyps cannot live in deep water and yet their calcium skeletons are

Heron Island, the most southerly of the Great Barrier Reef tourist resort islands. A channel has been cut through the reef to allow tourists access to the island.

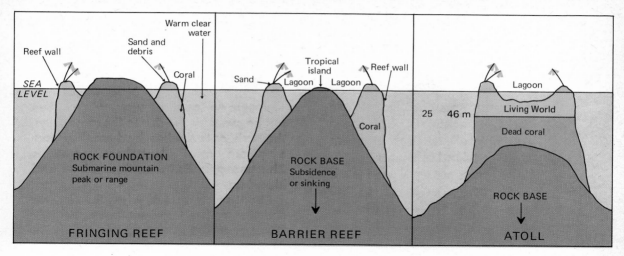

Figure 2.5 Diagrammatic sections to show three coral-formed features. The three features also show the developing stages of a coral atoll. The corals grow upwards towards light and food as the submarine rock foundation (undersea peak or range) sinks due to changes taking place in the earth's crust.

found at great depths, they must have originally grown near the surface, on top of submarine ranges or peaks in shallow waters.

(b) With the sinking of the land, the corals continued to grow upward to keep pace with the gradual sinking. Those polyps below a depth of 46 m died and formed the foundations of the reefs and islands.

The reefs and islands of the Great Barrier Reef rise steeply from the seabed on the east, but the inner channel towards the coastline is shallow and dangerous. The narrow channels between the reefs demand the skills of expert navigators.

In addition to surf and sunshine, the colourful wonders and surprises of the world's largest coral reef attract tourists from all parts of the world. Hotels have been built on many of the islands and tourists may enjoy sandy beaches, lagoons fringed by reefs, boat cruises, visits to an underwater observatory on Green Island, or observing the coral gardens and their variety of sea creatures by walking over reefs at low tide.

Here is a first-hand description of life on Hayman Island, the most northerly island in the Whitsunday Passage of the Barrier Reef. The description is written by a young student.

"It [Hayman Island] is one of the most popular tourist centres of the Barrier Reef islands. Walking tracks have been constructed to enable tourists to walk the 8 km around the island. Beyond the beach lies a coral reef 0.8 km wide, which is exposed at low tide. It reveals beautiful coral formations, shells, and trepang (sea slugs). During our school holidays I enjoy swimming, fishing, and boat trips to other islands. I am trying to make a collection of the different shells that are found here, as well as the different types of coral. Our school consists of one room and a small verandah at the back. The front has six large glass doors which enable us to catch a lot of breeze and light."

Questions
1. What might tourists enjoy doing on Hayman Island?
2. What types of work might the people of the island do for a living?
3. What does the school tell you about the island? What does the description of the school building tell you about the climate of Hayman Island?
4. Try and locate Whitsunday Passage on an atlas map.

The Great Barrier Reef presently faces two problems; namely, destruction by starfish and by tourists. Starfish are increasing in number on the reef at an alarming rate. These coral-eating sea creatures are destroying expanses of the reef. They are thought to be multiplying because of pollution in the surrounding waters. Efforts are being made to reduce and control these millions of starfish which, at present, seem to be migrating from island to island.

Some 250 000 tourists visit the reef each year. Souvenir hunters, insensitive to the enjoyment of others and indifferent to the delicate balance that governs animal life on the reefs, have scoured the more accessible areas for their colourful animal and plant life with devastating results. Areas which were once rich and colourful have been stripped of their beautiful coral gardens and of their plants and sea creatures.

Climate — A Land of Droughts

Because Australia is located in the Southern Hemisphere, the seasons are the opposite to ours — when it is winter in Canada, it is summertime in Australia.

Read the following paragraphs from a letter written by a young student in Sydney:

"Christmas in Australia is, I am sure, no different in some respects from Christmas in many other lands, for here, too, the shops and homes are decorated with the traditional holly and Christmas bells. However, to simulate snow in our midsummer Christmas weather, we sprinkle our Christmas trees and holly wreaths very liberally with glistening snow from a packet.

Old friends greet each other after Church service and then make for home for, by this time, the day is becoming quite hot, but not hot enough to deter the young children from running about the front lawns, backyards, and the streets.

Christmas wishes are exchanged on the verandahs or in some shady spots in the garden. Much importance is placed on the Christmas dinner, which is usually eaten about midday. Although the kitchen is

unbearably hot, the average Australian stubbornly insists on having a traditional Christmas dinner...

There are, nevertheless, quite a number of people who go to New Zealand or Tasmania on ten-day cruises, while others just go away for the day to the mountains, the bush, or to the beach where they have a picnic meal...Australians enjoy a Christmas period of warmth, sunshine, and blue skies.

About seven o'clock, when the sun sets and the temperature becomes noticeably lower, people drift outside again and visit neighbours...

Despite the fact that Boxing Day will bring new pleasures and new excitements like the start of the Sydney-Hobart Yacht Race and the finals of the Davis Cup, the Spirit of Christmas seems to linger."

Questions
1. Compare Christmas in Australia with Christmas in Canada, from the following points of view — customs, scenery, and weather.
2. Why is it warm in December in Australia?
3. What sports are enjoyed in Australia during the midsummer period (December to February)? Which sport do you associate with the Davis Cup?
4. Why do many Australians insist on the hot, traditional Christmas dinner in spite of the summer heat?

Australia has a wide range of climates — from hot, wet conditions along the northern coasts, to hot, dry deserts in the interior, to cool highlands with rainfall in the east. However, there is no period of extreme cold with ice and snow. Snowfalls are generally limited to the higher mountain regions where skiing is popular in winter (July). Because the Australian trees do not all shed their leaves at the same time of year, the change from season to season is less vivid there than in Canada.

The Australian seasons are: Spring (September to November), Summer (December to February), Fall (March to May), and Winter (June to August).

Study the maps and charts and answer the listed questions.

Questions

From Figure 2.6:

1. What is the name given to Latitude 23½°S?
2. Approximately within which lines of latitude does Australia lie?
3. Approximately how much of Australia lies within the tropics?

From Figure 2.7:

1. What type of pressure system exists over Australia in summer? What type of pressure area extends west of Australia at this season?
2. Winds blow *into* areas or cells of low pressure and *out* of high pressures. Explain.
3. Name the prevailing winds in summer.
4. Over what areas do these winds blow?
5. What would these winds carry?
6. What effect would they have on the coastal regions over which they prevail?
7. What type of winds would the interior overland winds be?

Note: The word monsoon probably comes from the Arabic word *mausin* which means "season" — hence seasonal wind.

From Figure 2.8:

1. What type of pressure system covers central Australia?
2. Which winds blow all the year round along the east coast?
3. Name the winter prevailing winds on the southern part of the continent.
4. In which direction do the monsoons blow at this time of the year? Blowing off the land, what type of winds would they be?
5. Which region receives the least rain? Which region receives the heaviest rainfall in January (summer)?
6. Locate the areas of winter (July) rainfall.

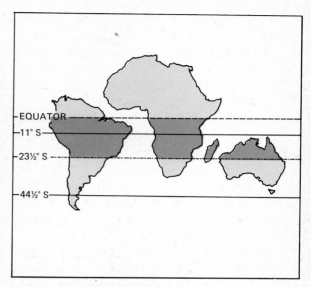

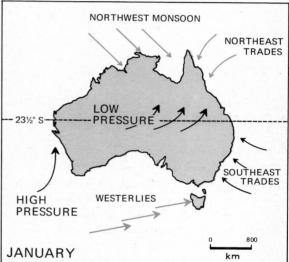

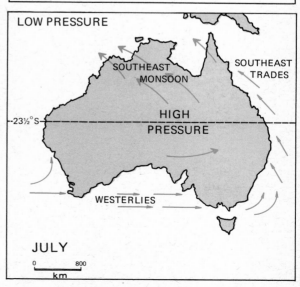

(Top) Figure 2.6   Sketch map showing Australia compared in latitude and area with southern Africa and southern South America.

(Centre) Figure 2.7   January (summer) pressure systems and winds.

(Bottom) Figure 2.8   July (winter) pressure systems and winds.

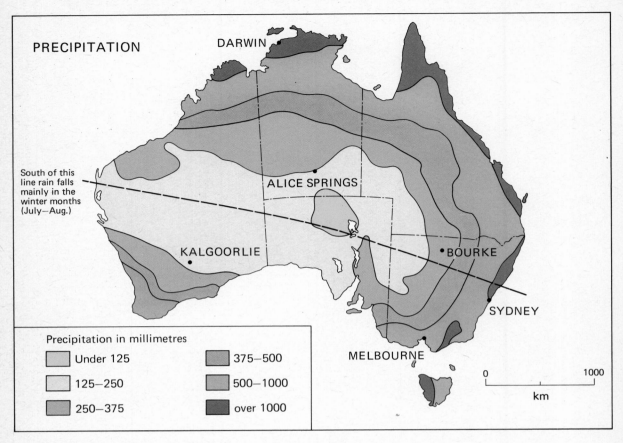

PRECIPITATION

DARWIN

ALICE SPRINGS

KALGOORLIE

BOURKE

SYDNEY

MELBOURNE

South of this
line rain falls
mainly in the
winter months
(July–Aug.)

Precipitation in millimetres

Under 125	375–500
125–250	500–1000
250–375	over 1000

0   1000
km

(Top) Figure 2.9   Map showing average annual rainfall of the continent.

(Bottom) Figure 2.10   Climate statistics.

DARWIN (30 m above sea level; Latitude 12°S)

	J	F	M	A	M	J	J	A	S	O	N	D
Temp. (°C)	28	28	29	29	28	26	25	26	28	29	30	29
Precip. (mm)	381	318	254	89	13	3	0	3	13	51	114	241

ALICE SPRINGS (580 m above sea level; Latitude 23°S)

	J	F	M	A	M	J	J	A	S	O	N	D
Temp. (°C)	28	28	24	19	15	12	12	14	18	23	24	28
Precip. (mm)	38	38	25	13	13	13	13	13	13	13	25	38

BOURKE (110 m above sea level; Latitude 30°S)

	J	F	M	A	M	J	J	A	S	O	N	D
Temp. (°C)	29	28	25	20	16	12	11	13	17	21	26	28
Precip. (mm)	38	38	25	25	25	25	25	13	13	25	38	38

SYDNEY (42 m above sea level; Latitude 33°S)

	J	F	M	A	M	J	J	A	S	O	N	D
Temp. (°C)	22	22	21	18	16	13	12	13	15	17	19	21
Precip. (mm)	89	102	127	140	127	114	114	76	76	76	76	76

From Figure 2.9:
Compare this map with a map showing the location of the Australian desert (page 10).

1. What is the lowest average rainfall in the desert?
2. What important annual rainfall figure approximately corresponds to the fringe areas of the desert? Name a town in this marginal area.
3. What pattern do you see in the rainfall from the interior to the coasts? Where are there exceptions to this pattern?

Relate the temperature and rainfall figures for Darwin Alice Springs, Bourke, and Sydney to the rainfall distribution map.

Study the climatic statistics for the four towns in Figure 2.10.
1. Which town receives the heaviest rainfall and the highest all-year-round temperatures?
2. Which town is within the tropics?
3. Which centre is almost on the Tropic of Capricorn?
4. Which centre receives the lowest annual rainfall? What, approximately, is the total annual precipitation?
5. If you were to live in one of these towns, which would you choose from a climatic point of view? Give your reasons.

(Top) Surf riding is a popular sport near Sydney, New South Wales. Such sports are popular during the Christmas holidays.

(Bottom) A view of the Snowy Mountains. Here are the sources of some of Australia's largest rivers. Since it is snow-covered in winter, the area is popular for skiing and winter sports.

Australia, as you already observed, is almost bisected by the Tropic of Capricorn, and therefore the northern regions are hot and tropical while the southern areas are more temperate. The continent is influenced by four main prevailing winds:

(a) The onshore, rainbearing, northwest summer monsoon which, with the high temperatures, produces a tropical climate in the northern regions.

(b) The rainbearing southeast trades which affect the east coast and the eastern slopes of the well-forested East Highlands.

(c) The winter, rainbearing westerlies which influence the southwestern parts of the continent. Because these regions have warm, wet winters and hot, dry summers similar to the lands of Europe, they are

referred to as the Mediterranean regions of Australia. (See Figure 1.3, page 6.)
(d) The offshore, dry, southeast monsoon which blows off the great interior desert, resulting in dry winter seasons in the north.

There is little chance for moisture-laden winds to bring rainfall to the interior or "centre" of Australia. Hence the presence of the Western Desert with its sand ridges, sparse and stunted vegetation of tough grasses and spiny bushes, and gibber plains of pebbles. The westerly winds blow too far south of the desert to bring rain, and the Eastern Highlands, or Great Dividing Range, act as a rain barrier against the influence of the southeast trades.

Questions
Study the cross section carefully.
1. What is meant by (a) rain barrier, (b) rain shadow area, (c) leeward, and (d) windward?
2. What happens to the rainfall as one travels from the east coast towards the interior?
3. What happens to the vegetation as one journeys from the coast to the interior?
4. Where would you expect to find the lowest population? Give your reasons.

Located between Latitudes 11°S and 44°S, where the sun's rays are more direct, Australia gets a considerable amount of sunshine and hence the problem of rapid evaporation is ever-present. During the hot, dry season, rivers often dwindle to a series of water holes and large lakes dry up to become desolate salt sheets. The Murray River is fed by the melting snows of the Australian Alps, but the River Darling may be dry for months at a time.

Droughts are Australia's greatest problem. They are irregular and unpredictable. Several years of good rainfall may suddenly be followed by a year of drought, which may spell disaster to the Australian farmer in terms of sheep and cattle loss or poor grain harvests. During the droughts of the 1890's, for example, Australia's sheep numbers fell from over 100 million to approximately 55 million.

Another problem is too rapid a rainfall, in the form of a thunderstorm, after a long drought period. The dried, caked, and cracked soils are unable to absorb the rapid downpour and much of the runoff water floods the dried-up valleys. This happens in the desert regions, where sometimes the whole year's supply of rain falls during one heavy thunderstorm.

Figure 2.11 A simplified diagrammatic cross section of Australia at approximately Latitude 30°S. West to east distance is 3860 kilometres (approximately).

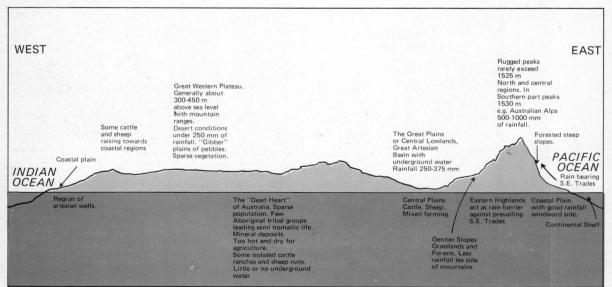

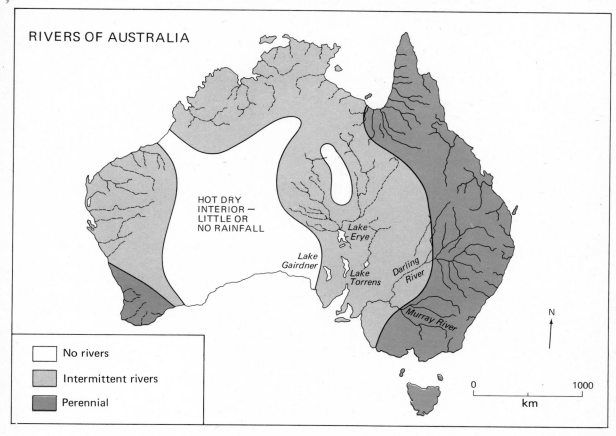

RIVERS OF AUSTRALIA

HOT DRY
INTERIOR —
LITTLE OR
NO RAINFALL

Lake
Erye

Lake
Gairdner

Lake
Torrens

Darling
River

Murray River

N

0   1000
km

No rivers

Intermittent rivers

Perennial

(Top) Figure 2.12   Map showing the rivers of Australia. Note the perennial rivers which flow throughout the year, and the intermittent variety which dry up during periods of drought. Even the large lakes shown vanish during the dry weather. Lake Eyre, for example, which may have a water surface of over 77 720 km² during a very wet season, can become a brackish marsh and even a sheet of salt during long periods of drought.

(Bottom)   The effects of drought in Australia.

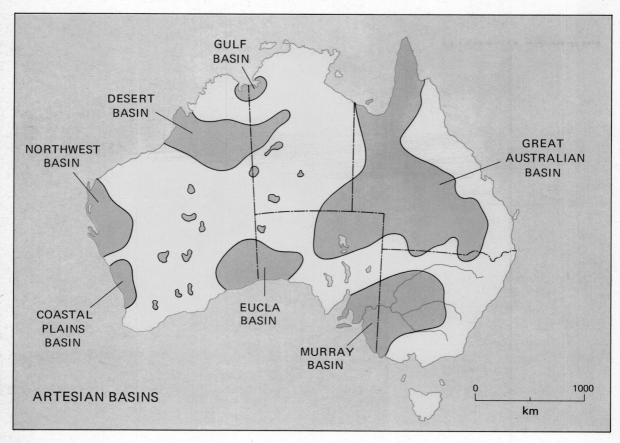

ARTESIAN BASINS

(Top) Figure 2.13 Artesian well regions where underground water is available.

(Bottom) Figure 2.14 Diagrammatic section of an artesian well in the Central Lowlands. Water enters the exposed porous sandstone layer of the Great Dividing Range and seeps to the lower level, where it is trapped some 450 to 600 m below the earth's surface between two impervious layers. The Great Artesian Basin is over 1.3×10^6 km² in area and is tapped by some 18000 bores.

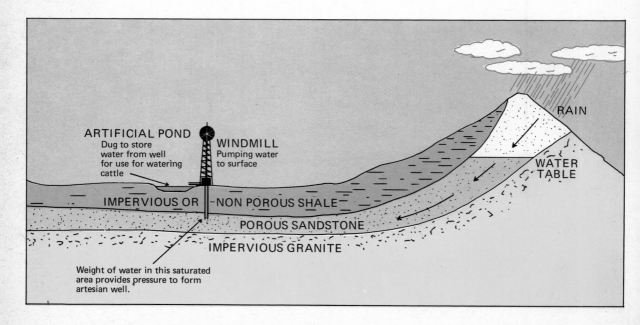

Australia's acute shortage of water would be far greater were it not for the continent's extensive supplies of underground water in the form of artesian wells. What is an artesian well? How is the water obtained from these underground reservoirs? Where are they located? These questions may be answered by a study of the diagrammatic section and map.

Questions
1. Name the two artesian basins that lie within the Central Lowlands.
2. In which region are the artesian well basins very much smaller and more isolated?

A typical Australian windmill pumping water from a bore on a sheep station in New South Wales.

Artesian wells are found in many parts of the world and provide valuable water supplies. Paris and London, for example, depend on such tapped subterranean water reservoirs. These wells receive their name from a dry region in France, Artois, where such wells have been tapped from very early times.

Water gushes from the base of a true artesian well because the underground pressure is sufficient to force up the stored reserves. However, if pressure is lacking, the water has to be pumped up with the aid of windmills or small motors. These are called subartesian wells or bores. The water is stored in large excavated ponds or tanks. Although the water from the Australian artesian wells is usually brackish and is not suitable for irrigation or domestic use, it is nevertheless essential for watering the vast herds of cattle.

Broadly speaking, only the northern regions, the southwestern area, Tasmania, and the eastern coastal margins of the continent are fairly safe from disastrous droughts.

Since climate is a factor in controlling the distribution of population, the greatest number of people are found in the pleasanter climatic regions of the east, southeast, and southwest. As stated earlier, some eighty-five percent of Australians are urban dwellers and the demand for water in these populated areas is a constant challenge. A vast system of pipelines from storage lakes, dams, and rivers, supplies the populated regions and irrigates the land.

Australia's greatest hydroelectric and water-supplying project to date is the spectacular Snowy Mountains Scheme. This project, which was started in 1949, is now nearing completion. Located in the Snowy Mountains in the southern part of the Great Dividing Range, this vast feat of engineering was planned to use the waters of the Murray, Murrumbidgee, and Snowy rivers, whose sources are within this area.

The Snowy Mountains Scheme, embracing more than 5180 km², involves the construction of power stations, dams, pumping stations, and kilometres of tunnels and aqueducts. Only now are vast amounts of hydro power available, and more will be in the future. An increased flow of water irrigates over 2590 km² in the Murray and Murrumbidgee valleys.

The scheme necessitated the building of extensive roads, and these cleared highways have opened up this mountainous area to tourists. Chalets now dot the slopes of the Snowy Mountains and skiing has become a favourite sport among Australians.

Vegetation

The availability of water controls the type of vegetation in a country and hence the species, number, and distribution of animals. In turn, these factors control the distribution of man and his way of life.

The rainfall map of a country generally reflects the type of natural vegetation that land supports. Compare the simplified map of vegetation in Australia with a rainfall distribution map in an atlas.

Questions
1. Where is the main desert area?
2. Note the wide region of sparse vegetation around the true desert. What is mulga? What is mallee?

Many geologists accept the theory that some fifty million years ago great movements in the earth's crust caused Australia and New Zealand to move away from the other landmasses and become isolated islands. This isolation led to the development of species of plants and animals which are very different from those found in other parts of the world. Australia has been described as the "Sunburnt Continent", and the "Orphan of the Pacific". These two names describe its generally dry, arid climate and its lonely, isolated position. Thus its plants are mainly drought-resistant and are unique to the country.

The two main types of vegetation are the eucalyptus or gum trees and the acacia or wattles.

The eucalypts are found all over the continent, from the tropical, summer rain areas of the north to the cooler, winter rain

Figure 2.15 The natural vegetation regions of Australia.

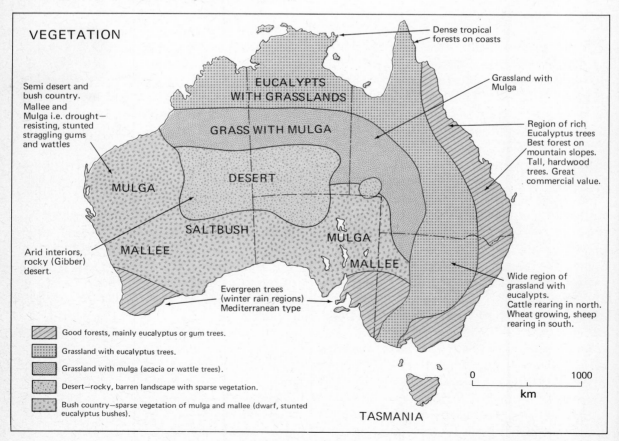

34

regions of the south. They thrive as tall giants on the well-watered eastern mountain slopes, and exist as stunted, dwarfed spring shrubs *(mallee)* on the desert fringes. The only region in which eucalypts are not found is the treeless, stoney desert.

Eucalypts, also know as gum trees because of the gum they secrete from their trunks, have a peculiar odour. The thick, leathery leaves contain a spicy oil known for its pungent smell and medicinal value.

There are more than 500 varieties of eucalypts in Australia. The most majestic is the mountain ash which grows to a height of over 90 m and is the tallest hardwood tree in the world. These trees fill all Australia's timber requirements and most of its newsprint and paper needs. All eucalypts are hardwoods and one, the jarrah, is particularly tough and water-resistant. The jarrah is particularly suitable for railway ties and for piles for wharves and piers.

The acacias or wattles, which also grow throughout the continent, are akin to the mimosa of America and Europe. Australia is the home of some 600 species of acacia, but the best known is the garden wattle and this is the floral emblem and national flower of Australia. The fluffy, golden flowers of this acacia are to Australia what the maple leaf is to Canada.

The acacia often reaches heights of 24 m, and has fine, delicate leaves. However, in the semidesert it is stunted, with spindly stems, irregular, struggling branches, and greenish-gray leaves. In this dwarfed form, it is known collectively as *mulga*.

It may be observed that the eucalypts and acacias are, in the main, drought-resistant plants, and the drier their habitat, the tougher and more stunted their growth. They develop smaller, leathery leaves to avoid loss of water, and deep roots to reach for moisture.

Another interesting plant is the bottle tree, which is native to Queensland. It stores

Eucalyptus trees (ghost gums) in the Northern Territory.

its water in its bloated, bottle-like trunk, and is also capable of holding 270 to 360 L of water in reservoir-like basins where the branches extend from the trunk.

Figure 2.16

Country	Percentage of forested land in relation to total area
Australia	1.5
Canada	33
U.S.S.R.	39
U.S.A.	24
New Zealand	19

Questions
1. Which country has the largest area of forests in relation to its total surface area?
2. How does Canada compare with other countries listed?
3. What are the advantages of large forest resources to a country?
4. How does Australia compare with Canada as regards forest lands?

(Top left) The kangaroo is as representative of Australia as the beaver is of Canada. Largest of the marsupials, a full-grown kangaroo stands over 2 m high, and with its muscular legs and a long tail for balance, it can jump a distance of 6 to 9 m at a time. It is a grass-eating animal, and so lives in herds on the plains. The female doe gives birth to an embryo, 2.5 cm long, which completes its development in the mother's pouch or marsupium. The young *joey* is protected and carried around by its mother until it is nearly nine months old and ready to graze.

(Top right) Another pouched animal is the wombat, also known as the Australian badger. When fully grown, the wombat is about the size of a small pig. It is nocturnal, that is, it sleeps during the day and is active at night.

(Bottom left) One of the world's strangest animals is the platypus, which lives on the banks of rivers and creeks. This unique animal is strictly preserved by law in Australia, and is a living link among mammals, birds, fishes, and reptiles. This furry animal, about 48 cm long, has the bill of a duck and four webbed feet. It lives in a burrow near water. Mainly nocturnal in its habits, it feeds on grubs and worms. It lays eggs but later suckles its young. What has the platypus in common with mammals, reptiles, birds, and fishes?

(Bottom right) The koala, like the kangaroo, is a pouched animal and is found in the bush country. There the little animals feed on juicy eucalyptus and gum leaves, which have sufficient moisture to supply the liquid needs of the animal. The name "Koala" is derived from an Aboriginal word which suggests that the animal does not normally drink water. The koala is well adapted to a habitat where there is little or no groundwater. Koalas are nocturnal animals. Contrary to their delightful appearance, they do not make good pets.

What Australia loses in quantity of forested land is compensated for by the variety of quality woods. Hardwoods, such as jarrah, karri, and red gums, are in constant demand and fortunately the Australian gum trees grow comparatively quickly. Australia is fortunate in her timber reserves because her forests, which are carefully supervised and controlled by the government, fill the country's present needs for timber for construction, furniture, pulp, and paper.

Wildlife

According to some scientists, Australia became separated from Asia at a very early age in the earth's history. Because of its isolation from the rest of the world since prehistoric times, the animals, like the plants, have developed in their own way. They are unique in that most species are not found anywhere else in the world. Also, animals common to other continents are not found naturally in Australia. For example, there are no members of the cat family, such as the tiger, lion, cougar, or panther, on this island continent. Also, there are no native hoofed animals, such as the antelope or deer, and apes and monkeys are not found in the Australian forests.

Nearly half the native mammals are marsupials, that is, animals which give birth to their young before they are completely developed and bear them in pouches. The best known marsupials are those of the kangaroo family, which vary in size from the great high-jumping kangaroo to the smaller wallaby.

Like the platypus, the Australian spiny anteater lays eggs like a bird or reptile, but once the eggs are hatched it suckles its young like a mammal. The anteater has a long nose to burrow into anthills, and a long, narrow tongue to get insects out of narrow crevices. A startled anteater performs an amazing feat. With rotating limb movements and shovel-like paws, it can submerge itself into the ground like a submarine sinking slowly beneath the sea surface, and completely disappear.

Another common and unusual native animal is the long-tailed possum. Some species live in trees and are known as flying squirrels. They can jump and glide long distances from branch to branch and from tree to tree.

The common rabbit is probably one of the greatest pests in Australia. Originally there were no rabbits on the continent, but in 1866 a few were brought into the country by settlers. The few multiplied at an alarming rate and soon overran the country. There was plenty of food for them, and there were no natural enemies, such as the stoat or the weasel, to control their numbers. The rabbits soon became an economic menace because forty rabbits can eat as much grass as one sheep. In the earlier days the rabbits ruined many farmers because they ate the fodder needed for sheep rearing. Rabbit-proof fences, which extend well below the surface of the ground, were built to protect the sheep runs. It was a tremendous undertaking as thousands of kilometres of such fencing were required. It took twenty years to bring the rabbit pests under control. By then, however, many farmers had lost their farms and faced bankruptcy — all because of the rabbit. Rabbits were also diminished in number some years ago when a rabbit-killing, virus disease known as myxomatosis was introduced into Australia. Millions of rabbits died, but the strong survivors have bred in increasing numbers and the rabbit, once again, continues to be a problem in various regions.

Australia has numerous species of lizards, snakes, and insects and a few of tortoises, turtles, and crocodiles. One of the more common lizards is the 1 m long goanna, recognized by its "frilled collar". The Aborigine has always hunted the goanna because its flesh is considered a delicacy.

(Left) The wolflike dingo dog is the most savage carnivorous animal of Australia. Because it attacks sheep, it is an enemy of the farmer. When it is hungry, it will attack a kangaroo.

(Right) The kookaburra is found in eastern and southern Australia.

Crocodiles, of which there are only two species, live in the mangrove swamps in the tropical northern regions.

Australia's birds are as unique and fascinating as her mammals. The emu, which grows to a height of 1.5 m and is similar to an ostrich, is the largest bird. With the kangaroo, it appears on the country's coat of arms. Another similar bird is the cassowary which, like the emu, is not capable of flight.

The kookaburra or jacko is one of the favourite birds of Australia. It is a giant kingfisher, somewhat larger than a pigeon, with a strong head and a large beak. His raucous notes are startling -- they sound like a horrible laugh. The kookaburra is a snake catcher. It flies high with the writhing snake and then drops it to break its back. The act is repeated until the snake is dead.

A fascinating bird is the mallee fowl, which builds its nest of rotting leaves in a shallow hole in the sand. When the foliage is damp enough, it covers it with a mound of sand about one metre high. The decomposing leaves generate heat and the sun also heats the sandy mound. The male bird, with its sensitive, thermometer-like beak, tests the heat of the nest and when it is about 33°C it digs approximately thirty holes into the sand. The female bird then lays an egg in each hole and covers it up. Daily checks are made of the temperature of the incubator. It is carefully controlled by removing or adding more surface sand. When the chicks hatch, they have to dig their way to the surface.

The lyre bird is noteworthy because of the beautiful and colourful tail of the male which is shaped like the musical instrument known as a lyre — a type of ancient harp. The mating activities of the lyre bird are of interest because during this period, within a small clearing in the underbush, the male bird struts in all his glory and calls out in a variety of tones — mimicking other birds and animals and sometimes even imitating human voices.

Other birds native to Australia include brightly-hued parrots, black swans with red bills, majestic eagles, timid budgerigars, and bowerbirds that build elaborate, walled, corridor-like structures or galleries and decorate them with shells or stones or flowers or even berry stains to help to attract the females during the mating season.

THE ABORIGINES

Origin and History

It is believed that the continent of Australia had been occupied by a people we now know as the Aborigines for at least 20 000 years before the European discoverers landed on its shores in 1788. Strangely, no special name has ever been found to apply to these original Australians, and hence the use of the capitalized form of the noun "aborigine".

We do not know precisely where the Aborigines originated or how they got to Australia. However, it is thought that there were three different migrations of these early peoples and that some descendants of

the first group were still living in Tasmania when the first European explorers landed on that island.

A study of the map will help to establish where these native peoples possibly came from and where they first settled.

Questions
1. From what region did they migrate?
2. How might they have reached their new homeland? What landforms would have helped them?
3. In which parts of Australia did they originally settle?
4. Name the farthest region of settlement.

It is generally accepted that about 300 000 Aborigines, speaking some 300 different languages, were living in Australia at the time the European settlers arrived. Some anthropologists estimate that there were as many as 500 tribal groups on the vast continent.

Captain James Cook, the English explorer, who landed on the northeast coast of Australia in 1770 after his ship, the *Endeavour*, struck an offshore reef, encountered

Figure 2.17　Map showing the possible routes taken by the first Aborigines during their migrations to Australia.

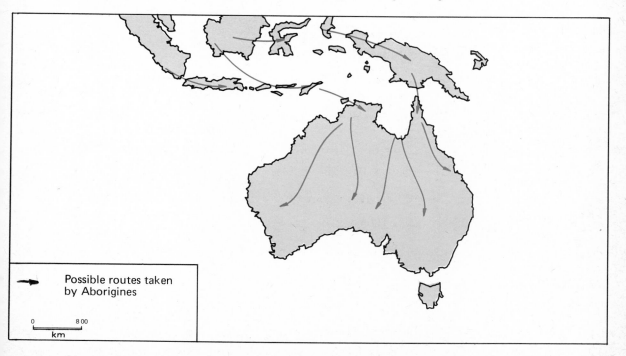

Possible routes taken by Aborigines

0   8 00
km

the Aborigines. He described them as a peaceful and happy people:

"The earth and the sea of their own accord furnish them with all things necessary for life; they covet not magnificent houses, household stuff, etc.; they live in a warm and fine climate and enjoy a very wholesome air, so that they have little need of clothing. . . . In short, they seemed to set no value upon anything we gave them, nor would they ever part with anything of their own for any one article we could offer them. This, in my opinion, argues that they think themselves provided with all the necessaries of life and that they have no superfluities . . . "

The history of the Aborigine after settlement by Europeans is, however, a sad one. Thousands died from diseases brought by the colonists and hitherto unknown to the Aborigines. Furthermore, as settlements expanded and the frontiers gradually encroached farther and farther into the interior, the loss of hunting grounds, water holes, and ceremonial sites created grave problems for the Aborigines. They moved or were pushed into the more inhospitable regions of the country and their whole lifestyle began to change. The introduction of alcohol and the use of force by the new landowners led to a rapid decline in the Aboriginal population.

Questions
Analyse the charts and map.
1. By how many thousands did the true Aboriginal numbers drop during the first 100 years?
2. Compare the figures for 1800 with the 140 000 true Aborigines in 1973. What is the estimated drop in numbers?
3. Account for this serious drop in Aboriginal numbers.
4. What steps might the Aborigines have taken to protect themselves against the early settlers?

Aborigine Population

1800	300 000
1900	70 000
1960	80 000
1973	140 000

State	Year	Aborigine Population
Tasmania	1788	4 000
	1830	500
Victoria	1788	10 000
	1830	2 000

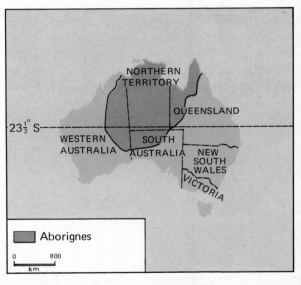

(Top) Figure 2.18   In 1800 the number stated in the chart was wholly Aboriginal. The figure for 1973 is for part Aboriginal and total Aboriginal. Today, only about 40 000 are wholly Aboriginal.

(Centre) Figure 2.19   Chart showing the dramatic decline in the numbers of Aborigines in two states during the first fifty years of European settlement.

(Bottom) Figure 2.20   Simplified sketch map showing the region of major settlement by Aborigines. Part and wholly Aboriginal peoples, however, live in all parts of the continent. The shaded area indicates where many Aboriginal reserves and settlements are located today and where some Aborigines, even today, live a simple, semi-nomadic life.

40

The dramatic drop in Aboriginal numbers, however, was halted in most areas by 1950 because of legislation and the work of various concerned societies and groups. It is now estimated that the total wholly and part Aboriginal population will reach 200 000 by 1990 and possibly 300 000 by the end of the century. In many areas the wholly Aboriginal birth rate is higher than that of the total Australian population.

Way of Life — Past and Present

The Aborigines are one of the most interesting peoples in the world. They have captured our imagination with their simple, Stone Age type of living and implements, their fascinating legends about the Dream Time, i.e., their period of the world's creation, their use of the boomerang, their sacred rituals of song and dance known as *corroborees,* and, above all, their ability to adapt to a dry, inhospitable, desert environment.

Before the settlement of Australia by Europeans, the Aborigines lived in all parts of the continent, especially near the coasts and in the fertile valleys. However, the stronger and more numerous settlers gradually pushed them farther and farther into the less desirable regions of the interior and the north. In these less desirable regions, especially the desert, they lived a semi-nomadic, primitive way of life. They wore little or no clothing, owned few possessions, and only built temporary shelters when the need arose. Only territorial boundaries, decided by tribal use and rites, limited their movements and mode of living. Each tribal group, consisting of several families, recognized its boundaries for hunting and food gathering. One group would seldom encroach on another's area. Rites were respected.

The Aborigines practised neither farming nor animal rearing. They hunted wild animals such as the kangaroo, lizards, and snakes and gathered such foods as roots, berries, and seeds. They were, and are, experts in tracking wild animals, finding water, and digging for edible roots.

At night they slept in the open, keeping a series of small fires burning beside them when they needed warmth and comfort. Some groups, however, constructed simple shelters out of saplings and mud, but these were mainly a means of protection against mosquitoes. Other groups built constructions of bark and branches as temporary

(Left) Two Aborigines playing a didgeridoo and music sticks.

(Right) Aborigines painted for a corroboree.

A gallery of Aboriginal cave paintings in Arnhem Land, a large reserve in the north of Australia's Northern Territory.

shelters against wind. Some tribal units gathered and bunched branches together for protection. Such shelters, possibly the simplest type ever built by man, were known as *wurlies*.

In such a simple, wandering life there was little need for possessions. The Aborigines' needs included a kangaroo skin for warmth on cold nights, a skin water bag, a dilly bag for carrying food, a digging stick, and some weapons, such as the boomerang, the barbed wooden spear, the throwing stick, or *woomera,* the stone axe and chisel, the fishing net, and the animal trap. The *didgeridoo,* a long, hollow, wooden, tubelike instrument which made dronelike sounds, was also an important item in their equipment.

The boomerang, which for many people has become a symbol of Aboriginal life, is still used as a weapon in some areas. Elsewhere it has only ceremonial uses. Designs vary and some groups do not use the boomerang.

In the past the Aborigines worshipped mystical and natural powers that appeared to control their lives — the wind, rain, animals, etc. They performed sacred rites and conducted ceremonies known as corroborees. Such corroborees, which lasted from several hours to several days, involved music, mime, and dance. They were performed to bring rain or to ward off drought, pestilence, or plague. Some Aborigines still hold corroborees. Others perform these ceremonies for cultural, historical, and traditional reasons.

Today very few Aborigines live by hunting and food gathering, although a few tribal groups living on the vast government reserves prefer the nomadic life. Others, after a period of settlement, take off into the desert and revert back to the old tribal ways. They go, as they say, on a "walk-about".

As stated earlier, the Aborigines are found in all parts of the continent, but most live in northern and central Australia in remote government reserves, mission settlements, or cattle and sheep stations. In the states where tribal Aborigines are fewer in number, movement to the larger towns and cities is increasing and creating housing, work, and welfare problems.

The following chart shows the distribution of the Aborigines.

State	Part Aboriginal	Wholly Aboriginal	Total
New South Wales	28 000	100	28 100
Victoria	6 100	–	6 100
Queensland	30 000	12 000	42 000
South Australia	6 000	3 000	9 000
Western Australia	18 000	10 000	28 000
Tasmania	600	–	600
Northern Territory	4 500	21 500	26 000
Australian Capital Territory	200	–	200
Total	93 400	46 600	140 000

From: Australian News and Information Bureau Publication, 1972.

Questions
1. Relate the above figures to the total population of the respective states.
2. Name the three states with the largest number of wholly Aboriginal people. Locate these states on an atlas map and refer back to the previous map in this chapter.
3. Which state has the smallest Aborigine population? What happened to the original inhabitants of the island during the period of European settlement?

(Top) Figure 2.21

(Bottom) Aborigines work as cattle drovers (shown here), sheep shearers, labourers, railway gangers, and shop assistants. Some now become nurses and teachers. Many, however, rely on seasonal work and spend the remaining period of the year by going "walk-about".

The way of life of the Aborigine is changing, and many stages of change may be observed. Some, as stated, still live the old, free-wandering, traditional way; others live in homes and work on mission settlements; many have homes on cattle and sheep stations; some live in modern houses in self-governing communities supervised by the federal government, and many more have recently migrated to the outskirts of the urban areas, where they congregate in poor, overcrowded settlements.

Since 1967 the Australian government has improved the position of its original people by passing laws to:

(a) provide special funds to the individual states to help them improve living and working conditions for the Aborigine;

(b) establish a Capital Fund to help Aborigines with loans so that they may develop group or individual businesses and projects;

(Top left)   Aborigine painter at work on a bark painting.

(Bottom left)   Pottery — a new medium for Aborigine artists.

(Right)   An Aborigine rock painting of a turtle.

(c) improve medical facilities by building more clinics and hospitals;

(d) open more schools and encourage more Aborigine students to attend secondary schools;

(e) provide scholarships for those who wish to pursue a college or a university education — at present just over twenty Aboriginal students attend universities;

(f) provide them with equal citizenship opportunities;

(g) encourage them to take pride in their culture and heritage.

Aboriginal art is now being recognized in Australia and the world over, and many Aboriginal dances and ceremonies have been adapted into modern ballet productions.

The Aborigines form a minority in the population of Australia, i.e., 140 000 Aborigines in a country of 12 800 000 white Australians — approximately one in a hundred Australians has Aborigine blood. The Australian government admits that, in the past, it has neglected the Aborigines and that these people have been handicapped in terms of education and employment, housing, and health services. Important changes, however, are occurring and will continue in favour of the Aborigine.

> "The changes in emphasis have been made to recognize the need for Aborigines to have greater opportunities as Australian citizens with full freedom to choose their own way of life."

From: *Commonwealth Policy and Achievements*, 1972.

The Aborigines, on the other hand, wish to share full Australian citizenship but, at the same time, they desire to preserve their identity. They state: "We want to share with the *balanda,* but we are not balanda. We are *yulngu* — ourselves."

AGRICULTURE

Australia — Land of Wool and Meat

A visit to a variety of stores and some enquiries would give a fairly clear picture of Australia's agricultural exports. Such goods would include materials made from Merino wool, joints of mutton and lamb, bottles of wine, cans of pears and peaches, packets of raisins and sugar, and many other items. Australia, in brief, is a land of sheep and cattle raising, wheat and barley growing, and sugar, vine, and fruit cultivation.

The Land of the Golden Fleece

The ancient myth relates how the hero Jason searched for, and after many great hazards and dangers found, the fabulous golden fleece. Australia, it might be said, also found the golden fleece, for the wool of the Merino sheep is like gold to the Australian sheep farmer. Wool growing has long been the country's biggest industry and it is still often quoted that "Australia rides on the sheep's back". Although wool is the country's biggest single export income earner, mutton is also a major product for shipment abroad.

In March, 1970, it was reported that Australia's sheep numbered 181 000 000 and produced thirty percent of the world's wool — nearly two and a half times the production of her nearest competitor, the U.S.S.R. In spite of the greater use of man-made fibres, Australia's top quality wool is in great demand and her woollen exports in 1970 exceeded $740 000 000, while the mutton and lamb export figures reached $82 000 000.

The Merino has a small body but a heavy fleece. The wool yield is about 4.5 kg at a shearing. Prize Merinos have known to yield up to 7.2 kg. This breed is purely a wool-yielding animal as its meat is poor.

Nearly twenty percent of all Australian exports is wool.

Australia's wool industry is based on the famous Merino sheep — the best wool-producing sheep in the world and a breed that can withstand heat and drought.

The Merino sheep, which are a Spanish breed, were brought into Australia in 1796, when some twenty-nine sheep were transported from South Africa. The suitability of these sheep for a hot, dry country had been recognized. Captain John McArthur was the first to realize the great wealth that wool could bring to the young country. He improved his stock by bringing purebred stock from the royal flocks at Kew, London. The flocks thrived and increased and the wool quality improved with crossbreeding. In 1820 the average fleece had a mass of 0.9 to 1.4 kg. Compare that with today's average.

Figure 2.22 Some figures to illustrate the growth of wool exports from 1807 to 1970. How many times has the wool production increased over this period? Notice the rapid increase during the first 25 (approx.) years.

Year	Wool Production (in kilograms)
1807	110
1831	1 134 000
1966	753 883 200
1970	926 704 800

To improve the meat and to provide mutton and lamb for export, other breeds were brought from England and crossed with the hardy Merino. The following section identifies and describes the most common breeds of sheep in Australia today, showing for each breed its percentage of the total sheep population.

Merino 75.6%
Wool-producing sheep. Fine, long fibres, 7.6-12.7 cm in length. Excellent quality wool. Merino sheep have five to six times more wool fibres than other breeds. A hardy sheep that adapts readily to extremes of temperature. It is the best breed for warm climates and dry conditions.

Merino Comeback 3.5%
A cross between a Merino and a British breed (generally Lincoln or Leicester). Seventy-five percent Merino and twenty-five percent British stock. A dual purpose sheep — wool- and meat-producing.

Crossbreed 9.5%
A true crossbreed. Fifty percent Merino and fifty percent British breed. Good for wool and mutton.

Other breeds 11.4%
Various breeds introduced into Australia from Britain. Reared for meat and some wool. Mainly located on sheep farms in the more temperate regions where rainfall is more assured and pastures are richer and irrigated.

Figure 2.23   The sheep breeds of Australia.

Questions
1. Which is the most common breed of sheep found in Australia?
2. What is meant by crossbreeding? Why was it necessary?
3. Which breed is best suited for Australia? Why?
4. In what form is the meat exported?

Questions
From Figure 2.25:
1. Locate the areas of heaviest sheep rearing.
2. Why are there so few sheep reared in the interior part of the continent?

Approximately seventy-five percent of Australia's sheep are reared in the region west of the Great Dividing Range, between Victoria and central Queensland. This area of rolling hills and plains receives adequate rainfall and is well irrigated. The other sheep-rearing areas include southwestern Australia and the island of Tasmania. In these regions crops such as wheat, alfalfa, fruits, and vegetables are also cultivated.

The chart gives a broad indication of how rainfall determines the number of sheep reared in an area and the size of the sheep stations. Sheep are dependent on pastures and these in turn depend on rainfall.

Annual Rainfall (mm)	Average Size of Station (ha)	Average Number of Sheep per hectare (ha)
510	40.5-810	12-15
380	2 025	2-7
Under 250	20 250	0.25

Figure 2.24

Sheep farms, therefore, vary from comparatively small properties, with good pastures to feed a number of sheep per hectare, to vast stations where the low rainfall supports poor fodder in the form of tussock grasses and mallee scrub. This is sufficient to rear only one sheep per several hectares. Such vast stations are found in the isolated interior, known as the "Outback". This is real sheep and cattle country. The sheep runs, which fringe the desert area, where the annual rainfall is 250 mm or less, may vary in size from 20 250 ha to more than 101 250 ha. The sheep stations in the Outback are isolated and some of the homesteads may be 240 km from the nearest small community. The larger, isolated sheep

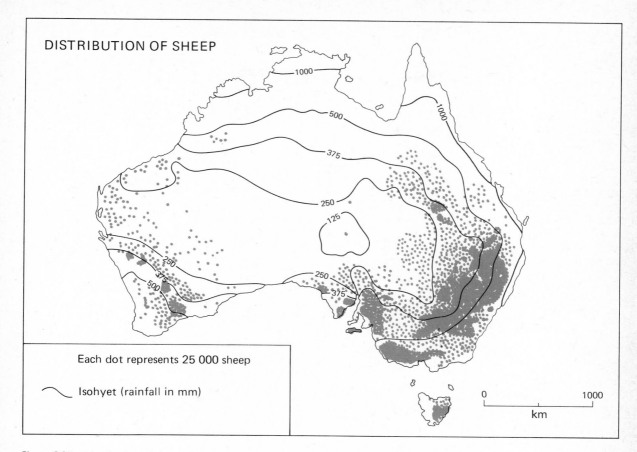

DISTRIBUTION OF SHEEP

Each dot represents 25 000 sheep

Isohyet (rainfall in mm)

Figure 2.25 Distribution of sheep in Australia. Relate the numbers of sheep to the rainfall.

stations are sometimes self-contained communities. Besides the owner's house and the inevitable woolshed, there are the quarters for the station hands and the jackaroos (young apprentices learning the wool trade). There may be a general store carrying medicines, sheep dip, foods, tobacco, wire fencing, and so on, which may act as a post office. A large station may also have a garage for servicing vehicles and equipment, a carpenter's shop, and a welding shop. The inevitable windmill indicates the dependence on artesian well water.

Seasonal Work on a Sheep Farm

December-February (Summer season)
This is the dry, hot season and the grazing pastures are slowly being depleted of their grasses. The sheep have to be moved from paddock to paddock to take advantage of all available pasture.

Wigging and crutching of sheep — clipping the wool around the eyes and the tail areas respectively to prevent "fly strike" and irritations caused by blowflies and skin parasites — are performed during these months.

Some paddocks are ploughed to absorb the early rains. In regions where irrigation is possible or rainfall is adequate, some land is ploughed in preparation for the cultivation of clover and oats (winter feed for animals).

March-May (Autumn or Fall season)
Flocks are checked. The lambing season begins in April and continues until the end of May. In suitable areas wheat is sown after the autumn rains.

June-August (Winter season)

Lambs are marked — generally by a notch in the ear. Tails are cut off. Sheep are sheared. The shearing starts earlier in the northern part of the country, and the travelling teams of shearers work their way southwards from one sheep farm to another. Shearing season ends in September in Tasmania.

September-November (Spring season)

Wool is transported to the auction centres. The lambs are sold to meat packers.

By late November in the southeastern areas, the wheat and oats are ready for harvesting. Hay is also harvested. (Winter fodder for sheep and cattle).

Records of herds, etc. are brought up to date.

The busiest time on any sheep station is shearing time. Teams of shearers visit a station, do their work, and travel on to a new station.

The flocks of sheep are brought into the mustering yards early each morning during shearing season. The sheep are gathered into the catching pens by workers called "penners up". The shearers in the shearing shed pull out a sheep and with the aid of electric clippers remove the fleece in one piece. An experienced shearer can shear as many as 300 sheep in a day. The shorn sheep is then directed into a tally pen for recording purposes and then checked for "shear cuts". It is finally dipped in a trough of chemicals or "fogged" (in a shed filled with a chemical mist) to destroy any parasites such as lice and ticks. A man picks up the fleece and throws it out on the rolling table where the "wool roller" skirts the fleece — pulling away the dirty or poor wool from the edges, which generally correspond to the underside of the animal. The skirtings are stored in large bins and are baled separately. The skirted fleece is then rolled and carried to the grader's table where it is examined, graded, and stored. Records are kept of the fleeces and they are baled accordingly. A huge wool press helps in packing the wool into 136 kg bales. Trucks transport the bulky bales to the wool auction rooms in the nearest large centre. Such auctions are held at Sydney, Melbourne, Perth, Brisbane, Newcastle, Adelaide, Hobart, and other cities. The wool is sold through brokers at these annual auctions, which open in September and last for several months.

Japan is the biggest buyer of Australian wool, buying approximately one-third of each year's export. Other markets include Great Britain and many European countries such as France, Italy, and Belgium.

Figure 2.26 Simplified plan of a shearing shed on a sheep station.

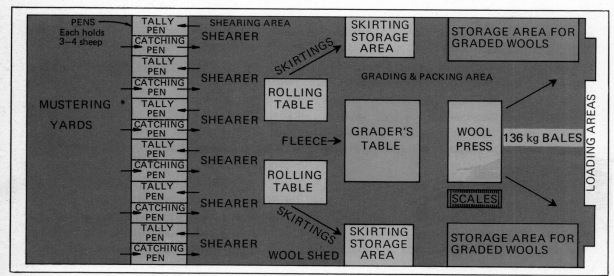

(Top left)   Dogs keep the Merino sheep in line in front of the shearing shed.

(Top right)   Wool bales in jute bags, ready to transport to the wool auctions.

(Bottom)   Shearing sheep using electric clippers.

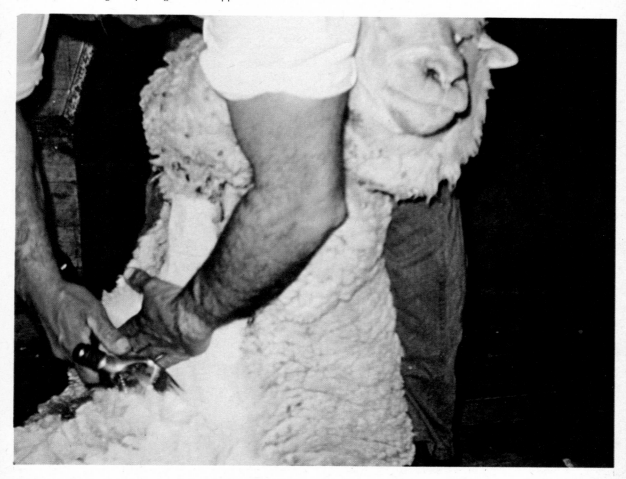

Cattle

Cattle, like sheep, need water and pasture; the availability of water and pasture determines the number of livestock a country may support. Cattle, as a general rule, need richer grasses than sheep, and they must be well-watered, because too much walking in search of water makes their meat tough and, therefore, undesirable for marketing.

Most cattlemen or stockmen try to find water holes for their herds within a distance of five kilometres. Cattle can withstand hotter temperatures than sheep, and are therefore more common in those areas in the interior that have an adequate water supply provided by artesian wells. Cattle numbers, as do those of sheep, decline drastically as desert conditions increase. Cattle stations vary in size, depending on the amount of pasturage to feed the animals. In the vicinity of Alice Springs, some of the cattle stations are larger in area than Prince Edward Island, supporting perhaps 20 000 head of cattle.

These huge cattle runs, like some sheep stations, are isolated in the Outback, great distances from the nearest railway. After "mustering the cattle on the runs" the stockmen "herd the mobs on the hoof to the railway halt". The cattle routes, known as Travelling Stock Routes, are broad tracks of unpaved road so planned as to take advantage of the water bores. Since the journey from the station to the railway may take several days, these wells are essential. Today, cattle are also being transported to the railway halts by giant, multi-trailered trucks called road trains, but this method is costly and the stock routes are still much in use. Cattle provide beef for home use and for export. The hides are made into leather.

A young girl living on a cattle station describes her home as follows:

"I live on a cattle station. It is called Macumba, which is the Aboriginal word for "Big Fire". Besides cattle, we have many horses, for the boys have to ride when mustering. Our nearest town is about 40 km away and is called Oodnatta. Oodnatta is 160 km north of Adelaide. Dad drives in at least once a week to pick up mail. I learn my school work by correspondence lessons. I finish a set of work each fortnight (two weeks) and then send it away to Adelaide for correcting at the Correspondence School. I have a *School of the Air* lesson every day on the transceiver. Our teacher is about 800 km away, but we talk to him as though he were in the schoolroom. Station life is interesting and often exciting, but it can also be very lonely."

Dairy cattle, as opposed to beef cattle, need richer grasses and a good water supply to ensure a maximum milk yield. Thus dairy cattle, the source of the country's milk, butter, and cheese, are confined to the richer pastures of the southeast, south, and southwest. About twenty-five percent of Australia's vast herds are dairy cattle.

> **Questions**
> 1. Compare Figure 2.27 with the map showing the distribution of sheep (page 47).
> 2. Which type of livestock is more common in the desert regions?
> 3. Where is the distribution of cattle heaviest in Australia? Why would the eastern coastal areas be suitable for cattle?

In conclusion, Australia supports some twenty-two million beef cattle. She is second only to Argentina as a world beef and veal producer.

(Top left) Figure 2.27   Distribution of beef and dairy cattle.

(Centre left)   A road train (each wagon is about 12 m long) heading north from Alice Springs to pick up cattle.

(Bottom)   Cattle at a water bore.

(Top right)   Another service provided for the isolated homesteads is the "Flying Doctor Service". The doctors operate their ambulance aircraft from a number of bases and keep in touch with their patients by two-way radios.

(Centre right)   Children living in isolated cattle and sheep stations in the Outback tune in to scheduled School of the Air "two-way broadcasts". They follow up their lessons by posting assignments to central educational offices. They can ask and answer questions on their transceiver sets.

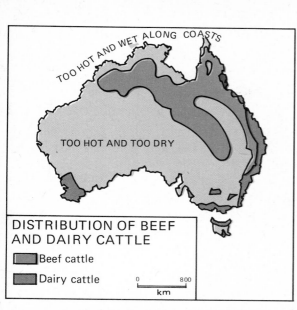

DISTRIBUTION OF BEEF
AND DAIRY CATTLE

TOO HOT AND WET ALONG COASTS

TOO HOT AND TOO DRY

Beef cattle

Dairy cattle

0   800
km

A Country of Many Crops

Australia spans many degrees of latitude, from 11°S to 44°S. It is almost bisected by the Tropic of Capricorn and so nearly all the northern half of the continent lies within the tropics. The southern regions of Australia are warm but enjoy a more temperate climate than the tropical north. One would, therefore, expect a variety of crops to be harvested within these latitudes. Crops vary from pears to pineapples, from potatoes to peaches, from wheat to rice, from sugar cane to tobacco, and from grapes to barley.

Questions
The graph lists the principal crop productions for 1969-70. Study the list and answer the following:
1. Name two tropical and two temperate fruit crops.

Figure 2.28

2. Which grain crop has the highest production figure? How many million cubic metres is it above the second highest yielding grain harvest?
3. Give examples of some citrus fruits. Where in North America are such fruits cultivated? What type of climate is necessary for growing citrus fruits?
4. In what forms would these fruits be exported to such foreign markets as Mainland China, Japan, Great Britain, etc.?

Wheat Cultivation

Australia's wheat crop is second in importance only to her wool. It is an important export dollar earner, and in a wheat-hungry world, Australia is an important contributor. She exports wheat to Mainland China, Japan, India, Britain, the Middle Eastern countries, and South America.

Principal Crop Production

Crop	Total Production
Wheat	$14\,000\,000 \text{ m}^3$
Oats	$3\,256\,000 \text{ m}^3$
Barley	$2\,780\,000 \text{ m}^3$
Rice	$388\,000 \text{ m}^3$
Apples	$684\,000 \text{ m}^3$
Pears	$345\,000 \text{ m}^3$
Citrus fruits	$529\,000 \text{ m}^3$
Pineapples	$226\,000 \text{ m}^3$
Bananas	$176\,000 \text{ m}^3$
Potatoes	572 727 000 t
Sugar cane (for crushing)	14 121 000 t
Grapes	666 364 000 t
Dried vine grapes (raisins, currants, etc.)	83 636 000 t
Cotton	27 800 t
Tobacco	15 900 t
Wine (made)	238 000 kL

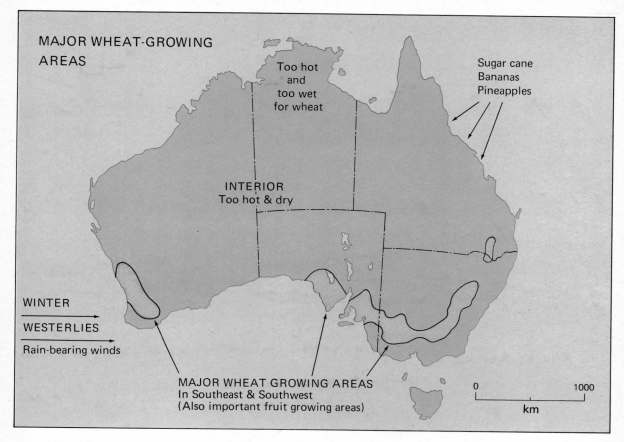

MAJOR WHEAT-GROWING AREAS

Too hot and too wet for wheat

Sugar cane
Bananas
Pineapples

INTERIOR
Too hot & dry

WINTER

WESTERLIES

Rain-bearing winds

MAJOR WHEAT GROWING AREAS
In Southeast & Southwest
(Also important fruit growing areas)

0   1000
km

Figure 2.29 The main wheat-growing areas in Australia. Wheat cultivation is confined to the southern areas of the continent. 1. Give some reasons why wheat is not cultivated in the northern and central regions of the continent. 2. Where are pineapples grown? Note that the southeast and southwestern "corners" of the continent receive rains in winter. Summers are hot and dry. These lands are irrigated in the summer. Fruits such as oranges, peaches, apricots, lemons, tangerines, and grapefruit are cultivated in these so-called "Mediterranean" regions.

In many respects, the wheat-growing areas overlap the best sheep raising regions, i.e., the meat-producing sheep. The best conditions for wheat growing include:
(a) a good heavy soil to support the top-heavy plant,
(b) an annual rainfall of 500-760 mm, with precipitation during the growing season and a dry, sunny harvesting period,
(c) flat land for efficient harvesting by mechanical means — combine harvesters, tractor drawn equipment, etc.
The Australian wheat farmer's working calendar is determined by the seasons:
(a) Seeding is done during the autumn, after the first rains have moistened the soils.
(b) Growth takes place during the warm, wet winters, since a good rainfall helps to swell the grain.

(c) The crops are harvested in late spring, when sunshine is essential to ripen the grain.

Australian wheat farms are large. Many are thousands of hectares in size. The farms, like those in Canada, are highly mechanized. The combine-harvester cuts, threshes, and bags the wheat. The grain is transported to railway halls for shipment to collecting centres. From these centres, the grain is transported to flour mills for home use and to the ports for export to foreign markets. Grain elevators, so typical of the Canadian West, are not part of the Australian landscape, for the grain, as stated, is bagged and ready for export. Australia is fourth after Canada, Argentina, and the U.S.A. as a world wheat exporter.

53

54

Sugar Cane Farming

Sugar is obtained from the sap of the long, fibrous, joint-like stems of the sugar cane. The canes grow so thickly that, in their struggle for light, they reach heights of 2.4 to 3.3 m. They are straight and upright and are topped by dense clusters of leaves.

Sugar cane grows best where the following conditions prevail:

(a) a hot, humid climate where the annual rainfall is at least 1000 mm,

(b) no frost,

(c) deep, well-drained, flat soils,

(d) heavy rains to speed up growth and fill the stems with juice,

(e) cooler weather before harvesting to slow down growth and thus increase the sugar content of the plant juice.

Study the map and cross-section and determine why the coastal areas of Queensland and northern New South Wales are ideal for sugar cane cultivation.

Page 54

(Top)   Mechanical wheat harvesters in New South Wales.

(Centre)   Sugar cane fields in Queensland.

(Bottom)   Mechanical cane cutter harvesting the sugar cane in Queensland.

Page 55

(Bottom) Figure 2.30

(Right) Figure 2.31   The sugar-growing areas of Queensland and the northern coast of New South Wales, are some of the main sugar milling and exporting centres. About 95 percent of Australia's sugar is produced in Queensland.

Questions
1. Name the line of latitude on the map. What does this tell you about the climate of the region?
2. What is the minimum annual rainfall along the coast?
3. Why is the rainfall heavy in this region?
4. Why is the land suitable for sugar cane cultivation?

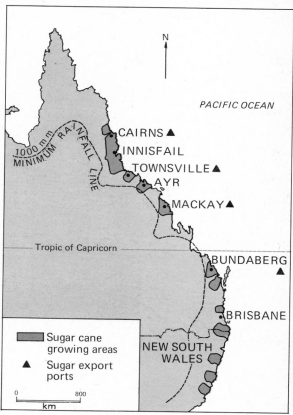

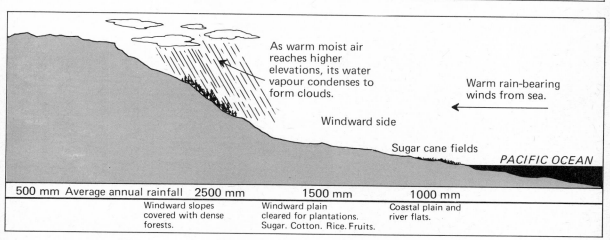

As warm moist air reaches higher elevations, its water vapour condenses to form clouds.

Warm rain-bearing winds from sea.

Windward side

Sugar cane fields

PACIFIC OCEAN

500 mm Average annual rainfall 2500 mm	1500 mm	1000 mm
Windward slopes covered with dense forests.	Windward plain cleared for plantations. Sugar. Cotton. Rice. Fruits.	Coastal plain and river flats.

Sugar cane is grown from stalk cuttings — each cutting being of two or three joints. Each cutting, known as a *sett,* may grow as many as fifteen to twenty canes. The new canes grow from buds at the joints or nodes of the stem.

Sugar plantations vary in size from about 20 to 80 ha, but most farms are approximately 30 ha. Because the land is flat, mechanical sowers and harvesters are now used, although many farmers still cut the cane by hand with the use of machetes.

During planting time, a single machine cuts up the canes into suitable lengths (setts), sprays them with fungicides, drops them into furrows, covers them with soil, and then adds the fertilizer. Such a planter fulfills all these functions in a series of rapid operations.

Before harvesting, the plantation is set on fire. The fire is kept carefully under control and the flames are kept long enough to get rid of the thick undergrowth and the rats in the fields. Although the canes are charred, the juice in the stems is not damaged. Teams of eight to ten cutters may work on a plantation as seasonal workers. On the other hand, the farmer might own or rent a mechanical harvester. In recent years, seventy percent of the sugar cane crop has been harvested by machine.

Raw sugar is Australia's most valuable export crop after wheat. The 1969-70 harvest yielded some 1 934 000 t of actual raw sugar. The annual home requirements total approximately 591 000 t. Exports for the year ending June, 1970, totalled 1 241 000 t of raw and refined sugar.

Figure 2.32   Simplified diagram to illustrate the processing of raw sugar cane. Follow the arrows carefully. 1. From where is the sugar cane transported? 2. Bagasse is the refuse left over after the juice has been extracted from the cane. What use is made of bagasse? 3. The excess sugar is spun off by means of a centrifuge. What is the name given to the spun-off syrup? 4. What is the clear liquid of unrefined sugar? Where is sugar refined?

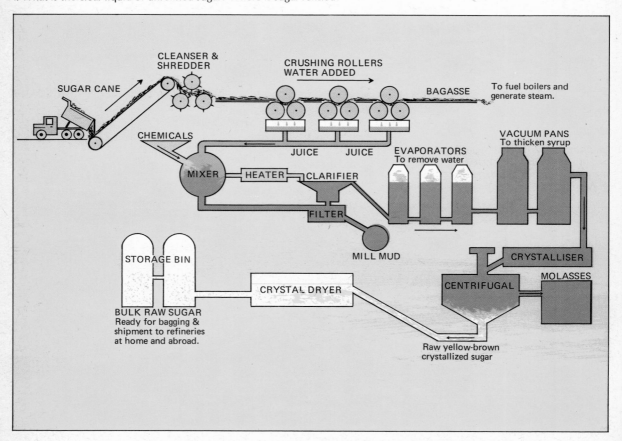

The chart shows the distribution of Australian raw sugar in 1969.

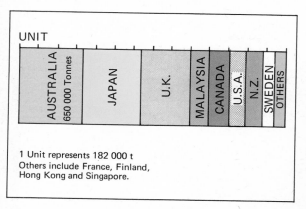

UNIT

| AUSTRALIA 650 000 Tonnes | JAPAN | U.K. | MALAYSIA | CANADA | U.S.A. | N.Z. | SWEDEN | OTHERS |

1 Unit represents 182 000 t
Others include France, Finland,
Hong Kong and Singapore.

Figure 2.33 1969 Distribution of Australia's Sugar Harvests

Questions
1. How many tonnes were kept for home use? Roughly what fraction of the total harvest was consumed in Australia?
2. Which country is Australia's greatest market for sugar? Which country closely follows this?
3. Why are these two countries great importers of sugar?
4. Approximately how much sugar did Australia export to Canada in 1969?
5. Why does the United Kingdom import more sugar than Canada?

A commercial pineapple plantation near Brisbane, Queensland.

The great sugar-producing countries of the world are: U.S.S.R., Cuba, U.S.A., Brazil, India, Australia, Mexico, West Germany, Poland, and South Africa. The U.S.S.R. produces nearly four times as much sugar per year as Australia, and yet the climate is unsuitable for the growing of sugar cane.

Questions
1. What type of sugar does the U.S.S.R. produce?
2. How does it differ from sugar cane in form and growth?
3. What other countries grow this source of raw sugar?

Fruit Growing

As already stated, Australia produces a variety of fruits — tropical fruits in the northeastern region and temperate types in the south. Although the fruit growing areas are limited, the industry is run on a highly scientific basis to produce maximum harvests. Australia's biggest crop is apples, and over a third of the harvest is exported. Furthermore, over a third of Australia's apples are grown in Tasmania.

Located in the Southern Hemisphere where the seasons are reversed, Australia's

Vineyards in New South Wales.

fruit exports find ready markets during the out-of-season periods in Japan and European countries.

Vineyards in southern Australia produce grapes for wine and fruit. The wines are imported to over fifty countries, including Canada. Great Britain is the greatest importer. Certain grapes are dried and are exported as raisins and currants.

Although some fresh fruit is exported, most is canned (pears, apricots, peaches, pineapples, grapefruit, and tangerines).

In conclusion, it should be stated that the Australian farmer today does not rely on one crop. He may grow wheat and rear sheep, or he may grow several types of crops, or he may grow oats and barley and rear beef cattle. Such practice is known as *diversified farming*. If one crop is poor in one year, the other helps to compensate for that loss.

MINERALS AND MINING

Australia is a "treasure island" of mineral deposits. The continent's resources vary from gold and silver to iron ore and bauxite, and from lead and zinc to coal and petroleum. A glance at the mineral resources map will show you the wide range of deposits and the areas where they are mined. The bar graph shows the export figures for the major minerals.

Page 59

(Top) Figure 2.34   Minerals in Australia.

(Bottom) Figure 2.35   Bar graph showing Australia's mineral exports for 1969-70 and the estimated export for 1973-74. Name the two minerals whose 1973-74 exports were expected to be less than those of the years 1969-70. Name the three minerals with the highest export value.

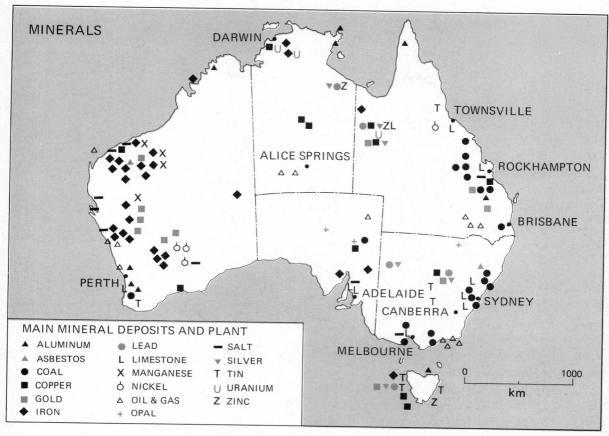

MINERALS

MAIN MINERAL DEPOSITS AND PLANT

▲ ALUMINUM	● LEAD	▬ SALT
▲ ASBESTOS	L LIMESTONE	▼ SILVER
● COAL	X MANGANESE	T TIN
■ COPPER	⚲ NICKEL	U URANIUM
■ GOLD	△ OIL & GAS	Z ZINC
◆ IRON	+ OPAL	

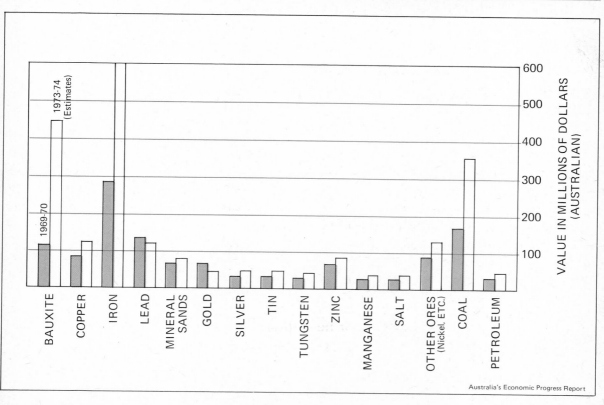

VALUE IN MILLIONS OF DOLLARS (AUSTRALIAN)

1973-74 (Estimates)

1969-70

BAUXITE COPPER IRON LEAD MINERAL SANDS GOLD SILVER TIN TUNGSTEN ZINC MANGANESE SALT OTHER ORES (Nickel, ETC.) COAL PETROLEUM

Australia's Economic Progress Report

59

Gold was the first mineral to be discovered on the continent, and its discovery in 1851 lured thousands of prospectors to the new land "down under". Australia's population doubled between the years 1851 and 1861, due to the immigration of over half a million people. Although the earliest gold discoveries were near Bathurst in New South Wales and at Ballarat and Bendigo, near Melbourne in the State of Victoria, the big "strikes" were made some forty years later in the Western Desert.

On September 17, 1892, two prospectors, Bayley and Ford, struck gold in the Western Desert at a place called Fly Flat. This prospecting centre later became known as Koolgoorbiddie (*Koolgoor* meaning a mulga tree and *biddie* a water hole). The name was later shortened to Coolgardie. The earlier names were truly descriptive of the place in such a barren desert landscape. A year later, Patrick Hannan found the richest deposits at Kalgoorlie, and so great were the outcrops of mineral that the centre was well named "The Golden Mile". Kalgoorlie is still Australia's foremost gold-producing centre, but the output of the neighbouring towns is diminishing, and some have become "ghost towns". This, of course, has also happened in other parts of the world, especially in California and in the Yukon region of Canada. Kalgoorlie's gold output is also on the decline, but as the world price of gold is getting higher, so the mine shafts are getting deeper.

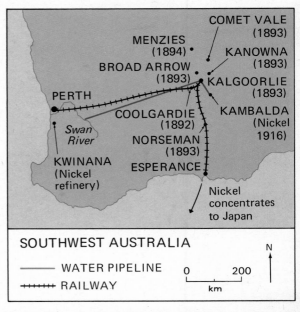

SOUTHWEST AUSTRALIA

—————— WATER PIPELINE

++++++ RAILWAY

0   200
km

N

Figure 2.37 Map showing some of the major and original gold mining centres of Australia.

Questions
1. Where was gold first discovered? What was the year of the greatest discovery?
2. Name the major gold-producing centre today.
3. What other mineral is now mined in this region? Where and when was it discovered?
4. Where is it refined? Name an important importer of nickel concentrates.
5. The world price of gold was once fixed at 35 dollars an ounce, (1933-1970). What is the price per ounce today? (Gold prices are still quoted "per ounce", and there are as yet no plans to change this.)

Figure 2.36 Flow chart to illustrate the processing of gold from the mined ores to the gold bar. Chemicals are added to the ore which has been ground and much water is needed for the washing and flotation (separation) process. One tonne of gold ore, on an average yields 6 grams of pure gold. However, this varies according to the gold content of the ore.

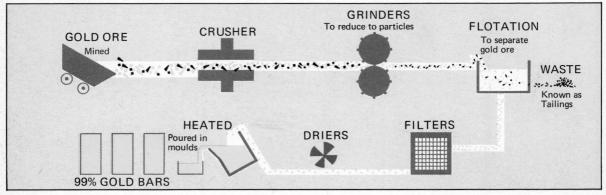

A second mineral boom occurred in Australia in the 1960's when nickel ore was discovered around Kalgoorlie. While searching for uranium, the modern prospectors came upon a high-grade nickel ore, and in 1966 the Western Mining Company of Kambalda announced a great discovery on their property. Kambalda is now the foremost nickel ore centre in Australia. Many Canadian nickel companies are involved in Australia's nickel industry. The processing of nickel from the crude ore is in many ways similar to that of gold, but the yield per tonne of ore is much higher. Nickel is a hard, magnetic metal which is resistant to corrosion and retains a high, bright polish. It increases in toughness and durability when alloyed with steel, and combines easily with other metals.

Questions
1. From resource books find out more about nickel and its uses.
2. Why would Japan be a major importer of nickel?
3. Why would Canadian companies be interested in Australia's nickel production?

Australia is fortunate in having deposits of coal. In the industrial development of the country, coal has been the most important mineral. Although it is mined in every state in the continent, approximately ninety percent is located in the eastern regions, notably in Queensland and New South Wales.

The coal is the soft bituminous variety which, when heated to remove the gases, leaves an excellent coke that burns with a high heat and little smoke. It is excellent for smelting furnaces and the production of thermal electricity.

The coal deposits found south of Perth are important for the iron smelting works at Kiwinana, which is also a nickel refining centre.

One coal-bearing region of importance is the industrial Latrobe Valley of Victoria State, some 145 km east of Melbourne. The largest known continuous deposits of brown coal in the world are located there. Although it is a low-grade fuel, earthy in texture, and of high moisture content, this soft lignite can be used in power stations. Nearly 80 percent of the state's electricity is obtained from these deposits. Furthermore, when the lignite is dried and processed, the resultant briquettes are ideal for household use.

Australia's major coal exporting port is Newcastle and her greatest market is Japan.

Names such as Iron Prince and Iron Monarch in South Australia indicate the presence of iron ore. In these, and in other areas, notably Yampi Sound in northwestern Australia and the Hamersley Range, huge hills of high-grade iron ore are mined. With her coal deposits and limestone beds, Australia has the essentials for an iron smelting industry. This industry is being developed rapidly, and contracts with Japan appear to forecast a profitable future. These contracts cover the export of 755 000 000 t of iron ore and pellets, valued at $6 450 000 000, by 1993.

Yampi Sound iron ore deposits in north Western Australia. The high-grade ore is mined from the ocean cliffs. The opencast type of mining is done by cutting into the cliff in 12 m step-like excavations. Where is this iron ore smelted? What is the use of limestone in the smelting process?

Page 62

(Top)   Mount Isa, in northwestern Queensland, offers an example of man living in an inhospitable, desert region because of the mineral resources. Here in the dry and isolated Outback lives a community of 17 000 people mining lead, zinc, and silver.

(Bottom left)   Iron ore from the Pilbara Region in Western Australia is loaded onto bulk carriers at Port Hedland.

(Bottom right)   Steel mills at Newcastle use iron ore from Yampi Sound.

Page 63

(Top right)   Offshore oil rig on the Marlin oil and natural gas field in the Bass Strait.

(Centre) Figure 2.38   Simplified diagram showing a cross-section of a typical area where oil or natural gas is found. Over countless ages, microscopic, unicellular oil-secreting plants and marine animals became entombed in layers of sedimentary rocks. Pressures squeezed the oil into more porous sandstones, forcing it to seep upwards until it met an impermeable rock layer. Oil reservoirs were thus formed. Since gas is lighter than oil, and oil is lighter than water, it is common to find reserves with gas on top, then oil, and below this salt water.

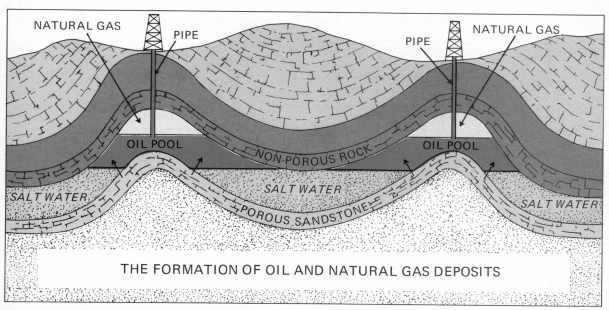

THE FORMATION OF OIL AND NATURAL GAS DEPOSITS

Unfortunately, in certain regions the iron ore deposits and the coal beds are not located close to each other, and as it takes 3.6 t of coal to smelt 1 t of iron ore, transporting the ore to the coalfields is necessary by land or water. The ore from Yampi Sound, for example, is carried by cargo ships to Newcastle, where the neighbouring coal beds provide the coke for the blast furnaces. Similarly, the ores from Iron Prince and Iron Monarch are transported to Newcastle and Port Kembla for smelting.

Australia's iron deposits are of high quality. Her reserves in the western region, for example, have an iron content of over fifty percent.

Bauxite, the ore from which aluminum is produced, is another mineral now being developed on the continent. The reserves in northwest Western Austrialia are so great that an aluminum plant is being planned to refine the area's estimated 182×10^6 t of crude bauxite.

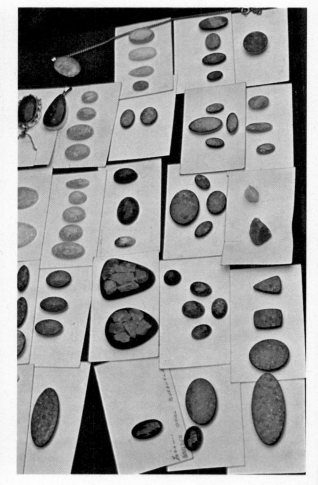

Oil and gas deposits were discovered in the 1960's, but Australia is far from being an oil-rich country. However, the Australian government is taking every advantage of her energy resources. Natural gas, for example, is piped to Perth and to Adelaide from deposits within their respective states.

With regard to semiprecious stones, Australia is famous for her black opals, zircons, and garnets.

Australia is developing her national resources at a demanding pace. As a young country, she is developing her industries in order to make the country more self-sufficient, to increase employment and trade, and to maintain a high standard of living for her citizens.

In addition to the so-called heavy industries such as iron and steel production, coal, and shipbuilding, many newer industries have been developed during the past few years. These include food production, automobile assembly and production of auto parts, petroleum refining, plastics, textiles, and the production of electrical equipment such as refrigerators, radios, stoves, toasters, and other appliances.

PRESENT AND FUTURE PROBLEMS

Australia's present and future problems may be summarized as follows:
(a) population — size and distribution,
(b) continued industrial development,
(c) markets for exports,
(d) defence.

Australia is anxious to increase her population by encouraging immigration under carefully defined and supervised immigration policies. Professional and skilled persons and young families are needed to settle and make the country their permanent home. The Government also seeks people who are prepared to settle in areas outside the already overcrowded big cities such as Sydney, Melbourne, and Adelaide. Although fair and objective in her demands regarding immigrants, Australia has always been selective and careful. Commonwealth citizens were generally given preference, but in January, 1975, the Australian Government decreed that every person visiting the country must apply for, and will need, a visa.

In the past, Australia has had to import most of her industrial and technical equipment and many manufactured goods, mostly from Great Britain. Transporation costs were high and goods were, therefore, costly. During World War II (1939-45), Australia, out of necessity, had to develop her own industries (iron and steel, electrical goods, textiles, food, etc.) and they have been further encouraged by government aid. The plan is to make Australia as independent as possible and to provide employment. Australia appreciates the need to continue to develop her agricultural interests as well as expanding her industrial projects.

Until recent years, Britain has been Australia's greatest trading partner. Close ties of kinship with Britain have always helped to cement trade agreements. However, when Britain discussed entry into the European Economic Market* and eventually became a partner, Australia realized that she had to develop other markets, and this she has done. Although she still exports

(Top) Bauxite is converted to alumina at this plant in Queensland.

(Bottom left) Molten iron ore is tipped into a ladle at the Port Kembla ironworks.

(Bottom right) A collection of valuable opals.

*The European Economic Community, also called the Common Market, is a partnership of several countries in Europe (Belgium, France, West Germany, Italy, The Netherlands, Luxembourg, Denmark, Eire, and Britain) for mutual economic benefit and security. The major aims include less restricted trading conditions between member countries, easier movement of the working population, and common transport facilities.

to Britain, Europe, Canada, and the United States, she is seeking greater trade with such Pacific countries as Japan, China, New Zealand, and the countries of Southeast Asia.

Australia's isolated position in the Pacific Ocean creates problems and demands a strong defence programme. Her policy is "to ensure the security of the mainland and island territorities and to protect national interests". Australia supports an army, navy, and air force. She is involved in the security of Southeast Asia and the Pacific, and is therefore a member of SEATO (Southeast Asia Treaty Organization), ANZUS (Australia, New Zealand, and United States Treaty of mutual aid in the case of an armed attack on any one of them in the Pacific), the Commonwealth of Nations, and the United Nations.

3. NEW ZEALAND

INTRODUCTION

An atlas map shows New Zealand as a slender, slanted outline close to the "bottom" of the world. It appears small and isolated in the vast Pacific Ocean, astride a line midway between the equator and the South Pole.

Composed of three main islands and several smaller ones, New Zealand lies some 1900 km from Australia and 10 600 km from South America. Far to the south lies the icy, snow-covered continent of Antarctia.

How were these islands, stretching roughly 1770 km from north to south, formed in the middle of this vast ocean? According to geologists, millions of years ago earth movements buckled the ocean floor in this area and thrust it above the sea surface, forming a new land — a land of volcanoes and earthquakes. However, apparently this land later disappeared into the ocean depths. Thousands of years later, another series of earth movements in the earth's crust, accompanied by volcanic activity, created further upthrusts and buckling to form land. Slowly the region became stable and, after cooling and countless years of weathering by wind and rain and changing landscape, New Zealand came into being. Evidence of the earlier volcanic activity may still be seen in the volcanic peaks and in the crater lakes of boiling, bubbling, heaving mud and boiling, steaming geysers in the Rotorua region of the North Island. New Zealand still experiences earthquakes and volcanic activity.

Atlas Exercise
1. Name the three main islands. Which is the largest of the three? Which is the smallest?
2. State the approximate lines of latitude within which New Zealand lies.
3. Name the sea which separates New Zealand from Australia, and the two straits which separate the three islands.
4. Locate Rotorua, the region of spouting geysers and bubbling mud pools that plop like boiling porridge.
5. Locate and mark the largest lake. Which island has the largest number of lakes?
6. From your study of the lines of latitude, which island enjoys the warmer climate?
7. Name the four largest cities of the country.
8. Name the mountain range which forms the "backbone" of the largest island.

New Zealand covers an area of about 268 750 km² — about one-quarter of the size of Ontario. Its total length is nearly 1600 km, and no point is further than 109 km from the sea.

The scenery is rich and varied. Snow-covered mountains and glaciers in the Southern Alps contrast with the steaming, thermal volcanic region of the North Island; the coastal areas vary from wide, flat beaches to the deeply indented fiords of the southwest; the lush, semi-tropical forests of the North Island offer different views from the rich grasslands of the Canterbury Plains of the South Island.

With a total number of 2 974 000 inhabitants, New Zealand's population is not large. In fact, some of the world's cities support a far larger number of people. Compare this population with that of Toronto or Montreal or Vancouver.

Pages 68-69

(Top left) A scene in the semitropical forest of the North Island.

(Top centre) A model Maori village in the Rotorua region of the North Island.

(Top right) A pool of boiling mud in the thermal volcanic area of Rotorua.

(Bottom left) The Franz Josef Glacier in the Southern Alps.

(Bottom centre) A typical sheep station in the South Island.

(Bottom right) A suburban scene in Gisborne, North Island. Houses are not unsimilar to those in Canadian suburbs. They may be made of brick or wood. Roofs are generally of tiles, but in the rural areas they are often of metal sheeting (corregated iron). Styles are derived from those of Europe. Over eighty percent of households cook by electricity and eleven percent by gas.

Of New Zealand's total population, approximately eight percent are Maori or part Maori, descended from the original settlers of the islands. The majority are of British descent.

The following account, written by a young student, gives an account of life in New Zealand.

> "I live in Milford, a seaside suburb of Auckland. This city is the largest in New Zealand, but it is not the capital.
>
> Most of our houses are made of wood and are on one floor level — bungalow style. Our office buildings and stores, which seem large to us, would be minute compared with the large skyscrapers of your cities, as they are seldom more than six or seven storeys high. The reason for this is that we are in the earthquake belt and tall buildings would be hazardous.
>
> Central heating in houses is practically unknown in the northern part of New Zealand, as our winters are mild with no snow and only occasional light frosts. Our yearly temperature range is between 10°C in winter and about 29°C in summer.
>
> As our country is long and divided into two main islands, there is an appreciable temperature difference between the northern and the southern regions. The South Island has a much colder winter than the North Island, and snow falls every year in the Southern Alps.
>
> My country mainly produces farm products for export. Fruits of the citrus, stone, and pip varieties are widely grown. Tobacco and hops are also cultivated. Winemaking is a growing industry, particularly around Auckland.
>
> New Zealand is a growing tourist centre with its thermal wonders, Swiss-like mountains, Norwegian-like fiords, big game fishing in its central lakes, and animals and flowers which are peculiar to the country. There are many smaller attractions, too, such as the Waitomo caves with their stalactites and stalagmites, and the grotto with weird, blue glowworms.
>
> The silver fern is our national floral emblem. Our most interesting bird is the kiwi. This wingless, flightless bird, which is about 30 cm high, is found in its wild state only in this country.
>
> The Maoris were the first settlers. They emigrated from some of the South Sea Islands. They named this country *Aotearoa* — the Land of the Long White Cloud. The Maoris no longer live in *pas* or fortified villages, but some pas are kept intact for tourists to visit. There is a new revival of Maori culture. Since they are becoming more integrated with the *Pakeha* (New Zealanders of European descent) and moving into the cities, it was feared that their way of life, customs and dances would die out.
>
> The Maoris live like everyone else. Maori children go to public schools. There are Maori teachers, preachers, and members of parliament. Any walk of life is open to all.
>
> Auckland is the largest city, but Wellington is the capital. Christchurch is the city which is most English in character, while Dunedin is the most Scottish.
>
> So you see, New Zealand has many aspects.
>
> *KIAORA* — the Maori for Greetings."

Explorers and Settlers

The first settlers in New Zealand, as already stated, were the Maoris, who migrated southwards across the Pacific, voyaging from island to island and performing feats of navigation rivalled only for their courage and skill by the exploits of the Vikings. The true Maori colonists, however, arrived about 1350 and this movement was known as the Great Migration.

For several centuries the Maoris lived undisturbed. Then, in December, 1643, the Dutch explorer, Abel Tasman, in search of a southern continent, saw the west coast of South Island. Tasman tried to land, but after an encounter with the Maoris, during which four of his men were killed, he sailed away. The country he later named *Nieuw Zeeland* was represented as an uncertain line on a chart.

(Left) Canoes like this were used by the Maoris to reach New Zealand.

(Right) A model of Captain Cook's ship, the *Endeavour*.

It was over a hundred years later, in 1769, that New Zealand was rediscovered. Captain James Cook, the great English navigator, discovered the islands at the same time as a Frenchman, De Surville. Their voyages took place at almost the same time and without the other's knowledge. However, it was Cook who sailed around New Zealand and found that Tasman's wavy line on a map was a group of islands. Cook's chart of the islands was superb and he made friendly contact with the Maoris.

Cook's accounts attracted pioneers in search of timber, seals, flax, and whales. Lonely settlements grew up along the coasts. Relationships between the rough, adventurous newcomers and the Maoris were often explosive and as settlement increased there were more quarrels and fights.

Meanwhile pressure was growing in Britain to make New Zealand a British colony before the French could claim the new land. Eventually, in 1840, Captain William Hobson of the Royal Navy was sent out to negotiate with the Maori chieftains. This led to the signing of the Treaty of Waitangi. In return for transferring the sovereignty of New Zealand to Britain, the Maori people were guaranteed "possessions of their lands" and were "accorded the rights and privileges of British subjects".

During the next ten years settlement increased rapidly. Wellington was made the capital city, and by 1852 New Zealand was granted self-government.

In the 1860's gold was discovered, and, as was true in all gold rushes, thousands of prospectors flocked to New Zealand from Australia and the west coast of North America. However, by the 1870's the gold rush days were over. Timber, the main export of the time, yielded first place to wool as an foreign money earner. The "future" of New Zealand was established in 1882 when the refrigeration of foodstuffs during the long sea voyage between New Zealand and Europe was successfully introduced. From that year, New Zealand developed her farming industries and began specializing in meat and dairy produce (butter and cheese) for the British and other overseas markets. Although gold helped in the settlement of New Zealand, it was the invention of refrigeration that actually developed the country and paved the way for the future.

In 1947 New Zealand became independent and self-governing, establishing equality with Britain and other members of the Commonwealth of Nations. New Zealand today is, therefore, a free, independent sovereign state with a parliamentary democracy. All citizens over the age of twenty years have the vote and, incidentally, it was the first country to give women the vote, in 1893.

New Zealand Today

Although New Zealand is essentially an agricultural country exporting such products as meat, butter, and cheese, seventy-seven percent of the people live in the cities and towns, which are the factory and office centres of the nation. The factories, which vary from meat freezing and general food processing to automobile assembling, and from the production of electrical equipment to clothing, are small plants compared with many in North America. Remember that the total population of all New Zealand is under three million. The country is divided into two major islands, and so the large centres cater to the variety of needs of their surrounding area. Some of the larger factories employ about 500 workers, but, in the main, the number of employees is considerably less.

Figure 3.1   Map showing the areas of densest population in New Zealand.

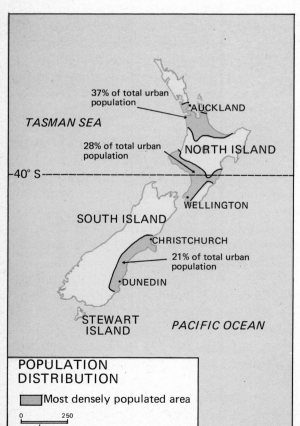

The rural population of a little over half a million people are mainly farmers and their families. Others living in rural areas include workers in forestry and mining and some Maoris who live in rural communities.

> *Questions*
> 1. Around which city is the densest population found?
> 2. Which island is the more densely populated?
> 3. Which city has the greatest population?
> 4. Why are there few people in (a) the central region of North Island, and (b) the central and western regions of South Island?

New Zealand is known for her "Four Cities" — Auckland, Wellington, Christchurch, and Dunedin. Note that two of these major cities are located on each island and they are approximately about the same distance from each other. Each serves an "all purpose" need for its own region. Nearly forty-five percent of the total population of the country lives in these four metropolitan centres.

These four cities have many factors in common:
(a) All four serve many functions — industrial, commercial, and administrative.
(b) All are ports.
(c) Each has good access to land area.
(d) Each is a railway centre.
(e) All four have airports — all except Dunedin have international air connections.
(f) Each is a centre of local government and of branches of the central government.
(g) All are university centres.

Page 73

\(Top)   Auckland, the northernmost and largest city in New Zealand (population Greater Auckland 720 000). The fastest growing city in the country, Auckland has as many people today as the urban areas of Auckland, Wellington, Christchurch, and Dunedin had together thirty years ago. Suburbs sprawl all along adjacent coasts. Auckland has a fine, protected harbour.

(Bottom)   Wellington, the capital city (population Greater Wellington 328 000). Situated on a magnificent harbour, Wellington is the administrative and geographic centre of the country.

(Left) A school in New Plymouth, North Island. Education is compulsory in New Zealand from the ages of six to fifteen, although nearly everyone starts school at five years of age. Education in the State (public) schools is free. Most children go to State schools but a small percentage attend fee-paying private schools run by the churches. Maoris attend the same schools. Some children living in the more isolated areas receive their education by correspondence courses. New Zealand has six universities and several technical institutes.

(Right) The New Zealand climate favours a wide range of sports all the year round — soccer, golf, cricket, tennis, surfing, swimming, skiing, and so on. The national game is rugby (football) and the "All Blacks", the national rugby team, is internationally famous. New Zealand sportsmen compete regularly in Olympic and British Commonwealth games. Sir Edmund Hillary, the first mountaineer to climb to the top of Mount Everest, was a New Zealander.

New Zealanders, in the main, enjoy a high standard of living. They are proud of their ancestory and ties with Britain are still warm and strong.

New Zealand today is a "welfare state", that is, the state provides social security and health, old age, and family benefits. All these benefits and pensions have existed since 1938, including free hospital and medical treatment. Life expectancy in New Zealand (69 years for men and 74 years for women) is exceeded only by Scandinavia, and the infant death rate is one of the three lowest in the world.

New Zealand, at one time, traded mainly with Britain, but since Britain has joined the European Common Market, i.e. entered into an agreement with certain European countries to trade with them for mutual benefits, New Zealand is now trading more with countries in Asia. She is developing as an independent country, trading within the Pacific area rather than with Europe.

THE PHYSICAL ENVIRONMENT

Landforms

New Zealand is predominantly a mountainous country. A central "backbone" of mountain ranges runs the length of the two main islands. In the North Island the ranges are located towards the eastern regions, while in the South Island the Southern Alps lie to the west.

The Southern Alps run almost the entire length of the South Island, with New Zealand's highest peak, Mount Cook (3764 m), midway along the chain. There are twenty-seven mountain peaks with heights of more than 2890 m above sea level in this mountain chain, and in keeping with this great alpine system is a network of imposing glaciers.

However, huge and imposing as the mountains may seem, there are also parts of

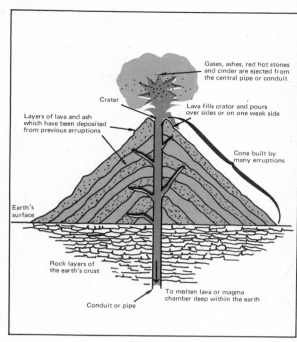

(Left)   Mount Cook. The Southern Alps is a region of high peaks and of glaciers. The largest glacier, located in the far south, is the Tasman Glacier, 29 km long and 1.6 km wide. Towards the southwest, the mountains cling close to the fiorded coastline and the scenery is very similar to that of Norway's coastal area.

(Right) Figure 3.2   This diagram shows the formation of a volcanic peak or cone formed by a series of volcanic eruptions. Sometimes the lava just flows over wide areas to form volcanic plateaus. What causes volcanoes? From where does the lava flow? What is pumice stone?

New Zealand where the earth's crust is thin and there is a region of volcanic activity and earth tremors. This area stretches in a line from south of Lake Taupo in the North Island to White Island, off the Bay of Plenty. In this plateau region, centred around Rotorua, are three great volcanic peaks, Ruapehu and Ngauruhoe, which are both active, and Tongariro.

The country's deeply folded landscape has many lakes and rivers. The rivers vary from the short, torrential streams along the west coast of the South Island, to the long, slower-flowing, glacier-fed waters of the eastern plains. The two deep-flowing rivers that drain the volcanic region of the North Island, namely the Wanganui and the Waikato, are important, especially as future energy sources. Lake Taupo, the largest lake, is a widening of the Waikato River. Some 168 m deep, Lake Taupo covers an area of 622 km². New Zealand's rivers, unlike those of Australia, never dry up.

Although nearly three-quarters of New Zealand is over 198 m above sea level, there are large expanses of flat country, and the most extensive are the Canterbury Plains. These green plains, level as a table and ideal for animal grazing, cover about 12 435 km² of the South Island's east coast.

Climate

New Zealand enjoys a temperate climate in that the summers are not too hot and dry and the winters are generally mild. The reasons for this type of climate are:
(a) New Zealand lies in favourable latitudes.
(b) The islands are long and narrow and no place is too far from the influence of the sea.
(c) It lies in the path of the rain-bearing westerly winds.

Because of its 1600 km north to south stretch, one would expect some difference in temperatures. For example, the Auckland Peninsula, being nearer the tropics, has a higher all-round temperature than Stewart Island in the far south. However, the difference in temperatures between the two islands is only 5 to 8°C.

As in Australia, the seasons in New Zealand are the reverse of those in Canada, i.e. winter in the Northern Hemisphere is summertime south of the equator. Christmas Day, as in Australia, is generally spent out-of-doors and preferably on a sunny beach. December 21st is their longest day.

The average temperature for the whole of New Zealand varies from 9°C in winter (July) to 18°C in summer (January). As already mentioned, the climate is warmer in the North Island and summer readings are often over 27°C.

While Australia is cursed by droughts, New Zealand is blessed with plentiful rains.

(Left) Figure 3.3 Map showing the distribution of rainfall and the prevailing rain-bearing winds.

(Right) Figure 3.4 Two simplified diagrammatic cross sections of the North Island and the South Island of New Zealand.

Rains may fall during any season, but are heaviest during the fall and winter. Nearly every part of the islands receives from 625 to 2500 mm a year. The rainfall keeps the country green, and it is on the rich, green grasses that the sheep and cattle feed. These, in turn, are the bases of the country's essential lamb, butter, and cheese exports.

The distribution of rainfall in the two islands depends on (a) the path of the prevailing winds, and (b) the location of the mountains which act as rain-barriers.

The map and cross sections will help to explain the rainfall distribution and patterns.

Questions
From Figure 3.3:
1. On which coasts is the rainfall heaviest?
2. How does the west side of the South Island compare with the eastern region?
3. Compare the annual rainfall in Hokitika with that of Christchurch. Account for the difference.
4. Locate the area where rainfall is light. What type of farming is practised in this region?

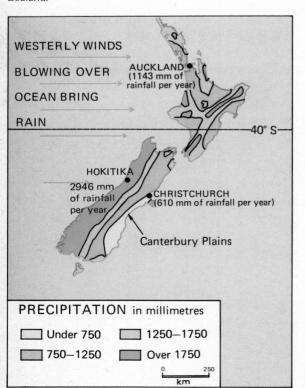

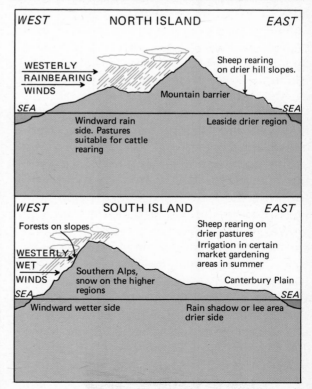

Unfortunately, the gravel soils in the east of South Island are coarse river deposits, built up with the passage of time to form plains. Water percolates very quickly through these soils. Also, during the summer New Zealand has abundant sunshine, resulting in the quick drying of soils. Irrigation is, therefore, necessary where market gardening and mixed farming are important occupations.

Vegetation

The islands of New Zealand are said to be "green", that is, they are well-covered with vegetation which includes thick forests, grasslands, and heaths with ferns. Rainfall is plentiful, vegetation thrives, and thus a "green landscape" is assured.

Much of the native vegetation, however, has been removed or replaced in recent years — partially by clearing for agriculture, but much more by firing or overgrazing. Most of the pastureland today has been seeded with new types of grasses — richer grasses to promote heavier sheep and cattle grazing.

(Top) A beach in the North Island.

(Centre) Milford Sound, a fiord on the southwest coast of the South Island.

(Bottom) In the warmer North Island, especially the Auckland Peninsula, the most valuable tree is the Kauri pine. Prized for its hard wood, it also yields a valuable gum when "bled". Kauri gum is used for varnishes and lacquers. Kauri gum, which once exuded from earlier trees and which now lies buried in the soil, is also dug up and sold to the paint manufacturers or for craft production.

The New Zealand government is very much aware of the need for reforestation and for soil conservation and use. Animal, insect, and weed pests are kept under control. Grasslands must be preserved to maintain the country's sheep population.

On the uplands of the drier east of North Island heath and fern scrub abound.

The South Island provides a variety of temperate vegetation. Along the wet west coast, thick forests of pine and beech prevail. In parts the "bush" is dense and tall. Fernlike, dark green trees provide lush forests of great beauty. The softer woods of the South Island are used for the making of butter and cheese boxes for export. Laurels and other evergreens add a rich and varied greenery to the western slopes.

In the drier east, the tougher, wiry tussocky grasses of the higher slopes have been removed, and, especially on the plains, have been replaced by European grasses and clovers. Because of the mild climate, the grass grows all through the year and animals may graze during all seasons.

Wildlife

Whereas the native animal life of Australia may be considered strange and unique, that of New Zealand may best be described as "absent". When the Europeans settled on the islands there was almost a complete absence of land animals. There were no kangaroos, wallabies, or platypuses, no reptiles except for a few species of lizard, and no amphibians except for a few frogs.

Most of the wildlife was introduced by settlers. It is believed that, in their migrations, the early Maoris brought the dog and the rat to the islands, and the first settlers introduced the Australian opossum. As they did in Canada, the pioneers brought birds and animals with them from their home countries. British settlers introduced such birds as sparrows, skylarks, starlings, such fish for the streams as trout, and such mammals as the rabbit, goat, and deer. As in Australia, the rabbit became a pest and had to be controlled. In some areas the red deer and the opossum are also considered as "enemies" because the former eats valuable grass and the latter destroys trees.

However, New Zealand is rich in birdlife. The following paragraphs give a fine description of the birds of the country.

"New Zealand has always been a land of birds. Long before the first humans arrived on its shores it was the home of birds of many species. They ranged in size from the minute to the monstrous. Some had their origins in prehistoric ages and survived through era after era in these islands, separated from the other land masses of the world by the Tasman Sea and the wide Pacific Ocean.

Then came the first Polynesian migrants. They saw the giant, flightless moas*, as tall as man, and trembled; but they also saw the tiny, friendly robins and fantails, which came fearlessly into their newly-built homes. All about from dawn to dusk, and even through the uneasy night, echoed the calls of birds. Their dawn chorus sung in unison was both a delight and wonder to the newly-arrived humans. These brown-skinned humans began to add bird lore to their knowledge and so started the rich store of fascinating stories which passed into the legend and history of the Maori people."

From: *New Zealand Birds and Flowers*, 1971.

*Note: The moa is now extinct. There were apparently some two dozen species. Some birds were 3.7 m in height. Fossil bones of this ostrichlike bird are now found in swamp muds.

Questions
1. Who were the first Polynesian migrants?
2. Where is Polynesia?
3. The Maoris were once called "Moa-hunters". What do you know about these extinct birds?
4. Give some reasons why the moa became extinct.
5. What other native birds were found in New Zealand?

The kiwi is native to New Zealand. It is not found in its natural state in any other part of the world. It is one of the national emblems of New Zealand. New Zealanders are sometimes called "Kiwis". The kiwi is a winged, tailless, but flightless bird with a long narrow beak. The bird is nocturnal, and its call is shrill. From this came the Maori name "Kiwi".

Many of the native birds have such names as kaka, tui, pukeko, and takahe — names given to them by the first settlers, the Maoris.

All native birds are strictly protected by law and it is not permitted to kill them, capture them, or take their eggs. Birds are also protected in national parks and bird sanctuaries.

THE MAORIS

The Maoris were the first people to settle in New Zealand. Today they number approximately 250 000 and mainly inhabit the North Island. Actually, half the Maori population of the country lives within a radius of about 160 km of Auckland.

The Maoris and the New Zealanders of European origin (known as *Pakehas* to the Maoris) live together freely and on equal terms. The Maoris are, naturally, full citizens and have representation in parliament. However, the mode of life of these people of Polynesian origin has undergone great change and this change continues. The Maoris, in the past, have faced many problems — wars, diseases introduced by European settlers, lack of recognition, and poor educational facilities. Much is now being done by the New Zealand government and by the Maori peoples themselves to overcome past and present-day problems.

Origin and History

The arrival of man in New Zealand remains a riddle. Some believe that the first arrivals were castaways blown off course during voyages from one Pacific island to another. Others think that they came as a result of planned migrations.

Legends and investigations indicate that the Maoris came from East Polynesia at some time between 600 and 1000 A.D. During this period an adventurous group left its South Sea Island home and sailed some 4000 km to find a new home. These people were excellent navigators, and, guided by the stars and by their knowledge of bird migrations, they landed on Aotearoa — *The Land of the Long White Cloud*, as New Zealand was named. Successive migrations from the same area apparently reached New Zealand at intervals until about A.D. 1300 or 1400.

During the latter part of this period, several large sailing canoes arrived and the names of these ships and their chiefs have been preserved in Maori legends and history. Almost all the prominent Maori families today can trace their descent from these people.

The early Maori settlers knew nothing of metals, they had no working animals, and had only their outrigger canoes for transport. Yet as seamen they were superb, and were, perhaps, the greatest of their time. Their implements were made of bone, wood, or

(Left)   A Maori girl in traditional costume, which is made from cloth spun from the fibres of the New Zealand flax plant.

(Top right)   Maori houses are made of wood. The front of the home, especially the door and door posts were heavily carved. Wooden sculptures of native gods protected the villages. The ancestral gods always had three fingers and a thumb per hand. Houses were grouped together within a stockade to form a fortified village.

(Bottom right)   A group of Maoris celebrating a traditional festival. Maoris are proud of their ancestry and culture. Old customs and festivals are still remembered.

stone. In New Zealand they settled and developed a culture which became, in many respects, the most highly developed in Polynesia.

Early Customs and Way of Life

The Maoris settled exceedingly well in their new land. Although they consisted of several different tribes (*iwis*), they spoke the same basic language.

They were and are an artistic people. They carved their canoes and the woodwork of their homes, and tattooed their faces and legs with intricate, spiral designs.

To provide comfort and warmth during the cooler weather, the Maoris made blankets, cloaks, and garments out of the flaxlike fibres of a native plant called *Phormium tenax.*

The Maoris Today

It is estimated that there were originally about 200 000 Maoris living in New Zealand. Intertribal wars during the years 1818-1835 and later wars between the tribes and the European settlers caused a rapid decrease in the Maori population.

The first European settlers in New Zealand were a very mixed group of people, varying from whalers, seal hunters, traders, adventurers, and escaped prisoners to earnest missionaries. Relationships between the rough newcomers and Maoris were often explosive, and European habits, customs, and diseases took their toll of the Maoris and their way of life. When the Maoris acquired firearms, traditional intertribal warfare became a blood bath, and thousands of Maoris died.

New Zealand came under British control in 1840 when Britain signed the Treaty of Waitangi with the leading Maori chiefs. Peace and harmony existed for a short time between settler and Maori, but disputes over land rights and land sales led to the Maori wars which lasted for ten years (1861-71). The Maoris, in spite of their valiant courage and defiance, were fighting against trained troops with guns and cannons. Not only did they suffer great losses in numbers but also a loss of pride. Their numbers dwindled dramatically.

Figure 3.5

Maori Population 1835-1990	
Year	Population
1840	(Estimated)200 000
1870	(Estimated)60 000
1896	(Census)42 113
1900	(Census)40 000
1951	(Census)115 740
1966	(Census)201 159
1973	(Census)250 000
1975	(Projected)281 873
1990	(Projected)491 700

Questions
1. Why was there such a rapid decrease in Maori population between 1840-70? What was the population difference?
2. What was the increase between 1951 and 1966?
3. What is the present Maori population. How does this compare with the original number in 1840?

The Maori population is now increasing because of better hospital and clinical care and because of legislation to improve their standards of living, resulting in improved health care and a reduced number of deaths among children.

The Maori population doubled in number between 1945-66 and it will double again between 1966-85. Very recently, however, the Maori birth rate has begun to drop, possibly in response to pressures felt by the rest of the population.

Although much is being done for the Maori today, many areas still need improvement. The New Zealand government recognizes these problems and solutions are being sought. The Maoris' problems include:

(a) Too many young Maoris do not complete their high school education — nearly fifty percent drop out before they reach fifth form.

(b) Too many Maoris are employed in nonskilled jobs, in factories, and as farm help — many also are employed in domestic duties. Few seek professional and white collar jobs.

(c) Maoris tend to live in inadequate and overcrowded housing.

(d) Maoris tend to have lower incomes than other workers.

(e) A higher proportion of Maoris die from tuberculosis, heart disease, diabetes, and pneumonia than non-Maoris.

The way of life of the Maoris is changing. Today, while land and property are still important issues with the Maoris, more emphasis is being placed on housing, health, welfare, and educational needs.

A noticeable change among the Maoris in recent years is the movement from the country areas into the larger towns and cities. For a people more accustomed to a rural and small community life, the change is difficult, and accommodation and the availability of suitable work are problems that have still to be solved.

The Maori is slowly taking his place and accepting his responsibilities in today's society. Maoris are among New Zealand's top artists, politicians, athletes, and poets. During both World Wars, Maori troops fought with honor for their country on foreign battlefields.

The Maori is fully integrated into New Zealand's society, but he still clings to his past customs and traditions. The Maori has a phrase: *Kia mau to Maoritanga* — "Hold on to your Maori culture."

RESOURCES

Agriculture

Grassland farming is the most important "industry" in New Zealand and is the source of over eighty percent by value of the country's exports. Farms cover almost half the land area, and sheep and lambs outnumber people by thirty to one. There are nearly 3 000 000 people living in New Zealand, and it is estimated that there are approximately 100 000 000 sheep. Sheep are reared either for their meat or for their wool. However, some crossbreed sheep provide both good meat and wool. Beef and dairy cattle are also raised on the grasslands.

New Zealand's success in farming lies in the ability to grow superb, rich grasses and clovers, in spite of the fact that the land, in the main, is not blessed with fertile soils. The following factors account for the fine areas of excellent grasslands:

(a) an adequate rainfall throughout the year, with fairly even distribution,
(b) plentiful sunshine,
(c) careful use of the land,
(d) regular topdressing to keep the grasses healthy and abundant — airplanes are used to spread the chemical fertilizers.

Farmers use all the modern techniques: machinery for plowing, sowing, reaping, and haymaking; electrical apparatus for shearing sheep and milking cows; and refrigeration. Electricity is available even in the most remote farms in New Zealand.

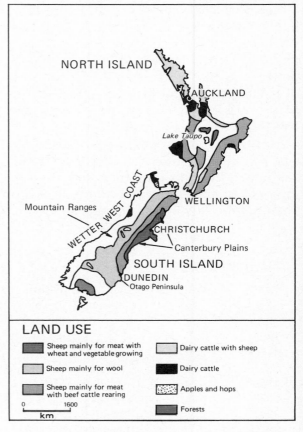

Figure 3.6 Map showing the way the land is used in New Zealand. Although half the land is used for farming, only about twelve percent of the total number of workers are employed on the land. Most of the working population live in the towns and cities, where they are employed in manufacturing industries, offices, and the professions.

Questions
1. On which island is dairy farming an important occupation? Give reasons.
2. In which parts of the island is dairy farming carried on? Name an important city centre.
3. What would be the advantages of having a rich dairy-producing area in close proximity to a large city?
4. Locate the Canterbury Plains. What type of sheep are reared on (a) the hillslopes, and (b) the flatter plains? Why are there different sheep found in these different regions?
5. Why is there no sheep rearing on the western regions of the South Island?
6. Why does the farmer rear cattle or sheep with an emphasis on one, or rear animals and plant crops and vegetables where soils and climate permit?
7. Looking at the total land surface, which type of animal farming occupies the greater land area?

Sheep Rearing

Sheep farms in New Zealand are not as large as those in Australia. The farms vary in size

82

Breed	Description	Uses
Merino	Hardy. Original breed in New Zealand. Ideal for higher mountain slopes in the South Island.	Mainly for wool.
Romney	Introduced from England. Wool is excellent but coarse. 70% of New Zealand's flocks are Romney sheep.	Wool and meat.
Corriedale	Excellent wool and good meat.	Wool and good quality meat.
Drysdale	Long, springy, coarse wool.	Wool for carpets.
Suffolk, Dorset— Down, Border, Leicester	Heavier carcasses, less wool.	Meat producers
Exports: **Meat**	Lamb is shipped to over 100 countries around the world, in the Far East, South America, and Europe. Britain is the greatest importer of lamb.	
Wool	Wool is exported to the U.S.A., Belgium (for carpets), Japan, Britain, and the U.S.S.R.	

(Top) Figure 3.7   Breeds of sheep raised in New Zealand.

(Bottom)   There are 40 000 sheep owners in New Zealand. About 28 000 of these have flocks of 500 or more sheep. The smaller sheep farms keep other livestock (cattle, pigs, poultry) and will also grow crops. The busiest seasons on a sheep farm are (a) lambing and (b) mustering for shearing or for shipment to the meat-preparing centres.

according to their location and the grass quality. The lower quality grasses of the hillslopes support only two to seven sheep per hectare and therefore, although the farms may be large in size, the number of sheep may be small. Pastures in the rich lowlands can carry fifteen to twenty sheep per hectare.

Cattle Rearing

Most of New Zealand's cattle are dairy breeds, particularly Jersey, but in recent years there has been an increase in rearing beef-producing breeds, especially Angus and Holstein. The world demand for beef is increasing; the Japanese, for example, are changing their food habits and eating more meat.

Besides frozen and canned beef, other meat products such as · sausage casings, tallow (fat for soap and candles), hides, and skins are also important exports.

The emphasis, however, is still on dairy farming. To produce top-grade milk, dairy cattle require rich grasses and plenty of water. These are available in the North Island, where the climate is mild enough to allow grazing all year round.

New Zealand's 22 000 dairy farms account for a quarter of the country's total earnings. The farms vary in size; a typical holding is about 53 ha, supporting about one hundred cows. Farmers generally own their properties and run them with the aid of one or two hired helpers. The farms are highly mechanized and are run on efficient modern lines.

Great Britain is the greatest importer of New Zealand's dairy products, but Japan, Greece, the West Indies, and Asian countries are also important trading partners.

New Zealand's major crops include wheat, hay (winter fodder for livestock), apples and pears, peaches, strawberries, plums, cherries, and such tropical fruits as kiwi fruit (Chinese gooseberries), passion fruit, and tree tomatoes (tamarillos). Apples and pears are exported, as are the tropical fruits.

Tobacco is grown for local markets. It is blended with imported leaves for variety. Hops and vines are cultivated for the manufacture of beer and wine respectively.

Forestry

When the early settlers landed in New Zealand, nearly two-thirds of the land area was forested. Tall, stately kauri and rimu trees covered vast tracts of land. Lumber was needed for building and for fuel and, to the pioneer, the existence of the forest was a disadvantage when grassland was needed for his cattle and sheep. Thus the forests of native trees dwindled in size. This practice of using the forests haphazardly occurred in the early days in many countries, when the pioneers were unaware of conservation practices. Since it takes about 150 years for a kauri tree to mature and 200 years for a rimu, New Zealanders have had to introduce quicker-maturing trees to forest their country and to provide the necessary timber. Thus a variety of pines has been introduced, the most successful of which has been the red pine. This redwood may be felled for wood pulp when about ten years old and is suitable for timber after twenty years.

(Top left) Cattle are milked twice a day – early morning and late afternoon. Practically all the milking is done by machines powered by electricity. Improved types of rotating or circular milking "parlours" are being introduced to enable one man to milk 100 cows in 1 h.

(Top right) The dairy industry is run on a cooperative basis. The dairy companies are owned by the farmers who supply the milk. The milk is taken from the farm to the factories by huge tanker trucks somewhat like oil trucks. The tanks carry up to 6819 L.

The milk is made into butter *(Centre left)*, cheese *(Bottom left)*, and powdered milk. Another important produce from milk is casein, which is processed into protein foods or used for industrial purposes such as paint, plastics, and glue. A new export product is milk biscuit which has high protein food value, and is easily packed and stored. Milk biscuits are important as a food for victims of disasters such as floods and earthquakes and for the peoples of the world's famine areas.

(Bottom right) New Zealand's forests provide wood for the pulp and paper industry and for construction. The wood is also important for the production of butter barrels, cheese and fruit crates, plywoods and veneers. Nearly half of the timber is exported to Australia.

84

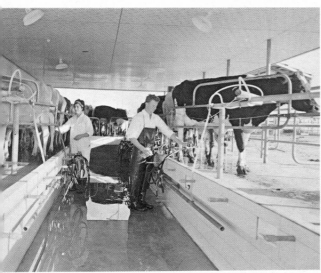

Industries

New Zealand is a country of many small factories rather than of heavy industries. However, some heavy industrial developments have taken place in recent years, for example, aluminum smelting at Bluff, South Island, and steel production near Auckland. Bauxite, imported from Australia, needs great quantities of heat to be smelted into aluminum, and the energy to supply this heat is plentiful in New Zealand in the form of hydroelectricity. The high-yielding iron sands, found along the west coasts of the North Island, are so abundant as to be a source of ore for many future years.

Gold, which caused the great influx of people in the country's earlier days, is no longer important, although it is still produced in very small quantities, and the present high price of the metal is causing renewed interest and exploration.

New Zealand's numerous factories manufacture a wide range of products. Most factories are linked with local industries, for example, meat freezing, butter, cheese, caseine and powdered milk production, fruit canning, food processing, pulp and paper production, woollen mills, plastics, building materials, etc. Other factories, such as auto assembling and petroleum refining, depend on imported goods.

The factories are found in the larger towns and cities. They were once located in downtown areas, but many factories, according to the new planning regulations, have been moved into certain suburban areas in parklike surroundings.

New Zealand's cities do not specialize in single industries, that is, no city is known for a particular product. The urban areas have many factories which cater to the surrounding region. Remember that New Zealand consists of two main islands and each island has two large cities, located about the same distance from one another, serving a certain area.

Although there has been a growth in certain industries, the small factory is still typical of New Zealand. In 1964-65 nearly forty percent of the factories employed fewer than six persons and eighty percent had fewer than twenty-one employees. On the other hand, less than two percent were large enough to employ more than 200 persons. However, as stated, changes are taking place and, although most factories still employ under twenty persons, there is a trend to larger plants and a swing from light to heavier industries.

(Top)   Coal is found on the west coast of the South Island. Although the total output is over 2×10^6 t a year, the soft, bituminous coal is not of high quality. It is used for domestic and factory purposes. However, the discovery of natural gas just offshore on the west coast of the North Island is diminishing the importance of coal.

(Bottom)   Within New Zealand's 19 km limit there are rich fishing grounds. The most common fish are the snapper and the tarakihi. The most valuable shellfish exported in quantity is the rock lobster. Freezing, processing, and canning plants are expanding at the fishing ports. It is recorded that there are forty-two varieties of seafood in New Zealand's coastal waters.

AFRICA

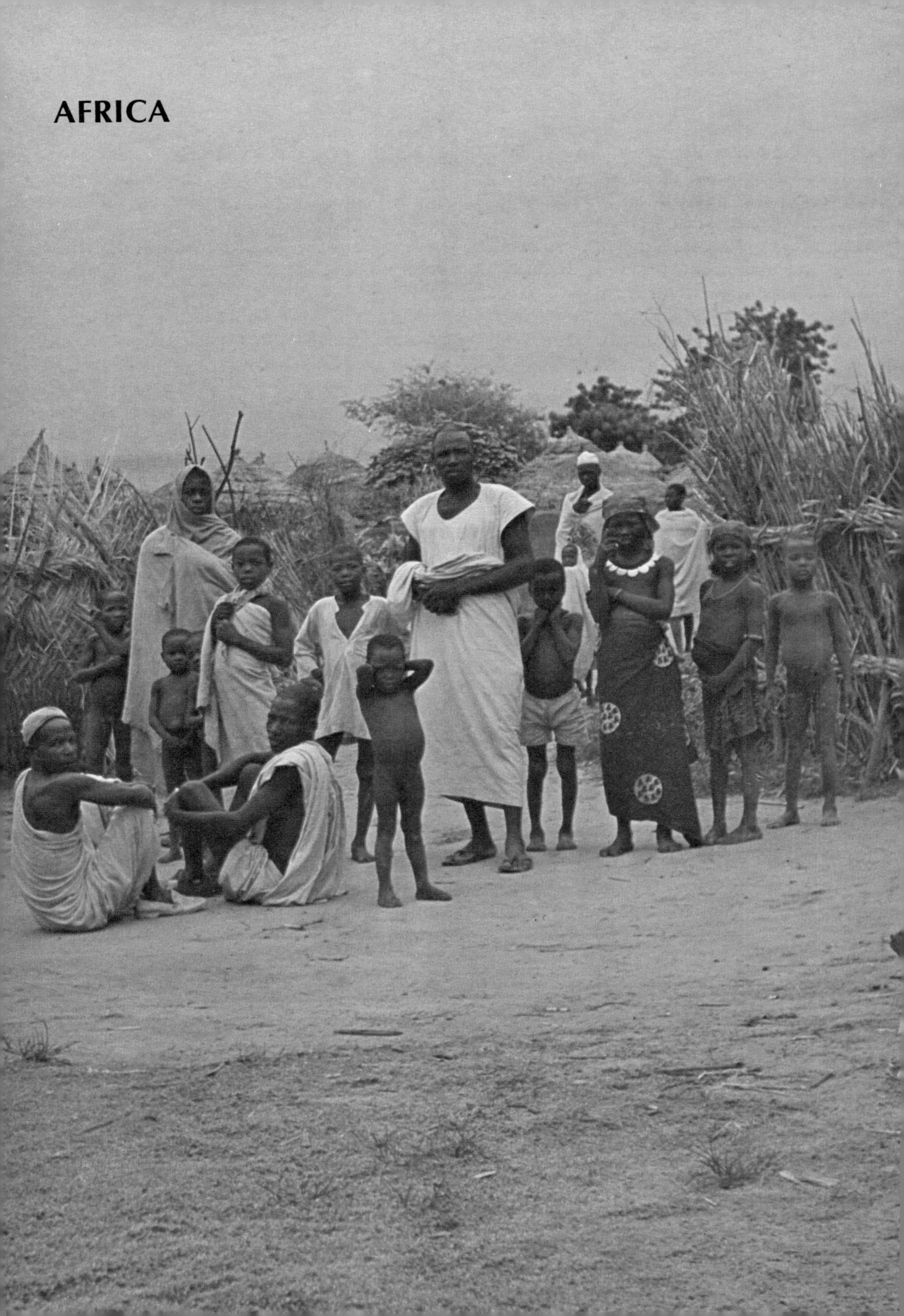

4. THE AFRICAN CONTINENT

AFRICA— PAST AND PRESENT

The Past

Nobody knows exactly where or when the first people lived. Archaeologists, who are interested in tracing mankind back to his beginnings, search for skulls and other bones, for these gradually changed in shape as man evolved and so can be used in dating finds. Some very important finds have been made in Africa, which is one of the places where mankind may have originated. Several of these discoveries have been made in the Olduvai Gorge, in Kenya, by Dr. Louis B. Leakey and his wife, Mary. For example, they discovered a skull which may be 2 000 000 years old. Tools, at least 600 000 years old, have also been found in the same gorge, embedded in soft rocks.

The examination of bones of animals also reveals much about the past. For example, it has been established that the rhinoceros used to live in many more parts of Africa than it does today.

The rhinoceros, and other animals, were widespread in northern Africa at a time when glaciers covered much of Europe. The climate of Africa was much cooler and wetter than it is today, and even the Sahara was covered with grass. However, since that time, the climate has warmed and the glaciers have melted, leaving us today in an *interglacial* period. The climate of the Sahara has become so hot and dry that the region is now a desert, and the rhinoceros and other animals, as well as the people who hunted them, have gradually retreated.

(Left) This skull was found by Dr. Louis Leakey, and belonged to the kind of man called *zinjanthropus*. It may be our earliest ancestor. It appears that zinjanthropus and similar prehistoric people knew how to keep themselves warm by making fires. They used bone tools and weapons.

(Right) A cave painting in the Algerian Sahara. In what way does the painting suggest that the climate of the desert may have changed? Thousands of cave paintings all over Africa are rich sources of information about the existence of early man on the continent.

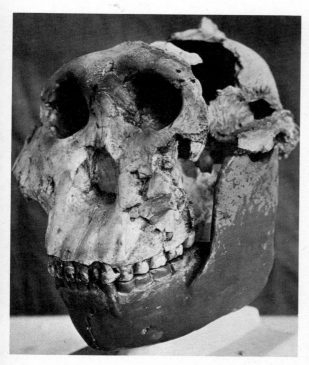

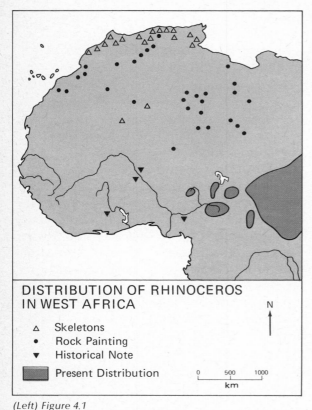

DISTRIBUTION OF RHINOCEROS
IN WEST AFRICA

N

△   Skeletons
●   Rock Painting
▼   Historical Note

[shaded]   Present Distribution

0   500   1000
km

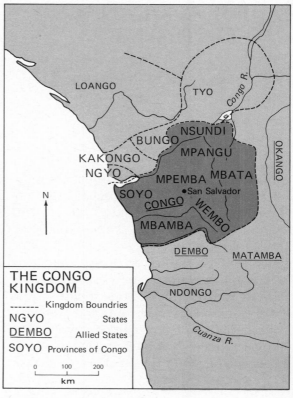

THE CONGO
KINGDOM

-------   Kingdom Boundries
NGYO   States
DEMBO   Allied States
SOYO   Provinces of Congo

0   100   200
km

(Left) Figure 4.1

(Right) Figure 4.2   The map shows the position of the early Congo Kingdom visited by the Portuguese merchants in the fifteenth century.

Questions
1. What does a rhinoceros eat? Why might they have disappeared from North Africa?
2. What would probably happen to the Sahara if the earth's climate began to get colder again?
3. Why would prehistoric man paint on cave walls? In which other parts of the world are there examples of early cave paintings?

The rock paintings, pottery, carvings, and buildings of the early Africans were so skillfully made that some European archaeologists found it difficult to believe that they were made without help from outside Africa. The Africans that were met by nineteenth-century European travellers and settlers seemed so poor, and so far behind Europe in terms of machinery, literature, and political organization, that it seemed impossible they had once been well on the road to developing modern states comparable to those of Europe. Two examples of early African states were (a) the Congo Kingdom and (b) the Songhai Empire.

The Congo Kingdom

Portugal was once one of the most powerful trading nations in Europe. When the wars between Western Europe and the Turkish Empire cut off the supply of spices, silks, and other valuable goods from China, India, and the Far East, Portuguese merchant seamen, such as Bartholomew Diaz, Vasco da Gama, and Pedro Cabral, began to search for a new way to the East around the shores of Africa. (At the same time, in the fifteenth century, the Spaniards were sailing westward and were soon to discover the Americas.)

Whenever the Portuguese ships stopped and went ashore in search of food and water, or simply out of curiosity, they met not savages but people who lived in well-organized states like those in Europe. The first Portuguese merchants to settle in West Africa did so as guests, not as conquerors. It was not long before Portuguese ships reached the Congo, the biggest of the African states on the Atlantic side of the continent.

The people of the Congo, known as the Bakongo, were farmers and herders. Mbanza Congo, the capital city, was situated in the centre of the kingdom, and was linked to the sea by a royal road, 240 km long. Built on a hill, where it enjoyed cool breezes, the city was secure from attack. Most of the valleys nearby were cultivated. Beans and other vegetables were grown, and the Bakongo also kept large herds of pigs and cattle. From their cultivated palm trees they obtained oil, wine, vinegar, and a type of bread. The oil, pressed from the palm fruits, was for food and for light. The bread was prepared from the kernels of the fruit, while wine was drained from a hollow cut at the top of the tree. When allowed to become acid, this could be used as vinegar. Cloth was made from fibres of the palm leaf. Citrus fruits and bananas, introduced by the Portuguese and the Arab traders from the north, were also cultivated.

The Bakongo were skilled ironworkers, producing both agricultural implements and weapons. They knew how to manufacture a wide range of medicines and ointments. Their astronomers studied the movements of the sun, moon, and stars, and worked out a 4 d week. *Sonna* was the first day, usually a holiday. The other three were called *gandu, chengo,* and *conzo.*

The Bakongo were most interested in all the new Portuguese ideas and inventions. A few Bakongo went to Portugal to study, and asked the king of Portugal to send out pharmacists, engineers, doctors, and a surgeon. One such expedition was sent, and for a time relations between the Congo and Portugal were very friendly. Perhaps, if this kind of cooperation had continued, the Congo might have become a strong modern state long before the twentieth century.

Riverside villages like this one were part of the Congo trading empire. The Bakongo traded up and down the many rivers of the Congo Basin. They traded salt, shell money, cloth bought from the Portuguese, and other goods to the villagers for skins and ivory. These, in turn, they sold to the Portuguese.

The Bakongo soon discovered, however, that most Portuguese merchants preferred to receive slaves in payment for their goods, for they could sell slaves at high prices in the new Portuguese colony of Brazil, across the Atlantic.

Many Bakongo princes started small wars in order to capture prisoners to sell as slaves. The king soon realized that such evil practices would destroy his country, but, although he tried to put an end to slave trading within the state, the greedy Portuguese slave merchants encouraged the princes to fight one another. The Congo Kingdom began to disintegrate — province after province broke away, and it was not long before Mbanza Congo itself was destroyed. The story of the Congo Kingdom is one small part of the tragic history of Africa.

Questions
1. Why was the palm tree so important to the Bakongo?
2. What was used for money in the Congo Kingdom?
3. Account for the weakening and the final destruction of this former kingdom.
4. How does a 4 d week work out as well as a 7 d week?

The Songhai Empire

In the broad belt of land that lies between the vast Sahara Desert and the forests of west and central Africa, the savanna country of scattered trees and grassland became the homeland of several powerful states. Long before the arrival of any Europeans in the area, the empires of old Ghana, Mali, Funj, Wadai, and the Songhai had left their mark on the African landscape. Perhaps the most impressive of all was the Songhai Empire which began to grow in the middle of the fifteenth century near to the modern town of Niamey on the River Niger.

By 1475 the Songhai Empire included the cities of Timbuktu, Gao (the capital), Djenné, and all the lands in the "big bend" of the Niger. Their wars of conquest were won by fishermen called the *Sorko,* who manned a fleet of war canoes, and hunters called the *Gow,* who organized a very powerful cavalry division.

Like the Bakongo, the Songhai built up an elaborate government service to take care of defence, finances, local government, farming, and other activities. Below the king, who ruled over the empire, were governors who administered the provinces. The civilian government was well organized, with a prime minister and ministers of finance, forestry, agriculture, justice, and foreign residents. The armed forces were run by the Army Chief, the Fleet Admiral, the Cavalry Commander, and the Superintendent of Waterways.

The Songhai had their own language, which is still spoken today, and also their own religion. This included a river god and a god of thunder named, Django. Some of the Songhai, however, became Muslims, believing in one God (Allah), whose prophet was Mohammed.

Like a huge ocean, the Sahara long kept the Songhai Empire safe from invasion. However, in 1591, the impossible happened. A Moroccan army, which contained many Spaniards who had become Muslims, found its way across the sands along an old trade

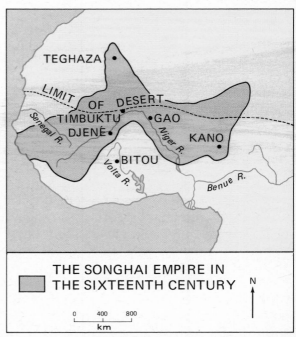

Figure 4.3 The Songhai Empire was prosperous. Timbuktu and Goa were the "ports" for the trade routes across the Sahara Desert to North Africa and Egypt. Djenné was a great market centre for salt and gold.

route through present-day Mauretania. They were looking for the source of the gold that had flowed for centuries from West Africa to the big North African cities of Fez, Algiers, Kairouan, and Tunis.

Armed with the most up-to-date guns, the Moroccans soon defeated the Songhai, and occupied the city of Timbuktu which became their capital.

The Songhai retreated towards their old homeland on the Niger. After many desperate battles with both the Moroccans and other African states, the Songhai Empire eventually crumbled.

Songhai power died in 1599, but its civilization lived on in the huts of humble fishermen and farmers, hidden in desolate bush country. The history of a glorious past lives on in their songs and stories, and still influences the way they live.

The very last flicker took place in 1905, in a Songhai revolt against the French. Today the Songhai are playing an important role in the new independent states of Mali and Niger.

(Left) Inside a Songhai home today. 1. What materials are used in the construction of this home? Why would they use these materials? 2. What utensils can you see? 3. Observe carefully. How do they light the home at night?

(Right) A Songhai woman spinning thread. 1. Describe this simple spinning process. 2. What tools are being used? 3. In what type of climatic region does this woman live?

European Penetration

Long before the first Europeans arrived in Africa, traders from North Africa, from Egypt, and from Oman went regularly to West and East Africa, along the trade routes shown on the map. Trade with West Africa was by camel caravan, while trade with East Africa was by water. Egyptian merchants reached the Sudan by boat up the Nile River, and East Africa by sailing down the Red Sea. The Omani Arabs, sailing from their great seaport of Muscat, waited for the northeast monsoon winds to carry their beautifully

Figure 4.4 African lines of trade and contact in the fourteenth century, before the arrival of the European traders.

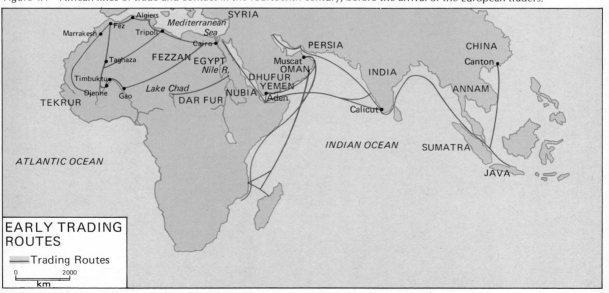

EARLY TRADING ROUTES

Trading Routes

0 — 2000 km

93

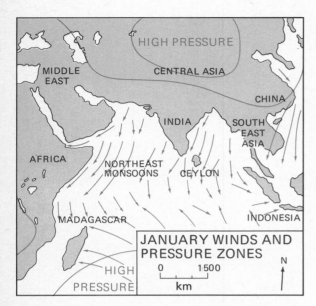

JANUARY WINDS AND PRESSURE ZONES

HIGH PRESSURE

CENTRAL ASIA

MIDDLE EAST

CHINA

INDIA

SOUTH EAST ASIA

AFRICA

NORTHEAST MONSOONS

CEYLON

INDONESIA

MADAGASCAR

HIGH PRESSURE

0   1500
km

N

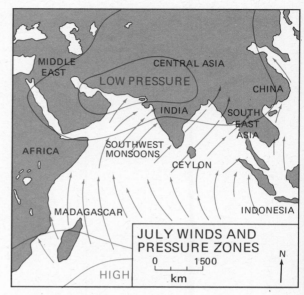

JULY WINDS AND PRESSURE ZONES

CENTRAL ASIA

MIDDLE EAST

LOW PRESSURE

CHINA

INDIA

SOUTH EAST ASIA

AFRICA

SOUTHWEST MONSOONS

CEYLON

INDONESIA

MADAGASCAR

HIGH

0   1500
km

N

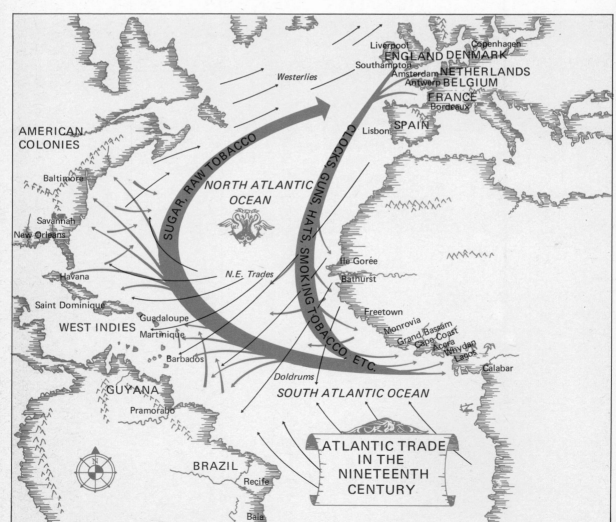

Westerlies

Liverpool
Southampton

Copenhagen

ENGLAND DENMARK

Amsterdam NETHERLANDS
Antwerp BELGIUM

FRANCE
Bordeaux

Lisbon

SPAIN

AMERICAN COLONIES

Baltimore

SUGAR, RAW TOBACCO

NORTH ATLANTIC OCEAN

CLOCKS GUNS HATS, SMOKING TOBACCO, ETC.

Savannah
New Orleans

N.E. Trades

Ile Gorée

Bathurst

Havana

Saint Dominique

Freetown

Monrovia
Grand Bassam
Cape Coast
Acora
Whydah
Lagos

WEST INDIES

Guadaloupe
Martinique

Barbados

Calabar

Doldrums

GUYANA

SOUTH ATLANTIC OCEAN

Pramoraho

N

ATLANTIC TRADE IN THE NINETEENTH CENTURY

BRAZIL

Recife

Baia

carved sailing boats, called *dhows,* to East Africa. They would trade along the coast, waiting for the southwest monsoon to blow them back home.

Some historians think that Indian, Malayan, and even Chinese traders also took advantage of the monsoon winds to reach the African coast.

Questions
1. Locate Djenné, Timbuktu, and Gao on Figure 4.4. Name the river on which they are located. In which great empire were they located?
2. Locate Oman. Name the capital city of these trading Arabs.
3. What desert did the North African traders have to cross to get to Timbuktu? What form of transport do you think they used?
4. Compare the early trade route map with Figures 4.5 and 4.6, showing the prevailing winds. How did the Arab traders take advantage of the seasonable monsoon winds? *Explain fully.*

Portugal was the first European country to send ships along the African coast. At first the traders were friendly with the many African people they met, and some married and settled down in the African trading posts. They learned a great deal about the interior of the continent, but like their maps, the Portuguese kept their information secret.

The Portuguese were also the first to round the Cape of Good Hope and to establish forts on the coast of East Africa. For a time the Portuguese controlled all the trade in the Indian Ocean. However, as her power weakened in Europe, she was unable to prevent the arrival of British, French, Dutch, German, Danish, and Swedish ships in search of gold, slaves, ivory, and spices.

Page 94

(Top left) Figure 4.5 and (Top right) Figure 4.6 In winter, the climate in Central Asia is very cold, causing a high-pressure zone. The mass of cold, heavy air forces winds outward in all directions; to Africa, Japan, Indonesia, and the Middle East. In summer, Central Asia becomes extremely hot, and a low-pressure zone forms over northern India and Afghanistan. This air flows in from the surrounding regions. These seasonal winds are called *monsoons.*
(Bottom) Figure 4.7

The slave trade almost killed Africa. Millions of Africans were sold into slavery. During the seventeenth century, for example, it is estimated that three million Africans were sold into slavery in the New World, and some seven million during the eighteenth century. As many as thirty million people were carried across the Atlantic in nearly four centuries of slave trading. For every African shipped out as a slave, four others died as a result of violence in the slave-gathering wars, and in the destruction of African states such as the Congo.

Questions
1. What cargoes did the ships carry in each part of the triangular voyage? What use was made of each of these cargoes?
2. What work was done by the slaves in the West Indies, Brazil, and the United States?
3. Which would be the most difficult part of the triangular voyage for a sailing ship?

In later years, Europeans became interested in the interior of Africa, both for trade and as a place to settle. Men, such as Dr. Heinrich Barth, René Caillié, David Livingstone, and John Speke explored the land.

An engraving showing David Livingston, the famous African explorer, being carried in a litter during the last few days of his illness, before his death in 1873.

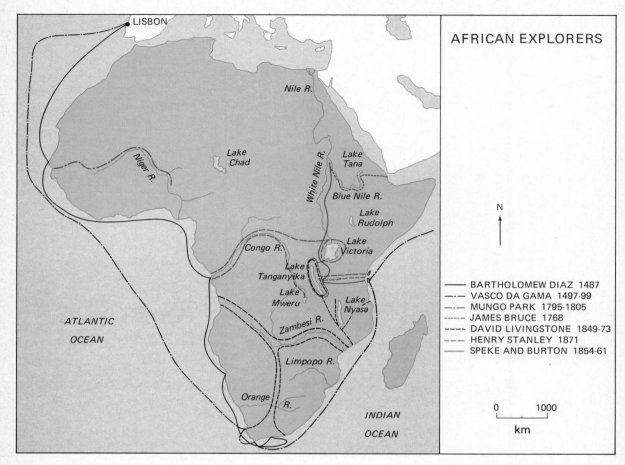

Figure 4.8 Map showing the routes of some of the early explorers of Africa.

AFRICAN EXPLORERS

—— BARTHOLOMEW DIAZ 1487
—·— VASCO DA GAMA 1497-99
—··— MUNGO PARK 1795-1805
········ JAMES BRUCE 1768
----- DAVID LIVINGSTONE 1849-73
– – – HENRY STANLEY 1871
—— SPEKE AND BURTON 1854-61

Questions
1. Who was the first European to round the Cape of Good Hope?
2. Name two explorers who explored the upper White Nile.
3. Who explored much of the Congo region?

The story of European penetration into the interior of Africa is one of exploration, missionary work, trade, and domination. African peoples fought fiercely against the invading Europeans who were taking over their lands and resources. However, their struggles were a long series of defeats because their weapons were never as good as those of the Europeans. Africans, armed with spears and old-fashioned rifles, were killed in desperate attacks against experienced troops armed with machine guns and canons. The map of Africa changed as it became partitioned and divided up among the European powers, especially Britain, France, Portugal, Belgium, and Italy.

In 1945 the Second World War came to an end, and thousands of Africans, who had fought in different European armies, were sent back to their homes. Some of them, shocked by the poor living conditions in their home towns, began to demand a greater say in local government. The demand for independence grew, and a strong nationalistic spirit took root all over the continent. Uprisings, riots, local wars,

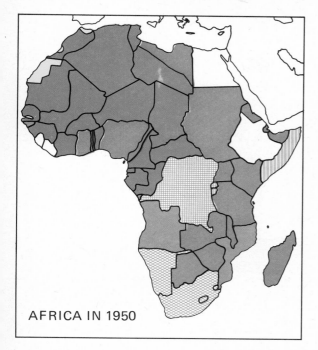

AFRICA IN 1950

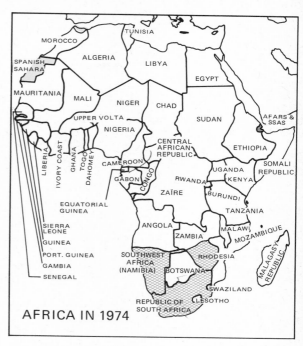

AFRICA IN 1974

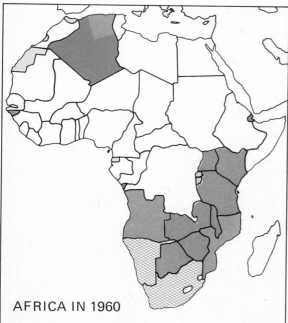

AFRICA IN 1960

(Top left) Figure 4.9

(Bottom left) Figure 4.10

(Top right) Figure 4.11

and imprisonments became common, and the European powers finally decided that it was too costly to try to retain their African colonies. These became self-ruling countries and the maps show the rapid changes that have taken place.

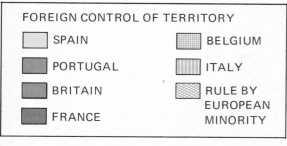

FOREIGN CONTROL OF TERRITORY

	SPAIN		BELGIUM
	PORTUGAL		ITALY
	BRITAIN		RULE BY EUROPEAN MINORITY
	FRANCE		

Questions

1. Name the three independent countries shown in Figure 4.9. The republic located on the west coast was formed in 1847 by the American Colonization Society as a home for freed slaves. Compare the name of this country with the original purpose of the territory. *Very appropriate*

2. Which European country had the largest number of colonies in 1950?

3. Compare Figure 4.9 with Figure 4.10. Which two European countries still held all their colonies? Which two had given up most of their colonies?

4. Which countries, in 1950, were ruled by a European minority?

The Present

The African scene is rapidly changing. Each newly independent country is trying to develop its resources as quickly and as efficiently as possible. Improved housing, education for all, better health and social services, and improved transportation facilities are some of their main concerns.

The isolation of many African villages and towns, caused by poor roads, has meant that aircraft play an important role. They are a means of carrying perishable cargo, and of getting government officials, mining personnel, and other important people to their destinations. African countries are now training their own pilots and mechanics, and are developing their own state airlines. It is now possible to fly to Africa from New York and Europe, using only African planes, and most of the pilots, ground crews, and hostesses are African.

Railways and highways are being built and improved. Nigeria, for example, has in recent years spent twenty-five percent of its budget on road building. There are several schemes for building highways across the Sahara Desert, and from Mombasa (Kenya) to Nigeria, passing through Uganda, the northeast corner of the Congo, the Central African Republic, and Chad.

Questions
1. What problems would you face in driving across the Sahara?
2. How do you think they might be solved?

The Alvaro Machado Bridge, near Lobito, on the Benguela Railroad.

As they grow, African cities show a fascinating mixture of architectural styles. Top left is the old part of the city of Kano (Nigeria) while the top right picture shows the modern section of Yaoundé, capital city of Cameroon.

(Bottom left)   Young girls in Lesotho training to be teachers. Teacher training is an important part of each African country's program, because millions of people still have had no chance to go to school. Until recently, in countries like Chad, Upper Volta, and the Sudan, of every hundred men only two could read and write. Among the women the *literacy rate* was only one in every hundred. The aim is to teach everyone to read and write as soon as possible. School attendance has been made compulsory for all children in some African countries and adults are encouraged to attend literacy classes. In some countries such as Senegal, the Sudan, and Mauritania, it is difficult to persuade families to send girls to schools. Because of the shortage of teachers, young foreigners are still teaching in Africa. Many are sent by organizations such as CUSO (Canadian University Service Overseas), the American Peace Corps, and the British V.S.O. (Voluntary Service Overseas).

(Bottom right)   Students at a university in the Congo. What are they doing? What do the boxes contain? Most African countries today have their own universities. Only a few small countries, such as Togo and Gambia, have to send their students to universities in neighbouring countries or overseas. Technical schools and villages are also being built to teach people the many skills that will be needed in Africa's future development.

Entebbe Airport, in Uganda, is one of the most modern in Africa.

Page 100

(Top left)   Africa is a continent rich in traditional and modern sports. The traditional sports include wrestling, canoe racing on rivers, lakes, and lagoons, and camel racing in the Sahara Desert. Wrestling is one of the most popular sports and forms part of most village festivals. Villages have their champion wrestlers and teams. Styles and rules vary from country to country. The picture shows Nuba wrestlers in the Sudan. Why do they powder their bodies?

(Bottom left)   Long contact with Europe brought a new range of sports to Africa — soccer, cricket, horse racing, polo, yachting, and so on. The cost of equipment for these sports, however, is too expensive for most Africans. The two exceptions are track and field, and soccer, and Africans have excelled in these sports. African teams are sent to most international events.

Changes in Africa are also seen in art. The carving *(Top right)* is one of its famous life heads of Nigeria, and is a fine example of traditional African art. The painting *(Bottom right), Allegorical Scene,* by Tall Papa Ibrahim of Senegal, is an example of how modern African painters mix new international styles with traditional themes.

Health Problems

Since independence, African countries have begun to spend heavily to make improvements in housing, education, and health conditions. A tremendous amount of work still needs to be done. For example, tropical diseases, and others that are not confined to the tropics, claim hundreds of thousands of victims each year. Some of these diseases are:

malaria	yellow fever
sleeping sickness	bilharzia
leprosy	dysentery
plague	yaws
cholera	trachoma
typhus	
typhoid	
para-typhoid	
tuberculosis	
poliomyletis	
gastro-enteritis	

Many tropical diseases are caused by parasites. In Africa, malaria is caused by a parasite carried by about eight varieties of anopheline mosquitoes. People only become infected if they are bitten by one of these tropical species. As the parasite takes at least 12 d to mature in the mosquito's body, the disease does not spread rapidly. Some forms of dysentery are caused by parasites taken into the body through contaminated water and foods. Sleeping sickness is also caused by a fly-borne parasite. Trachoma, an eye disease, uses flies as intermediate hosts. It is estimated that nearly three million people in Egypt alone suffer from blindness or partial blindness caused by trachoma.

Like most of the diseases that are listed at the beginning of the chapter, leprosy is most commonly contracted by children and by poor people who live in crowded conditions.

101

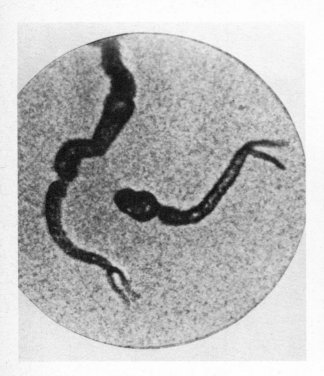

(Top léft) *Bilharzia cercarial.* These tiny organisms, seen here under a microscope, live and multiply in the blood vessels of bilharzia sufferers. They become so numerous that they eventually destroy the liver. Although the disease rarely kills people outright, it weakens them and lowers their resistance to other infections. It is estimated that in Egypt alone, bilharzia causes an annual loss of work time worth $100 million.

(Top right) If the life cycle of the bilharzia parasite could be interrupted, the disease would die out. There are three methods of attack. (a) To keep people away from contact with snail-infested water. This is difficult as villages are still too poor to install proper water supplies and sewage systems. (b) To kill the snails by using chemicals such as copper sulphate and barium chloride. Chemicals are expensive and not fully effective. (c) Install snail filters in irrigation channels, but this too costs money.
The picture shows a research worker gathering snails for examination.

(Bottom left) An infected person passes eggs from the parasites through the urinary tract, and as sanitary conditions in the villages are often poor, infection spreads. The eggs hatch into tiny larvae in ponds, ditches, and streams, and the larvae in turn invade small freshwater snails. They complete their life cycle in the snails' bodies, and are then released back into the water to infect humans. The snails act as *intermediate hosts.*
The picture shows villagers washing clothes in Guinea. Such conditions as these leave people open to attack by bilharzia. Locate Guinea on the map. How could conditions in this village be improved? What can you tell about the climate of Guinea from this picture?

Page 103

(Bottom left) Figure 4.12

(Bottom right) Figure 4.13

Hospitals and Medical Care

When the colonial period ended in Africa, the continent was terribly short of doctors, nurses, and hospitals. Not nearly enough money had been spent on medical facilities, and a few years of independence have not been enough to close the gap between Africa and the richer countries.

Study the maps and answer the listed questions.

(Top right) This young girl has leprosy. It shows as a lightening of the skin on her shoulder. About a million Africans have leprosy, a much-feared disease that was once common in Europe. It often does not cause pain, but its victims lose their sense of touch in the infected parts. It gradually destroys the facial features, and also the fingers and toes. Lepers today are placed in *isolation villages* where they can lead a social life together and get medical treatment. More severe cases are sent to a leprosarium.

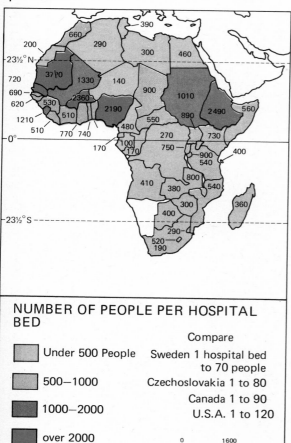

NUMBER OF PEOPLE PER HOSPITAL BED

Compare

Under 500 People   Sweden 1 hospital bed to 70 people

500—1000   Czechoslovakia 1 to 80

1000—2000   Canada 1 to 90

over 2000   U.S.A. 1 to 120

0   1600 km

Source: *Statistical Yearbook, 1969,* United Nations

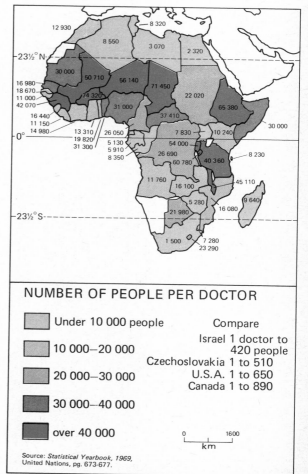

NUMBER OF PEOPLE PER DOCTOR

Under 10 000 people   Compare

10 000—20 000   Israel 1 doctor to 420 people

20 000—30 000   Czechoslovakia 1 to 510

30 000—40 000   U.S.A. 1 to 650

over 40 000   Canada 1 to 890

0   1600 km

Source: *Statistical Yearbook, 1969,* United Nations, pg. 673-677.

African governments are pouring as much money as they can afford into building new hospitals, health centres, and clinics, and the training of doctors and nurses. Even so, in some areas foreign missionaries are still the only people who provide medical help and schools. Missions, however, are no longer as important as they once were.

THE PHYSICAL ENVIRONMENT

Only the Eurasian landmass (Europe and Asia combined) forms a larger continent than Africa. The African continent, with an area of over 31×10^6 km², contains as great a variety of landforms as South America. Although most of the continent is a smoothly eroded plateau, there are towering mountain chains, volcanoes, vast river basins, lakes, narrow coastal plains, and gently rolling hills. It differs from North America, Southeast Asia, and Europe in that there are no large peninsulas jutting into the ocean, and very few sheltered inlets or bays to serve as harbours.

(Left) School children line up to look at *bilharzia cercarial* during a health lesson. Many different methods are being used to help people to keep themselves healthy — health and homecraft classes, radio programs, films shown in the villages by mobile film units, and by a display of posters in buses, village halls, schools, and even on tree trunks.

(Right) An Egyptian social worker teaching young villagers about nutrition and better cooking methods.

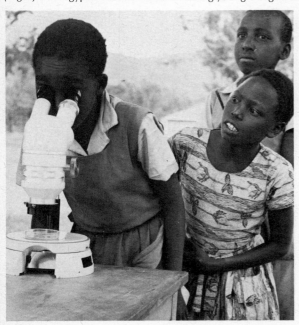

4. A trip, mainly by truck, from Dakar to Djibouti takes about five months. How many kilometres are travelled in a straight line?
5. Many travellers try to journey from the Cape (of Good Hope) to Cairo. How far would that be?
6. A narrow strait separates Africa from Spain. What is it called? What separates Africa from Asia?
7. What is a delta? Locate two in Africa.
8. Name the large lake whose waters cannot flow out into the ocean.
9. Which is (a) the biggest, and (b) the smallest country in Africa?

The African Landscape

Most of Africa consists of a block of very ancient rock, similar to the Laurentian Shield of North America. Many physical geographers believe that it was once the main part of a huge continent that included India, South America, and Australia. Forces in the earth caused these landmasses to separate and drift apart.

Over millions of years, the work of rivers and wind has worn down almost all the old mountain ranges, so that Africa is now a fairly smooth plateau. There are a few traces left of these ancient mountain ranges, for example, the Hoggar and Tibesti Mountains in the Sahara and the Cameroon Highlands. However, most of these owe their present height to more recent volcanic activity.

Volcanoes have built some of the highest peaks in Africa, of which Mount Cameroon (4070 m) is the best known example in West Africa. The isolated volcanic peaks of East Africa are even more impressive, and they include Mount Kenya (5200 m) and Kilimanjaro (5896 m).

Powerful pressures in the earth's crust, perhaps caused at the time of Africa's separation from other continents, warped parts of the eroded plain upwards, often to considerable heights. The most impressive of these uplifts of the African plain are the

(Top) The Drakensberg Mountains of Lesotho are the most impressive part of the rim of the African plateau. The rock strata are nearly horizontal, which show that these mountains are *not* fold mountains like the Alps or the Rockies.

(Bottom) The Atlas Mountains of Morocco. These are Africa's only example of recent fold mountains. Like the Alps, they are largely composed of limestone, which shows that the sea once invaded the northern part of the African plateau.

Drakensberg Mountains in Lesotho, which reach 3300 m. Others include the Fouta Djallon, in Guinea, and the Bauchi Plateau, in Nigeria (1780 m).

Most of the world's greatest mountain chains were created by much more recent folding of sedimentary rocks, such as those that formed the Andes and the Himalayas. The only example of this most recent mountain-building period in Africa is the Atlas Mountains. Composed mainly of limestone, the Atlas ranges reach heights of 4166 m.

Somewhat older fold mountains occur at the other extreme of Africa, at the southern tip. Here the Cape ranges, such as the Swartberge, have been heavily eroded and seldom rise above 1525 m.

The rift valley system, that stretches from Mozambique through East Africa and Ethiopia to the Red Sea and north into Israel, Lebanon, and Syria, is the most remarkable physical feature in Africa. It is marked by steep valley sides and deep valleys, some of which are filled by long, serpentine lakes. There are at least three different theories as to why the rift valleys were formed, but all agree that the steep valley sides are in fact *faults,* or cracks in the earth's crust. One theory even argues that East Africa will gradually drift away from the rest of the continent.

The deepest lakes in Africa are those that lie in this rift valley system. Other lakes, usually shallow, have been formed in slight depressions of the main African plateau. Lake Victoria, the biggest of these "depression lakes", has a maximum depth of only 76 m, compared to 1455 m for Lake Tanganyika, which is the largest of the rift valley lakes. Much of the Congo Basin was probably once a "depression lake" of which only Lake Leopold and a few smaller lakes remain.

Questions

1. Why are land surfaces formed by very ancient rocks likely to be fairly flat?
2. What would be the eventual appearance of the surface of the earth if the earth's crust did not fold, tilt, and crack?
3. Name the youngest mountains in Africa.
4. From your atlas, find the names of the six rift valley lakes in Africa, and one in the Middle East.
5. Why are the rift valley lakes all long and narrow?

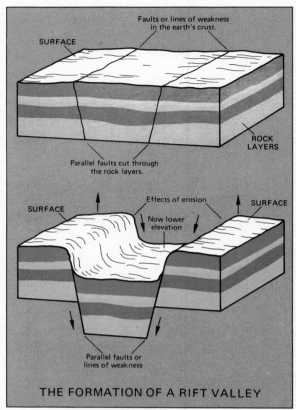

THE FORMATION OF A RIFT VALLEY

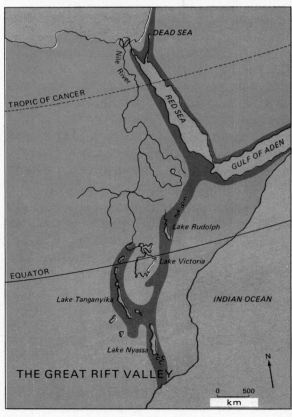

THE GREAT RIFT VALLEY

(Top) Figure 4.14 The formation of a rift valley. The two parallel lines of weakness, called faults, cause the area between them to lower and thus form a depression. Rift valleys generally leave sharp, steep sides.

(Bottom) Figure 4.15

The great French geographer, de Martonne, once estimated that less than half of Africa has drainage systems (rivers and stream systems) that lead to the sea. This very low figure is partly a result of the large areas of desert, where only skeleton drainage systems remain. Africa also has some of the world's largest *inland drainage basins*. The biggest of these is the basin containing Lake Chad. Here, the Shari and other rivers and streams flow into the lake, which has no outlet to the sea. The lake is gradually shrinking, partly because of high evaporation in the hot climate, and partly because the Benue and other rivers are cutting back and gradually "capturing" smaller streams that feed the Shari.

Other ancient lakes that lie at the centre of inland drainage basins are the Makarikari and Okovango swamps of southern Africa. Now these only contain water in the rainy season, but they were once permanent lakes like Lake Chad.

Underground drainage is important for irrigation, but not enough is yet known about Africa's underground drainage pattern. It is believed, however, that there are large underground rivers and lakes beneath the Sahara which could be tapped by extra-deep wells to permit farming in the desert.

Much of the African coast seems to be rising slowly above sea level, as is shown by the existence of a very narrow coastal plain that fringes the continent.

Climate

Temperature

A glance at an atlas will show that Africa has a greater proportion of its landmass lying within the tropics than any other continent. This means that large parts of Africa experience direct or slightly deflected rays from the sun throughout the year, tending to produce high temperatures on the ground. Those regions to the north and south of the tropics lie within the warm, subtropical latitudes, where summers are hot and winters are generally cooler.

The equator almost bisects Africa and, as the rays of the sun, according to the seasons, are almost directly overhead, temperatures are generally high throughout the year, averaging 26°C. This hot region is known as the thermal equator. However, the sun is directly overhead at the Tropics of Cancer and Capricorn in June and December respectively. The temperatures, approximately 32°C, are higher in the tropical regions than they are at the equator. The reason for this is that the sun stays longer overhead in these regions than it does at the equator. The earth revolves around the sun at different speeds, and during June and December, when the sun is said to be "approaching" either the Tropics of Cancer or Capricorn, the earth slows down in its revolution. Again, as the sun "reaches", or "moves" back to, the equator once again, the earth's revolution increases.

Figure 4.16 A simplified cross section showing a typical African coastline. Note the inland cliffs which represent the old fault that once was the original coastline. What is a dune? What typical crops are grown by the villages? Note the position of the village. Give some reasons why this would be a good location for settlement.

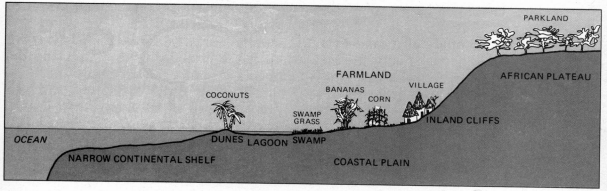

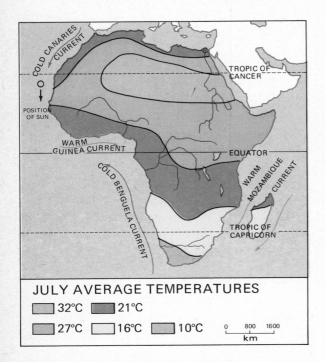

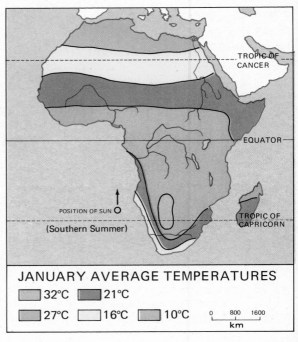

JULY AVERAGE TEMPERATURES
- 32°C
- 21°C
- 27°C
- 16°C
- 10°C

JANUARY AVERAGE TEMPERATURES
- 32°C
- 21°C
- 27°C
- 16°C
- 10°C

(Left) Figure 4.17 and (Right) Figure 4.18 The maps show the temperature distributions in Africa. Notice that the vast area north of the equator has larger regions of high and low temperatures than to the south. This is because: (a) Land gains and loses heat quickly and this vast landmass is less affected by the oceans which warm and cool more slowly. The southern part of the continent is narrower and is influenced more by the surrounding oceans and currents. (b) The northern region is closer to, and is affected by, the great landmass of Asia with its extremes of temperatures during summer and winter. Temperatures reach their maximum after the sun has reached and left its overhead position, as it takes time for the earth's surface to absorb the heat.

In Canada actual temperatures as well as humidity and wind strength are considered when estimating how cold it feels. Similarly, in Africa, humidity, winds, and altitude must be considered as factors that modify the actual effect of high levels of "insolation" on human beings. Thus, although extremely high temperatures are recorded in Africa (it now seems that the world record high temperatures are recorded in Somalia and not the Sahara), there are many other climatic factors that make it possible for people to lead normal lives.

Most of the equatorial belt experiences high levels of humidity, both during the day and at night. Although this means that people tend to perspire a lot (which has a cooling effect on their bodies), it also means that the full impact of the sun's heat is lessened. Even a very clear, hot day in, for example, Conakry will be cooler than a similarly hot, clear day in the Sahara.

Cool breezes from the sea, from rivers and streams, and from lakes make life quite pleasant, and most villagers try to locate their settlements to take advantage of this factor. This effect is strongest in the evening, just when people need to relax.

Much of Africa is well above sea level, and altitude is another factor in modifying the temperature. This effect of temperature decrease with altitude increase is particularly strong in the Ethiopian and East African Highlands, in the Central African Highlands, and, of course, in the mountain ranges of North and South Africa.

Much of the time, cooler air masses move into Africa from both the oceans and the upper layers of the atmosphere.

In areas with high temperatures and high evaporation rates, such as the Sahara Desert, Somalia, the Kalahari, and parts of East Africa, people have learned to adapt their daily routines to the climate. Most travel and hard manual labour is done early in the mornings, in the late evenings, or at night. Wedding feasts and other celebrations are held at night. The hottest part of the day is for rest, inside a cool hut or under a shady tree.

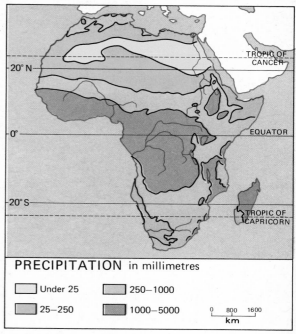

PRECIPITATION in millimetres

Under 25	250–1000	
25–250	1000–5000	0 800 1600 km

Figure 4.19

Questions
1. What might be some of the reasons why we still do not know very much about Africa's climates? *Factors Affecting?*
2. What do you think "insolation" means?
3. Why might a long midday siesta not be as popular with city workers as with peasants?
4. Why do you think cities such as Conakry, Dakar, and Lagos were originally located on promontories or islands projecting in the ocean?
5. Which months are likely to be the hottest in Chad and in Lesotho? Why?

Precipitation

The oceans surrounding Africa are vital, because they give up moisture to the air as it moves over them towards the continent. There are three main wind systems that bring rain to Africa:

1. The *winter westerlies,* blowing across the Atlantic towards Europe. In winter months these rain-bearing winds occasionally move southwards, affecting the Atlas Mountains, the Moroccan lowlands, and the smaller mountain block on the Mediterranean coast of eastern Libya. Very rarely a severe rainstorm can be brought by the westerlies to the Sahara. Egypt, at the eastern limit of North Africa, seldom receives rain, as by the time the westerlies reach Egypt they contain little moisture. There are no mountains to force the air to rise, cool, and discharge what moisture it contains. In the extreme south the winter westerly winds bring moisture to the southwestern Cape region.

2. The *monsoons,* which made it possible for Arab, Indian, and even Chinese sailors to reach Africa's eastern coast long before the arrival of Europeans. They bring rain mainly to Kenya, Tanzania, and the island of Madagascar.

3. The *trade winds,* blowing towards the equator, affect southeast Africa, west Africa, and the western coast of the Sahara. In southeast Africa, the southeast trade winds bring rain to Natal, Swaziland, Lesotho, Mozambique, and to the east coast of Madagascar. The same winds, deflected sharply north, also bring rain to the west African coast, particularly the mountainous areas of the Fouta Djallon and the Cameroon Highlands. The reverse effect is caused by the northeast trades, which blow *away from* the west African coast north of Sierra Leone, just as the southeast trades blow *away from* the coast of Namibia and Angola. Both of these areas, therefore, are very dry.

Questions
1. Where are the regions of heaviest rainfall located? *Name 3 main countries*
2. Locate the regions where the annual rainfall is under 250 mm. What type of vegetation would you expect to find there?
3. What winds bring rain to the Mediterranean coastal regions of North Africa and similarly to Southwest Africa? When does the rainfall occur?

4. How do winds blowing from the sea differ from winds blowing over landmasses?
5. Compare the rainfall distribution north of the equator with that to the south. Are they similar in any way?
6. Why does Ethiopia have an area of heavier rainfall than most of the southern Sudan?

A main source of rain in the tropics is convectional air currents, rising sharply from the land surface. This kind of rainfall is especially intense when the sun is directly overhead. Thus, close to the equator there will be two rainy seasons: one when the sun "moves" north towards the Tropic of Cancer, and a second when it "moves" back towards the Tropic of Capricorn. Closer to the Tropics themselves there will be one main rainy season and a much shorter, second rainy season.

Don't do

Questions
1. Why does air release its moisture content when it is forced to higher levels?
2. How is the air around us heated? What causes it to be forced upwards?
3. How does convectional rainfall differ from relief or orographic rainfall?

Figure 4.20

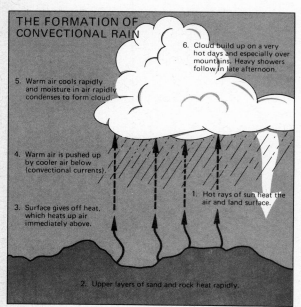

THE FORMATION OF CONVECTIONAL RAIN

6. Cloud build up on a very hot days and especially over mountains. Heavy showers follow in late afternoon.

5. Warm air cools rapidly and moisture in air rapidly condenses to form cloud.

4. Warm air is pushed up by cooler air below (convectional currents).

3. Surface gives off heat, which heats up air immediately above.

1. Hot rays of sun heat the air and land surface.

2. Upper layers of sand and rock heat rapidly.

Some parts of Africa, therefore, have regular rainy seasons that can be relied on to come each year, even though the quantities of rain may vary from year to year. Other areas, dependent on the same winds but further from the main areas where they blow, may only get rain in years when the winds are particularly strong. Somalia and northern Kenya, for example, depend for their scanty rainfall on slight changes in direction of the monsoons. Similarly, Botswana depends on strong southeast trades. Both of these areas, therefore, can suffer severe droughts lasting for several years.

Water is a problem that plagues most of Africa's farmers. There is either too much or too little. All the roads in southern Chad, for example, are flooded in the rainy season, while at the same time of year a traveller in northern Chad could die of thirst. For more than 5000 years, Egyptian farmers have lived at the mercy of the River Nile. When the river carried enough water, the farm fields could be irrigated, but when it did not they might starve. When it flooded, their homes and villages would be ruined. A recent drought that lasted several years killed most of the cattle in Mali, Niger, and Upper Volta. As the water holes and even deep wells began to dry up, people were also in danger of losing their lives.

Nevertheless, water is one of Africa's greatest natural resources. The Nile, Niger, Congo, and many other rivers are navigable for much of their length, making transportation easier. Rivers such as the Volta, the Nile, and the Zambezi have been harnessed by huge dams to create power supplies for industry. Lakes provide supplies of fish, as do many of the rivers and lagoons. Once Africa is able to organize its water supplies, by providing drainage to tackle floods and swampy conditions, and irrigation and wells to counter droughts, it will be able to profit from its water supplies rather than suffer.

Powerful and damaging winds, such as typhoons and hurricanes, are rare in Africa, although Mozambique has occasionally been hit by typhoon-force winds. Violent rainstorms, however, are a threat over most of the continent, even in the desert or semidesert regions. The exception is the equatorial belt, where the daily convectional currents usually produce a downpour for little more than a hour or two in the afternoon or evening. Even here, windborne rain, or exceptionally hot weather with thunderstorms, can bring flooding. In the deserts, violent winds can bring sandstorms or *simoons* by gathering up loose particles from the dry surface.

Vegetation

Natural vegetation varies according to rainfall, temperature, and soils. Because Africa extends about the same distance both north and south of the equator, generally we can find two of each vegetation zone. For example, Mediterranean-type vegetation is found in both North Africa and South Africa. Similarly, there are hot deserts in both the northern and southern parts of the continent.

A broad (and oversimple) differentiation of African vegetational zones might be: desert, grasslands, and forests. Each of these, however, would need subdividing to give us some idea of what the vegetation looks like. An English geographer, for example, subdivided "forests" into:

(a) Equatorial rain forests.
(b) Temperate high-altitude rain forests.
(c) Oak and conifer forests.
(d) Dry forests.
(e) Thorn forests.
(f) Mangrove forests.

The vegetation map shows the *equatorial rain forests,* which are much less extensive than many early European explorers imagined. Most explorers never ventured far from the rivers in the Congo region, for example, and therefore they saw only the riverine forests along the banks, remaining ignorant of the open grasslands lying a little distance away.

The higher altitudes of the mountain ranges produce different soils and a cooler climate, giving temperate high-altitude rain forests. Oak and conifer forests are confined to the Atlas Mountains, and are, therefore, much more typical of the Mediterranean region than of Africa. Both the dry and the thorn forests are associated with the desert margins, while mangrove swamps are found in the tropical river deltas and lagoons. One of the world's largest mangrove forests is in the Calabar region of Nigeria.

Some geographers have used names such as *parkland* and *wooded savanna* to describe grasslands with some scattered trees. In reality, this is an intermediate zone between grasslands and forests, for dense forests do not appear suddenly.

Others, more interested in grasses and their feed value for livestock, have drawn different grass zones, both in the semideserts and on the plateaus of southern and eastern Africa.

The map shows the vegetational zones of Africa. Study the map and answer the listed questions.

Questions
1. Compare the vegetation map, on page 112, with the map showing annual rainfall distribution. What type of vegetation is found in regions where there is: (a) heavy year-round rainfall, (b) little or no rainfall, and (c) winter rain and long summer drought periods?
2. Describe briefly the type of vegetation found in (a) equatorial rain forest, (b) Mediterranean-type regions, and (c) "parkland" or savanna.
3. Why were the grasslands of Africa called the Big Game Lands?
4. What type of vegetational zone borders the rain forest? How does the vegetation change in character as one travels north from the equatorial region to the Sahara?
5. How are the xerophytic desert plants adapted to arid habitats?

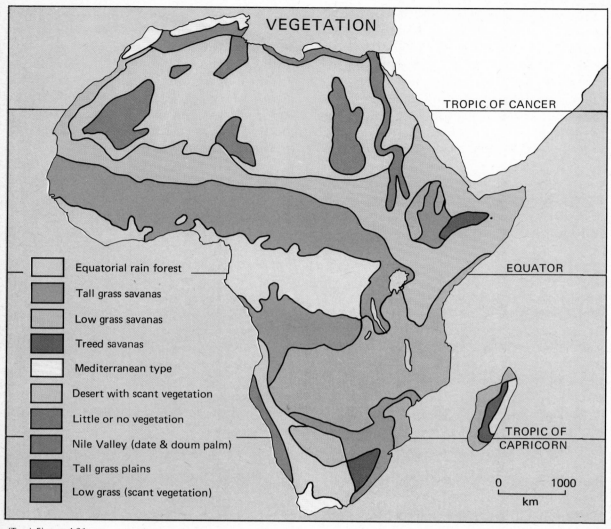

VEGETATION

TROPIC OF CANCER

EQUATOR

TROPIC OF CAPRICORN

Legend:
- Equatorial rain forest
- Tall grass savanas
- Low grass savanas
- Treed savanas
- Mediterranean type
- Desert with scant vegetation
- Little or no vegetation
- Nile Valley (date & doum palm)
- Tall grass plains
- Low grass (scant vegetation)

0   1000
km

(Top) Figure 4.21

(Bottom left) A typical view of a mangrove swamp. Mangroves grow in shallow water, supported by aerial prop roots extending down from the trunks and lower branches. During periods of low water these roots help the plants to breathe.

(Bottom right) A scene in the grasslands of Africa with a herd of elephants in the foreground. Notice the "parkland" nature of the grasslands. Huge herds of elephants like this were once common. Hunting and poaching for meat and ivory have reduced their numbers almost to the point of extinction, except in the national parks.

Wildlife

To most African farmers, wild animals are pests. Elephants and smaller grass-eating animals smash down fences and root up crops. Hippopotami foul the water holes used by cattle. Birds eat the crops, and farmers must spend anxious weeks before harvest trying to keep them away. Lions and other beasts of prey carry away livestock.

Although wild animals are a nuisance, they are also a useful source of fresh meat for African villagers, whose diet is often low in protein. In the heavily farmed parts of Africa, such as northern Nigeria, the Senegal River valley, and the Ethiopian Highlands near to Addis Ababa, very few wild animals are left. There is still a great demand for ivory, rhinoceros horns, leopard skins, zebra skins, and crocodile skins, and so professional hunters have already killed off most of Africa's valuable animals. The skins, tusks, and hides are exported to Europe and North America, as well as to India and China, where ivory carvers long ago ran short of ivory from Asian elephants.

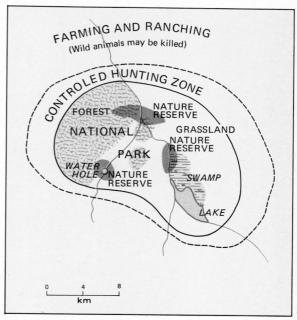

Figure 4.22 The nature reserves shown on the map would be out-of-bounds for tourists and so would be preserved areas for special study. In the National Park there would be as many animals as the land could support in order to attract tourists. Within the controlled hunting zone, licensed hunters could hunt under supervision. Annual numbers and species to be killed would be worked out by wildlife experts so that the wildlife would be kept at a steady level. This kind of hunting is called *cropping*. Beyond the legalized hunting area would be ranchlands and farmlands, where hunting regulations would be less rigid.

Questions
1. What are the differences between African elephants and Asian (Indian) elephants?
2. What are some of the main animal pests (a) in North America today and (b) in Australia?
3. What happened to North America's buffalo herds? Why are there so few wild animals in their natural regions in North America today?

Conservationists, in Africa and all over the world, are afraid that many species of animals and birds may soon become extinct. They are trying to control hunting in certain areas, and to prohibit any hunting of very rare animals. It is possible that soon every part of the world will have been disturbed in one way or another by human activities. The conservationists, who include many botanists, zoologists, biologists, and ornithologists, as well as geographers, are trying to set aside a few areas as undisturbed natural environments.

National parks, forest reserves, nature reserves, controlled hunting areas, and game reserves are beginning to dot the map of Africa. But still the farmers complain that animals from the reserves cross over into the farming areas and destroy crops and animals. The park and reserve managers complain that Africans enter the reserved areas and kill animals without a license. One plan that might satisfy everybody is shown in the diagram.

Uganda is one of the several African countries that have developed a system of national parks and other reserved areas. These areas have been carefully chosen, so that at least one good area for each kind of animal is included. For example, there are swamps and rivers for hippos, crocodiles, and water birds, and grassy plains for antelopes, deer, and lions.

One of the main reasons for animal protection in Africa is the tourist trade, which today brings in millions of dollars to countries with large game reserves and national parks like Kenya, South Africa, Uganda, Tanzania, and the Ivory Coast.

Another good reason for stopping the slaughter of Africa's wild animals is that they may be the best way of making money from certain kinds of land. Most larger animals and birds can be used for meat, which could be sold in the markets.

One expert counted all the hippos, buffalos, cobs, waterbucks, elephants, and geese that were living on a 1000 km² game reserve in Uganda. He then converted his results into cow-units. A buffalo, for example, might be counted as 1.3 cow-units as it is slightly bigger than an average cow. He showed that the total number of cow-units on the reserve was greater than the number of real cows that could be raised in the same area. In other words, it might be better to leave the wild animals alone, instead of killing them off to create new rangeland for cattle. The animals could then be cropped from time to time and sold for meat and hides.

Some animals and birds are now being farmed. South Africa is known for its ostrich farms, and several countries are planning crocodile farms. Farmed animals, however, do not attract tourists, and "animal tourism" may soon become one of modern Africa's biggest money-makers.

Page 114

(Top left)   The animals of the tropical grasslands of Africa can be divided into those that eat grass (herbiverous) and those that feed on other animals (carnivorous). The herbivores include the zebra, impala, wildebeest, water buck, gazelle, elephant, rhinoceros, giraffe, and hippopotamus.

(Top right)   A cheetah rests in the tall grasses. After the summer rains the tall grasses take on brown and tawny hues providing a natural camouflage for the animals. The cheetah is the fastest runner on the grasslands. Other carnivores include the lion, leopard, crocodile, hyena and the vultures.

(Centre left)   Young lion cubs relaxing in the sun. It is, however, quite difficult to shoot pictures like this even in a national park. The best time to see the animals is at dawn, near the water holes. Tourists visiting these game reserves must be accompanied by guides and are never allowed to leave their cars.

(Bottom left)   In recent years a number of myths about animals have been exploded. Careful animal watching has shown that hyenas do hunt for themselves, while the lions often hang about waiting for the hyenas' leftovers. Hyenas hunt in packs, at night, which is why they had never been seen hunting before. In the past people believed that hyenas follow lions, waiting to steal part of the kill.

(Bottom right)   Another popular myth concerns the ostrich. Careful bird-watching has finally proved that ostriches do not put their heads in the sand when frightened. Instead they arch their necks downwards, mainly to protect their eggs. Ostrich feathers were once extensively used for decorative purposes. South African farmers reared ostriches and made fortunes out of their feathers. Changes in fashion have greatly reduced the industry. However, a few ostrich-rearing farms still exist around Oudtshoorn. The feathers are plucked, cleaned and exported. The tough skin of the ostrich is also treated and made into wallets and purses. Ostrich eggshells are so thick and compact that a child can stand on one without breaking it!

Questions
1. What functions do national parks perform?
2. Name the nearest national park to your home.
3. What is meant by "conservation of our wildlife"? Why are conservation practices essential today?
4. If you were to visit a national park in Africa what animals would you expect to see?
5. Are any wildlife reserves found in North America?

POPULATION PATTERNS

The natural landscapes of Africa are tremendously varied. As a result, Africans have developed many different ways of making a livelihood. Lagoon fishermen, lake fishermen, river fishermen, and sea fishermen have all developed different techniques, and have borrowed techniques from one another. Similarly, cattlemen on the great rolling grasslands of Africa have traded ideas and methods as they have migrated from one area to another. Farmers have developed tools and techniques to suit the soil and climate conditions of their different areas, and hunters have had to adapt to the kinds of animals most common in the forests and grasslands.

As the population of different areas has grown, shrunk, or moved, the human impact on the natural environment has changed. African historical geographers have much work to do in tracing these changes. For example, the decline of farmlands or grazing lands, because of invasions of flies and fly-borne diseases, can be traced by seeking archaeological evidence, interviewing old people, or looking for clues such as abandoned villages or verses in popular poems and songs. Migrations of whole tribes and nations can also be traced using similar methods. Anthropologists, geographers, and economists can also study how people move into new areas and adapt to fit their new environment.

The main concern of a geographer, however, is the *present landscape,* and the changes that are taking place. Human occupancy has changed the landscape of most of the world and most of Africa, to the extent that physical geography forms only a background to our real landscape studies.

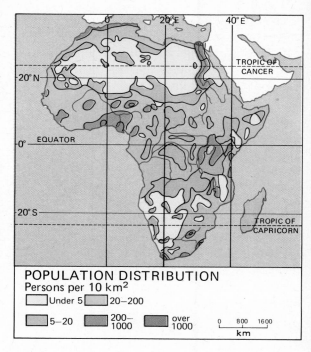

POPULATION DISTRIBUTION
Persons per 10 km²

☐ Under 5 ☐ 20–200

☐ 5–20 ☐ 200–1000 ☐ over 1000

0   800   1600
km

Figure 4.23

Today Africa presents a bewildering mosaic of peoples and human environments. Centuries of distrust and conflict led many peoples to keep to themselves as much as possible, and to make use of swamps, mountains, and forests as barriers between themselves and their neighbours. Each group of people developed their own language, religion, and way of life, making it still more difficult for them to intermingle. This is the main reason why it is still fairly easy for an African in, for example, Khartoum, to tell where a stranger comes from just by his appearance.

If the stranger is very tall and dark, he is likely to be a Nuer or a Shilluk from the south. If he is very short and dark, he is probably from the Yambio district near the border with Zaïre. Special body markings and hairstyles make recognition even easier. Long, bushy hair would indicate that the stranger was a Hadendowa from the Red Sea Hills.

Questions
1. Check this population map with a political map of Africa to find out which countries contain areas of very high population density.
2. What areas, other than the deserts, support very low densities?
: Why is there such a high population density in the region around Lake Victoria?
4. Which river flows through areas of high population density for half its length?
5. Compare the population map with the vegetation map on page 112. What conclusions can be drawn?

In the modern states of Africa, these ancient barriers between peoples are breaking down. Especially in the rapidly growing cities, more and more Africans are abandoning their old facial and body markings, their traditional styles of dress, their religions, and even their languages. More intermarriage is taking place between people of different origins, so that a hundred years from now it will be very difficult to tell who is who from their appearance, just as it is in Europe at present.

Some geographers find it interesting to study what they call "human types", and to discuss the origins and present location of Pygmies, Bushmen, Berbers, Tutsi, and other peoples. The Pygmies, who are about 130 to 140 cm in height, are nomads living in the equatorial rain forest of east-central Africa, particularly in the Ituri Forest region. Another nomadic people, the Bushmen of Kalahari Desert, live as hunters and gatherers. However, of the total 20 000 to 30 000 Bushmen, today less than 8000 live in the traditional nomadic way.

To many modern Africans, however, this is a relic of the past, and helps to perpetuate dangerous divisions. This kind of "tribalism" has been bitterly opposed by African leaders such as Kwame Nkrumah (Ghana), Leopold Senghor (Senegal), and Said Barre (Somalia). They argue that it makes no difference what colour a man's skin may be, how long his ears are, or how tall he is. What does matter is whether or not he is a good man.

Just as physical differences and variations in religion, language, and life-style are disappearing, so are many traditional ways of making a living. Camel nomads in the Sahara Desert are moving to the cities and farmlands where they can make a better living. Besides, the market for camels has almost disappeared. Even in the past, there were very few "true nomads" who practised no farming at all. Today, some of the nomadic peoples still follow their traditional movement patterns, following the rains to secure pasture for their animals, but many of them stay behind to farm.

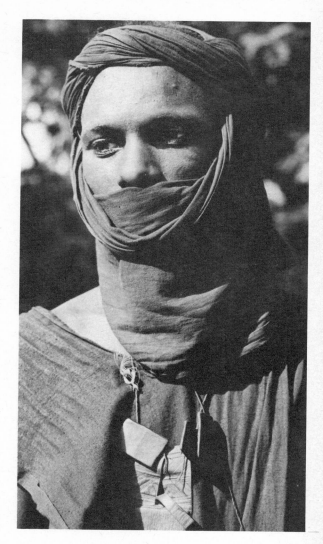

As barriers have broken down between African peoples, and under the pressure of severe droughts in the southern fringes of the Sahara, many Tuaregs have migrated southwards in search of new jobs and new homes. Gradually they discard the old styles of dress, to blend in with the new African nations. Their children will likely marry Hausas, Ibos, or anyone they choose. In this way, the old distinctions between African peoples are rapidly breaking down.

Subsistence farmers, who lived in isolated villages producing all their own needs, are finding it more profitable to grow crops for the market, and cattlemen like the Nuer and the Masai are being encouraged to raise cattle for sale rather than just to keep huge numbers of them for prestige.

All of these changes lead to more mixing, more contact. The most dramatic change is the drift to the towns and cities. In the past ten years, most African towns have tripled or quadrupled their size, mostly by absorbing migrants from the countryside. In Khartoum, for example, Nuers rub shoulders with Hadendowas, Kababish, Baqqaras, and Fur neighbours, gradually losing their fear and distrust of one another. For a while, the new arrivals, like immigrants into North America, try to keep up contacts with people from their own area. Children, however, mix and make friends more easily than their parents.

Human Settlement

Oases

A very distinct environment, quite different from the grazing lands and farmlands of Africa, is the string of oases in the northern parts of the Sahara Desert. Varying in size according to the amount of available underground water, the oases stand out from the surrounding desert because of their dense groves of date palms. The oases communities are long-established, and often speak their own dialects and have their own religion. In the past they became rich by servicing camel caravans crossing the desert.

Figure 4.24 A simplified cross section of an oasis.

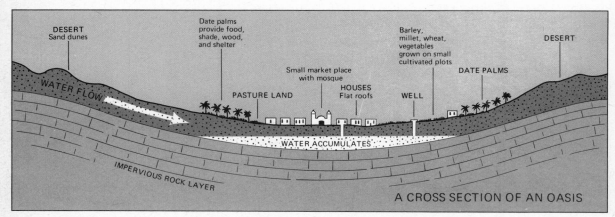

A CROSS SECTION OF AN OASIS

Villages

A human geographer looks at the whole pattern of human settlement, from small villages to cities. He is also interested in the links between settlements. These include *communications links,* such as telephones, postal services, railroads, highways, footpaths, riverboats, and airlines. They also include *commercial links,* such as markets and the flow of goods from one settlement to the other. The whole pattern of settlement points and their links is often called a *network.*

More than eighty percent of all Africans still live in villages. Some of them, like the villages in the rich farming areas of Northern Nigeria, the cocoa-producing villages of Ghana, and those villages that lie on main transport routes, are closely tied into the settlement and marketing network. Many others, such as the forest villages of Ethiopia and the villages in the Atlas Mountains, are isolated.

Isolation means that villagers must produce almost everything they need. It means, too, that they will have few of the advantages of modern civilization, such as medical services, schools, and libraries. The new African governments are trying to build roads to link up every village with the main transport and communications network.

In the past, it was often necessary for groups of Africans to seek isolation as a means of protecting themselves against powerful neighbours. They built fortress-like villages in swamps, mountains, or forests, or even halfway up steep cliffs. Today these villages are shrinking in size as the people move to better farmlands.

The photographs on this page and on pages 120 and 121 give some idea of the great variety of African villages.

The kind of material used for housebuilding varies according to the different types of climate and vegetation, as does the shape of the houses themselves. In the hot, dry Sudan

A quiet village street in southeastern Nigeria. What materials are used for building? What can you tell about the climate of this region from the picture?

belt, mud bricks make good building material, and conical-shaped homes are cooler.

Throughout most of Africa, however, modern building materials are used more and more. Gradually, the old architectural differences are disappearing, as can be seen in the picture of a Chagga farming area in Kenya, where some of the richer farmers have built homes with imported building materials.

African village life is rich and interesting. Almost every activity can become a social occasion, and there are songs and dances for most important events such as marriages, harvesting, funerals, and childbirth. It is not uncommon for people from the same village to call each other "brother" and "sister", even if they are not closely related, for living in a village is like living in a large family. The villagers miss their homes when they move away to live in the cities, and prefer to live close to people from the same village.

(Top left) The village of Ksar es-Suk in the Atlas Mountains. Notice the high, castle-like walls of the houses on the perimeter of the village, with slit windows to give protection against rifle fire.

(Centre left) The opposite extreme. Here, in Kenya, lush farmland combined with political peace have resulted in highly scattered country dwellings. Note the mixture of old-style and modern roofing.

(Bottom) The lagoon village of Ganvié in Dahomey. The jars on the boat are filled with drinking water because the lagoon itself is both salty and muddy. What is a lagoon? Why are the houses built on stilts? What materials are used in building the houses? Explain why these boats are unlikely to be used at sea.

Page 121

(Top) Villages in the open plains of Upper Volta, West Africa. In the past the Muslim farmers of these villages were protected from their enemies by powerful princes and emirs and were able to live close to the fields. How many hamlets do you see? How do you think they would obtain their water? Describe a typical house. What type of farming would be practised in this area?

(Bottom) Women working together on palm-leaf matting in a Togolese village. Men often work in the fields from dawn to dusk. Implements are simple and consist mainly of hand tools such as cutlasses and hoes. Women help during busy times of the year, especially with planting, weeding, and harvesting.

120

Village life in Africa is peaceful and secure, but it also has many drawbacks. It is difficult to get help in times of trouble, schooling for the children is often poor, and there is little opportunity for the men to find any other work besides farming. Many of the livelier people find village life rather dull and monotonous.

In recent years a new problem has appeared. Factory-made goods from the cities are becoming more expensive, while the goods produced in the villages still bring the same prices. This means that the villagers are finding it harder to make a living, and many leave for the cities. One of the reasons for low prices for village produce is the lack of cheap transport. The African governments are trying to help, by building better roads, by bringing in electricity, by building schools and libraries, and by trying to improve agricultural techniques.

It is probable, however, that village life will soon be nothing more than a memory for millions of Africans, just as it is for millions of Europeans and North Americans.

Cities

Most people in the world today live in towns and cities. One of the main reasons is that in a city, everything is close at hand. Large industries, and any activity that needs to make use of other people's skills to any degree, such as book publishing or designing, will prefer to locate in a city. Administrators, too, like to be at the centre of things. People are attracted to cities not only because of the opportunity of getting a better and more interesting job, but also because of better cultural, educational, and other social facilities. For example, there are usually theatres, orchestras, universities, and good libraries.

Today, millions of Africans are moving to the cities, both for these reasons and because it is hard to make a good living in the countryside.

Cities have grown up for several different reasons. They may have been established as centres of (a) trade and manufacturing, (b) administration and finance, (c) transportation, (d) culture, or (e) religion.

The old cities of Africa, such as Timbuktu and Kairouan, were mainly trading centres. In the network of human settlement, they served as market points and terminals of the great trading routes. Timbuktu and Kairouan, for example, were at opposite ends of a trans-Saharan route.

Where strong states grew up, administrative capitals also appeared. Examples of these capital cities were Kumasi, Benin, and Omdurman. As with cities throughout the world, they attracted skilled craftsmen and artisans. Traditional industries grew up, such as textiles, dyeing, metalworking, tanning, and pottery. The artisans were grouped together in *trade guilds,* similar to those that existed in Europe at the same time. In Fez, for example, dyeing and leatherworking were important industries long before the European conquest of Africa. "Morocco" had even become a trade name in Europe for very fine flexible goat or lambskin leather, used for binding valuable books.

Seaports grew up along the North African coast, where the Muslim navies fought a centuries-long war against European navies based on the north coast of the Mediterranean. Both sides treated the others as pirates. Along the East African coast, the great Omani trading empire founded a string of seaports. Only the West African coast had few ports, as these states were not part of a world-wide trading network until the arrival of Portuguese vessels in the fifteenth century.

The European conquest meant the destruction of the Muslim seaports of North and East Africa, which were replaced by a string of trading cities that circled the continent. The Europeans' later conquest of the interior of Africa led to the creation of new administrative centres. These were never built in the old African cities, but were set up a few miles away or in completely new locations. Tananarive, the capital of the Malagasy Republic, was one of the few exceptions to the rule. There the French built their administrative and business centre around the old capital.

Today almost all cities in Africa, whether they began as African or European centres, are growing rapidly. The chart shows the rate of growth of several West African cities. Note the changes since 1950. Growth, caused by thousands of farmers who are flocking to the cities in search of employment, brings a host of problems. These include water supply, drainage, housing, traffic congestion, and unemployment.

Questions
1. Locate these cities on an atlas map.
2. How many of these cities are also seaports?
3. Which is the largest city? What was its population in 1970?
4. List the reasons why people leave their villages and move to the cities?

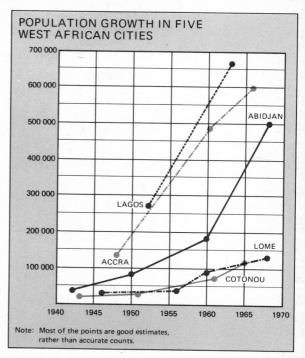

POPULATION GROWTH IN FIVE WEST AFRICAN CITIES

Note: Most of the points are good estimates, rather than accurate counts.

(Top) Figure 4.25

(Bottom) Old "colonial" buildings with their metal-sheeting roofs and sheltered sidewalks (in the foreground) are giving way to modern apartment and office blocks in the Plateau, the commercial centre of Abidjan. Similar changes are taking place in all the major cities of Africa.

A shantytown in Porto Novo, Dahomey. When poor farmers or workers first arrive in a big city, they usually have no jobs and no places to live. They must either crowd into existing houses, creating slums with a *high population density* (a large number of people per square kilometre), or must build their own shacks on the edges of the city. These shantytowns are called *bidonvilles* in French-speaking Africa.

Throughout the world, it is in the cities that art and learning flourish best. The rapid growth of Africa's cities is perhaps the most hopeful development of all, in spite of the serious problems discussed in this section. Great universities such as Dakar, Dar es Salaam, Lusaka, Legon (Accra), Cairo, and Nairobi are growing rapidly, and are producing the engineers, doctors, and technicians that Africa needs.

The cities are the major growth points of human settlement, and the independent African governments are spending their precious resources to turn the rapidly-growing urban centres into pleasant and exciting places in which to live.

AGRICULTURE

Crops

Considering the vast size of Africa and its variety of climatic regions, one would expect a wide range of crops. The harvests of Africa vary from temperate crops, such as wheat, rye, barley, and maize (corn), to tropical products, such as rubber, cocoa, cane sugar, and groundnuts (peanuts).

Commercial Crops

Only a small number of the many hundreds of plants cultivated in Africa are grown for export. The rest are for food, medicines, animal feed, dyes, materials for cloth and basketry, and drinks for the local population. Some of the most important food crops, for example, dates, yams, cassava, millet, and corn, are almost entirely consumed in the countries where they are grown, with only small amounts being sent overseas. Because of the importance of the commercial export crops, however, most governments spend far more of their money on them than on food crops.

Questions
1. How do the crops of northwestern Africa (Morocco and Algeria) compare with those of southwest Africa? How do the climates compare?
2. List the crops grown in Egypt.
3. What important crops are grown in West Africa?
4. What is Ethiopia's main commercial crop?
5. Why is the Nile delta region especially suitable for rice cultivation?
6. Where are groundnuts cultivated? What products are made from groundnuts?
7. Where is sugar cane mainly cultivated?

Export crops such as cotton, rubber, cocoa, groundnuts, tea, coffee, tobacco, and linseed are important to a number of African countries. This is especially true of those

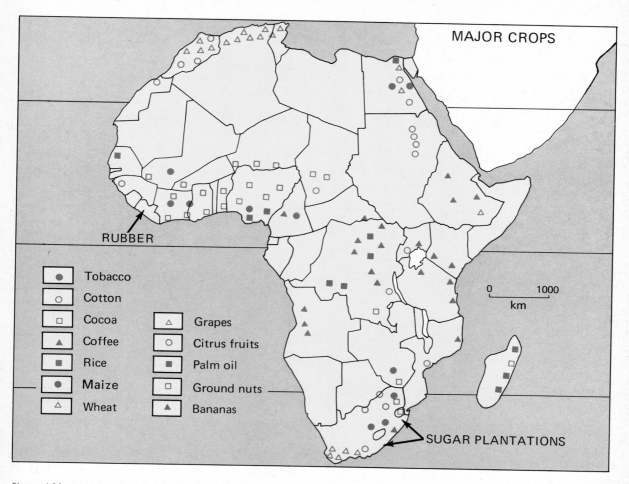

MAJOR CROPS

RUBBER

●	Tobacco
○	Cotton
□	Cocoa
▲	Coffee
■	Rice
●	Maize
△	Wheat

△	Grapes
○	Citrus fruits
■	Palm oil
□	Ground nuts
▲	Bananas

0   1000
km

SUGAR PLANTATIONS

Figure 4.26   Map showing the distribution of the major commercial crops of Africa.

that do not have valuable minerals to sell. Without an income from foreign sales, a country such as Senegal would not be able to afford to import anything at all. Between sixty-five and eighty percent of Senegal's foreign currency earnings comes from groundnut sales. Chad, another country that is short of minerals and forestry products, earns about eighty percent of its foreign currency from sales of cotton.

Omit

Questions
1. From reference books, find out how groundnuts are cultivated. Why are they also called peanuts?
2. What is linseed? What uses are made of this seed?
3. Why is it important to constantly seek out new varieties of cultivated crops?

Coffee is an indigenous African fruit. This means that it originated in Africa, actually in the mountains of western Ethiopia where many kinds of wild coffee still grow. There is even a wild coffee "forest" still in existence. Because the wild coffee is still available, coffee experts can use it to cross-breed with domesticated coffee varieties to strengthen resistance to disease and to obtain new flavours.

In Ethiopia, most coffee is collected by poor farm families, and then sold to local buying agents who ship it in sacks to the capital, Addis Ababa. There, some thirty merchants specialize in selling the coffee to overseas buyers. In other countries, such as the Ivory Coast and Guinea, most coffee is grown on large farms or plantations. From Africa, coffee spread to Brazil and other

125

parts of the Americas, so that today South American production is more important. Even so, there are many varieties of coffee, and some coffee lovers claim that the Ethiopian varieties are by far the best.

Cocoa was originally an Amerindian crop. In parts of Guatemala, for example, a bitter cocoa drink is still an important food for the local Indians. Cocoa was taken to Africa, and was first grown on small plantations for use in the European chocolate trade. The largest of these plantations were on the Portuguese islands of São Tomé e Principe; where slaves were brought from the mainland. Later, wealthy African farmers in Nigeria and Ghana began to plant cocoa, encouraged by the British colonial government, so that today' this is the most important cocoa-growing area in the world.

Like coffee, the cocoa beans are carefully graded according to quality before being shipped overseas, and must be dried so that they have a low moisture content. Grading is important because it gives the buyer, in Europe or America, who sees the crop only when it arrives in his country, confidence that he is paying for something the quality of which is guaranteed in advance.

Rubber, too, was originally an American crop. The first rubber shipments were from Brazil and Peru. The Amazon rubber "boom" lasted until rubber seedlings were smuggled out and nurtured in Kew Gardens, in England. From there, they were shipped to plantations in Malaya, which became the world's most important rubber-producing area. In later years, American companies decided to create their own rubber plantations, just as French and Belgian tire manufacturers had created theirs in Cambodia and South Vietnam. The Americans, led by Firestone, first tried the Amazon Basin, and then established plantations in Liberia, in West Africa.

The rubber is collected at regular intervals by cutting the trees so that the milky white latex oozes into a collecting cup which is emptied each day. After a tree has been tapped for a while, it is given a rest period.

> **Questions**
> 1. To which country did São Tomé e Principe belong? Why would the British have been anxious to encourage farmers in Ghana and Nigeria to grow cocoa?
> 2. Why do you think rubber plants had to be smuggled out of Brazil? Who ruled Malaya?
> 3. What other agricultural products can you think of that are graded?
> 4. Most coffee you buy in the stores is differentiated only by the brand names. See if you can find some coffee on sale that tells what varieties it contains. Look particularly for the robusta varieties. In a delicatessen, try to buy some real Ethiopian coffee.

Problems and Remedies

Africa's earth could feed several times the present population, even though today millions of Africans do not get enough to eat. The problem is that most food crops are produced on small farms by villagers who do not have enough capital to make their land give of its best. Because they do not have enough money for pumps, irrigation water must be raised from wells by hand, or using a pulley worked by animals. The same lack of money means that deep wells cannot be dug, that large-scale drainage and flood-protection works cannot be undertaken, and that concrete irrigation channels cannot be built to replace earth channels which lose a lot of the precious water.

Only a minority of African villages are connected to the main markets by motorable roads, and the dirt trails are frequently impassable during the rainy season. Even villages that are near to main roads cannot afford trucks. The lack of capital is felt seriously when insect pests attack the crops, when a plant disease appears, or when fields need fertilizing. All of these problems show up in statistics of crop yields. Low yields in turn mean low incomes, and the whole set of problems repeats itself.

One of the worst disasters that can strike African farmers is the arrival of a swarm of locusts. One locust has a mass of only 2 g but it can eat more than its own mass in 1 d. Approximately 200 to 250 locusts will eat over 0.5 kg of food in 1 d. Some locust swarms have measured over 260 km², and each square kilometre of locusts eats 140 t of food per day. Swarms can travel up to 5000 km, leaving a trail of ruin that can cross several African and Middle Eastern countries.

Locust swarms are normally attacked while they are still young "hoppers", unable to fly. Anti-locust operations are carried out like military campaigns with several governments paying the costs of modern equipment. Insecticides are sprayed from aircraft or by huge spray guns mounted on trucks.

Birds can also be a serious pest to the farmers' crops. Tiny *quelea*, not much larger than locusts, form colonies thousands strong. They are fought today with flame throwers.

For about a month before harvest time, African farmers and their children spend much of the day keeping birds from eating their crops.

Once the harvest is in, the villagers feel a great sense of relief, and most marriages are celebrated at this time of year. Special festivities take place, and farmers make trips to town to buy something new for their homes, some new cloth for their wives, and perhaps a sewing machine or a transistor radio if it has been a good year. Their possible crop losses, however, are still not over.

The crops must be stored, and very few African farmers can afford proper storage bins. The traditional storage bins, although very attractive to look at, are not proof against insects, rats, damp, and beetles. One international organization has estimated that over one-third of Africa's food supplies is lost during storage.

(Left)   A swarm of locusts.

(Right)   A basket-like grain store in Upper Volta.

CROP YIELDS*
(100 kg/ha)

	World	Europe	North & Central America	South America	Asia	Africa	Oceania
Wheat	14.2	22.4	18.2	11.6	9.0	7.3	15.5
Rye	12.9	18.3	14.1	6.6	11.8	3.9	4.6
Barley	16.5	26.9	20.8	10.0	11.8	4.5	15.5
Oats	15.8	21.0	16.6	12.0	12.5	4.7	11.9
Maize	23.3	29.9	35.3	14.6	10.9	10.9	23.8
Millet & Sorghum	7.6	19.9	31.8	20.0	4.6	6.6	16.5
Rice	20.0	45.3	34.7	16.3	16.9	17.5	58.8
Potatoes	127.0	174.0	217.0	67.0	102.0	71.0	188.0
Swt. Pots. & Yams	83.0	133.0	62.0	102.0	98.0	66.0	94.0

*Production Yearbook, 1967, Vol. 21, United Nations Food & Agriculture Organization (1968), p. 33.

Figure 4.27

Questions
1. Are African crop yields generally higher or lower than those of other countries? How do they compare with world average yields?
2. Which crops give the highest yields in comparison with other countries?
3. Why do you think that African crop yields are generally lower than other continents?

In many parts of modern Africa, farmers are grouping themselves into cooperatives. By pooling their labour, and sometimes their land and implements, they hope to be able to use more modern methods. If one farmer cannot afford a tractor, for example, maybe twenty can. Already over one-third of Tunisia's land is worked by cooperative farmers, and cooperatives are growing in many countries from the Malagasy Republic to Morocco.

Many governments have set up special departments to encourage the formation of new cooperatives and to help those already in existence with loans and technical advice. They feel that cooperative farming has many advantages, some of which are:
1. Seed and fertilizers, pesticides and equipment can all be bought more cheaply in bulk.
2. The farmers can sell their produce together, hiring or buying a truck, and therefore get better prices.
3. The cooperative can borrow money (capital) more easily. Some countries have set up special cooperative banks for this purpose.
4. The farmers, if they wish, can organize their work as a group instead of each farmer doing his own work.

Another important way of improving Africa's food supply is to work out better farming methods suited to each kind of land. This is usually done in agricultural research stations, which also develop better varieties of farm crops, and study the effects of different fertilizers on different crops. New methods of weed control and pest control are also developed. Every African country has its agricultural research stations, many of which were opened in the years before independence. Many Africans complain, however, that the new ideas have mainly been concerned with export crops and not the ordinary food crops grown by the peasant farmers.

As industry develops in Africa, it will become possible to supply pesticides, fungicides, locusticides, herbicides, fertilizers, farm machinery, pumps, ploughs, metal bins, trucks, packing materials, and the thousand-and-one items of equipment that make up a modern farmer's capital. At present, most of these have to be imported and are much too expensive for an African villager. Some African economists argue that until industry develops, millions of Africans will continue to have insufficient food to eat. They suggest that it is more important to get factories started to produce fertilizers and other needed goods, than to import fertilizers.

Livestock

There have been cattlemen in Africa for centuries, particularly in the high, grassy plateau country of East Africa and in the broad belt of country between the Sahara Desert and the farming areas to the south. Madagascar is famous for its lush pastures, which are the home of several cattle-owning peoples. To some Africans, such as the Nuer of the southern Sudan, cattle have become a whole way of life, and each of their animals is given a pet name. Other important groups of cattlemen are the Masai of Tanzania and Kenya, the Fulani, who move their herds in most of the West African republics, and the Baggara of the Sudan.

Africa's cattle herdsmen have many serious problems:
1. Flies. There are many kinds of biting flies which annoy cattle, especially during the

(Left) Figure 4.28

rains or near rivers. The most troublesome is the tsetse fly, for it also transmits *trypanoso-miasis* (sleeping sickness). The presence of tsetse flies means that an area will no longer be of any use for raising cattle.
2. Other cattle diseases, such as *rinderpest* (cattle plague), which can wipe out whole herds of cattle.
3. Huge distances to markets, and a lack of trucks, roads, or railways.
4. Droughts and floods.

The terrible effects of drought can be seen from this extract from Botswana's 1968-1973 Development Plan:

> "Botswana has recently experienced the most calamitous drought in living memory. It lasted from 1961 to 1966. Famine was widespread and about one-third of the national herd was lost. In many areas the vegetation was entirely grazed away, and permanent damage done to the veld (pastureland). The heavy rains which fell during 1966/67 brought temporary relief, but the rains failed again in 1967/68."

From: Republic of Botswana, *National Development Plan*, 1968-73 (Gaberones, Botswana: Government Printer, 1968), page 1.

(Top right) Nuer cattle returning to the village at the end of the day.

(Bottom right) The Masai, who live in Kenya and Tanzania, have been cattlemen for countless generations. Like the Baggara of the Sudan, their lives revolve around the needs of their animals.

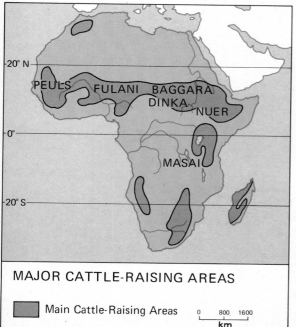

MAJOR CATTLE-RAISING AREAS

Main Cattle-Raising Areas   0   800   1600
km

More capital could solve many of these problems, just as in agriculture. In the meantime, the African cattlemen must solve their own problems. One traditional method has been to move the herds according to the season, so that the herds will always find sufficient good grass.

The Humr— A Group of Nomadic Cattle Herders

An eminent anthropologist, Dr. Ian Cunnison, spent over a year living with the Humr, a group of Baggara cattle nomads in the western Sudan. He made a careful record of the way they organize their movements. Their main farming area, for very few nomads are not also part-time farmers, is near Muglad. Each year they range as far south as the Bahr el-Ghazal, a tributary of the White Nile. Dr. Cunnison drew up a schedule of their movements (see table).

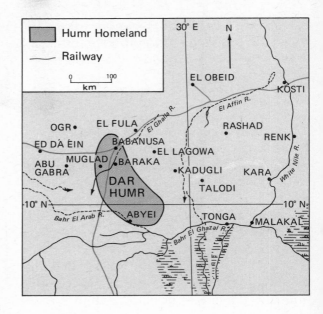

(Top right) Figure 4.30

(Bottom) Figure 4.29

From: Ian Cunnison, *Baggara Arabs: Power and Lineage in a Sudanese Nomad Tribe,* Clarendon Press, Oxford.

THE HUMR YEAR

MONTH	WEATHER	ACTIVITIES
January	Cold; dry; north wind	Arrival and establishment on Bahr; camps on northern *regebas* (water courses).
February	Dry; getting hot	Bahr. Camps going to late dry-season positions.
March	Dry; hot; dust devils	As surface water disappears, well are reopened.
April	First few rains, still very hot	Bahr.
May	Dust laid; fresh grass	Cattle move north with approach of insects; cotton cultivators remain on Bahr.
June	Rain more frequent	Migration orthward completed; cattle to gardens, thence to *Babanusa* (semi-desert area north of Muglad). Preparing gardens for millet and cotton; sowing and first weeding.
July	Rain more frequent	Cattle move to Babanusa; millet and corn cultivation.
August	Heavy rain	Cattle cand camps reunited in Babanusa; cotton people come north.
September	Rain, much reduced at end of month	Southwards to Muglad at end of month; cattle and camps still together; some cotton people return south.
October	End of rains	Cattle in the Muglad; first millet people back to gardens.
November	Dry; getting cold; north wind	Cattle in *Qoz* (sand plains between Muglad and Bahr); millet harvest, cotton harvest.
December	Cold; dry; north wind	Cattle eat remains of gardens and go south; cotton harvest; end of millet harvest and stacking grain.

130

"Humr daydream about the life of ease and comfort that cattle can bring them. Cattle attract women and enable a man to marry more than one wife. The women feed him and bring him tea as he lies under his tree, content in the knowledge that his numerous sons are taking their turns at herding. All he has to do is to wait until evening, sleeping or talking to the guests who honour him with their presence, and whom he can treat generously by bringing them milk, sour milk, and one of his flock of sheep or goats that his ample cattle have enabled him to establish. Evening is the best time of day, for then the cattle return, filled with the finest grazing his sons could find; they come lowing into camp and cluster round the wood and dung fires his dependants and Dinka servants have built. He wanders in among his herd and inspects them as his wives release the calves at milking. Perhaps he milks one or two himself. At night there is plenty of liquid butter for a wife to massage his legs; he sleeps in peace, to be awakened only by the churning of the sour milk *calabash* outside the door of his scent-filled tent."

From: Ian Cunnison, *Baggara Arabs: Power and Lineage in a Sudanese Nomad Tribe,* (Oxford University Press, London, 1966), page 32.

Questions
1. Which are the busiest months for the Humr?
2. In which month do you think they have weddings and other festivities?
3. From your study, name some items in the diet of the Humr.
4. Name some other nomadic peoples of Africa.

(Top) Humr families moving north in June. Notice the vessels used for milk, and the rolled-up mats.

(Centre) Herdsmen gather under a favourite tree for the midday meal.

(Bottom) Humr horseman on southward migration in December. The long spears are to keep off wild animals and to hunt giraffe.

131

(Left) Important discussions among Babanusa menfolk, about cattle, marriages and politics, are usually held under shade trees while the cattle herds graze nearby.

(Right) A Humr housewife churning milk for breakfast. Notice the gas can used for storing water, the heap of millet in the right foreground, and a small teapot near the door of the temporary hut.

When a whole way of life has grown up around cattle raising, cattle become important for prestige as well as for food and money. This is one reason why it is difficult to buy enough cattle to supply a meat-packing plant, even in the cattle-raising areas of Africa. It is also dangerous for a man to sell too many of his animals, for it then only needs a disaster such as a drought or an epidemic of rinderpest for him to lose the rest of his herd, and with it his social standing.

Camel herders live in many parts of the Sahara Desert and along its margins. They travel great distances in search of fresh pastures for their animals. Like the Humr, they follow roughly the same pattern of movement every year. Unfortunately for the camel herders, camels are no longer important for transporting people and goods across the desert. The great trading caravans have been replaced by trucks and cargo planes, and the impoverished camel men are seeking work in the oil industry, or as watchmen or traders in the towns surrounding the desert.

One big remaining market for camels is Egypt, where camel meat is eaten by the poorer people.

In the high mountains of Africa, goats and sheep become the most important domestic animals. They are kept mainly for meat and milk. It is possible that the introduction of new varieties of sheep, together with cross-breeding, will make the mountainous areas an important source of wool in the future. This has already begun to happen in the Drakensberg Mountains of southern Africa.

Goats are kept, often along with camels, in the drier semi-desert areas. They convert

Tunisian shepherds on their way to market. They have collected firewood in the hills to make some extra money.

otherwise useless vegetation into meat and milk. Goats will eat almost anything, and often destroy trees and shrubs. They must therefore be kept out of valuable forest areas, especially in the dry mountains of North Africa where the trees grow slowly.

The diets of Africans could be improved tremendously if modern methods of livestock raising were introduced. For example, irrigated feeding lots, such as those already used by European farmers in southern Africa, could be used to fatten cattle for market. Long-distance cattle trucks could be used to bring cattle to market in good condition, and veterinary medicine could wipe out many of the worst diseases. All of these developments, however, require capital.

Fairly soon, Africa may become a source of meat, wool, and hides for the rest of the world. As world living standards improve, people can afford to eat more meat. This demand has caused a rise in prices for beef in recent years, so that it is now profitable for African countries to invest some of their scarce capital in packing plants and livestock improvement programs. New breeds of range cattle are being developed that are more resistant to disease and that fatten more easily, while other breeds that give high milk yields are being introduced in densely populated areas.

(Top) Traditional breeds of cattle can be improved. This is a fine specimen of an Acholi cow from Tanzania. The large horns are much admired by East African cattlemen.

(Bottom) This fine herd of Boran cattle in Kenya is an example of the kind of fat, healthy and well-cared-for cattle that could turn Africa into an important cattle-producing continent.

MARKETS AND MARKETING

Local Markets

Even the most isolated and self-sufficient village in Africa needs to buy some goods from other places and from factories in the cities and foreign countries. For example, a village with good fishponds will sell fish to villages that have none, perhaps in exchange for wheat or millet. Because of this need to trade, markets are the strongest links between the African villages and the outside world.

People from isolated villages will walk miles to the nearest market, partly to trade and partly because of the opportunity of chatting with people from other villages.

When the transportation system is adequate, large quantities of goods will come into the countryside from the cities. Travelling merchants will come by truck or bus with cheap pots and pans which are brighter and more durable than the clay pots and carved calabashes made in the villages. In this way many old crafts are gradually disappearing from the villages, just as they disappeared from the European countryside.

The cloth-selling stalls of a West African market. As a market grows and more stalls are built, the area becomes a permanent trading place. The big city markets of North Africa have gradually developed into *bazaars,* in which winding streets and alleyways have replaced the paths that used to lead between the stalls and small lock-up stores.

Very few village markets are big enough to stay open every day. Instead, neighbouring villages have market days on different days of the week. This enables travelling merchants to move in a *circuit* from one market to the other, and also enables villagers to find a market open each day somewhere in their area.

The larger markets develop whole areas for each kind of merchandise. In some of the bigger cities, these specialized areas will even separate into different market places, so that a city the size of Omdurman will have a separate cloth market, a food market and so on. There are usually small food and vegetable markets in each part of the city, so that housewives do not have to travel far to buy their groceries. The pictures on this page and on pages 135 and 136 show specialized markets in several of the big cities of Africa.

In the bigger towns and cities, markets have been modernized. In the past, fly-borne and dust-borne diseases were easily spread in the overcrowded and insanitary markets. Today, proper drainage and cleaning make shopping in a large African market as healthy as shopping in a supermarket.

Some supermarkets have begun to appear. But most African shoppers still prefer the markets and lockup stores, because there they can bargain for lower prices, and choose their goods from many different merchants.

Visitors from North America often notice that there seem to be far too many people trying to sell things in an African town. A world traveller would point out that this is common to most of the cities in Asia, Latin America, and the Caribbean. It is caused by high unemployment. People prefer to try to sell goods rather than have no work at all.

Page 135

In the market of Tangier, like other North African cities, the stalls have become permanent stores. Morocco is famous for its fruit and vegetables. Name some of the fruit and vegetables displayed on the stalls. Notice the lady is wearing a veil, a custom practised by some Arab women. What men in the Sahara traditionally cover their faces?

(Top left)   Housewives buy their fish as it is brought ashore at Freetown. Refrigerated storage would make it possible to relocate fresh fish markets near the main market in town, so that housewives would not have so far to walk.

(Bottom left)   Coffee, corn, beans in Omdurman market, Sudan.

(Top right)   A temporary marketplace in a very poor part of Ethiopia. The farmers and their wives have walked distances of up to thirty-two kilometres to get here, often to sell only a few handfuls of peppers or spices.

Foreign Markets

Distributing goods to the villages and towns is only one side of marketing. The other is to bring the produce of the countryside to the towns and cities, for sale or for export. Here, the main problem is transport. Only the large mines and plantations can afford to have their own transportation; the smaller village producers have to send their produce by hired trucks, animals, or public transport. This is uncertain in countries like Nigeria, where there are only one-fiftieth as many trucks per head of population as there are in Canada. Furthermore, as there are few trucks, those merchants who do own one can pay low prices to villagers and then sell the produce at much higher prices in the city.

African countries are anxious to increase the number of foreign markets for their exports. There are, however, some major difficulties which include:

(a) much of their present trade is still with these European countries which were their former rulers,

(b) shortage of ships and other means of transportation,

(c) lack of finances for expansion and development.

The pattern of trade with former colonial countries is strengthened because the big companies that buy and sell African produce, such as Unilever, Anglo-American, and the British West Africa Company, are the same companies that traded in Africa in the colonial period.

Questions

1. From the study of the table of exports from Zaïre, 1969, and the map on page 138:

(a) Name the two greatest importers of Zaïre's products.

(b) Which European country once ruled this part of Africa?

(c) What is Zaïre's major export?

2. By analysing the table of exports from Tanzania, 1967, on page 138:

(a) Name the major exports of this country.

(b) Name the greatest single importer and from this, state the country which once ruled over the area.

(c) What are the names of the E.E.C. countries?

(d) What type of diamonds is exported?

3. From an analysis of the table of imports to Zambia, 1969, on page 138:

(a) Name the country from which Zambia imports the largest amount of goods, and also the country that once ruled the area.

(b) Which countries, within Africa, trade with Zambia?

4. Which West European countries would you expect to be important trading partners of Senegal, Uganda, Mozambique, and Dahomey?

(Top) Trucks, over bumpy roads, can be used for palm kernels, but not for highly perishable goods like fruit and vegetables. Why?

(Bottom) On their long trek to market, cattle lose condition and weight and their owners lose money.

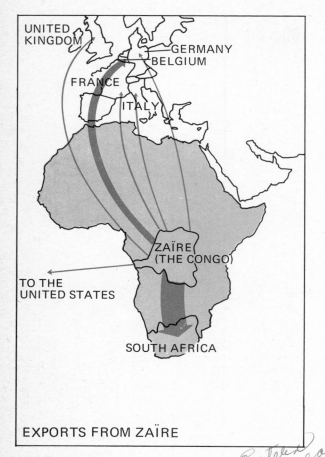

EXPORTS FROM ZAÏRE

EXPORTS FROM ZAÏRE
(THE CONGO), 1969*

(Thousands of zaïre at 1 zaïre = U.S. $2)

Belgium and Luxembourg	183.8
United Kingdom	25.1
Italy	35.2
German Federal Republic	20.8
France	25.3
United States	13.9
South Africa	482.0

Note: 70% of Zaïre's export earnings come from copper.

*From *Africa South of the Sahara*, 1971 (London, Europa Publications, 1971), p. 257.

(Top left) Figure 4.31

(Top right) Figure 4.32

(Centre right) Figure 4.33

(Bottom right) Figure 4.34

EXPORTS FROM TANZANIA, 1967*

(millions of shillings at 72 sh. = U.S. $10)

United Kingdom	473
India	108
Hong Kong	113
Japan	67
China, People's Republic	59
EEC Countries	250
CMEA Countries	56
North America	117

Note: Main exports are sisal, coffee, cotton and diamonds.

*From *Africa South of the Sahara*, 1971 (London, Europa Publications, 1971), p. 833.

5. Study the table on page 139 showing the value of goods exported from Canada to the various African countries.
(a) Which African country is Canada's best customer?
(b) Which is the second major buyer?
(c) What would Canada export to these African countries? List a few exports.

As a result of their colonial history and the lack of finances, African countries were unable to build their own ships and train their own crews, depending heavily on shipping lines owned by West European countries. Ghana, one of the first African

IMPORTS INTO ZAMBIA, 1969*

(thousands of kwachas, at 10 kwaches = U.S. $14)

United Kingdom	71 407
South Africa	69 946
Rhodesia	21 772
U.S.A.	30 083
Japan	22 588
German Federal Republic	12 151
East Africa	11 180

*From *Africa South of the Sahara*, 1971 (London Europa Publications, 1971) p. 901.

CANADIAN EXPORTS TO AFRICA, 1971*			
(Thousands of dollars)			
Ethiopia	206	Angola	862
Libya	1 618	Cameroon Republic	3 091
Somalia	78	Dahomey	1 063
Sudan	1 209	French Africa	1 041
U.A.R. (Egypt)	10 158	Gabon Republic	150
Gambia	89	Guinea, Republic of	217
Ghana	8 167	Ivory Coast	704
Kenya	7 037	Liberia	1 642
Malawi	276	Malagasy Republic	3 098
Mauritus and dependencies	252	Mauritania	182
Nigeria	9 799	Morocco	5 110
Republic of South Africa	62 828	Mozambique	2 241
Rhodesia	—	Portuguese Africa	368
Sierra Leone	99	Senegal	1 183
Tanzania	4 365	Spanish Africa	468
Uganda	693	Togo	1 111
Zambia	3 986	Tunisia	5 692
Commonwealth Africa	60	Zaïre (The Congo)	1 749
Algeria	30 407	Total	171 300
*Source: External Trade Division, Statistics Canada			

Figure 4.35

countries south of the Sahara to win its independence, decided to create its own shipping line so that its exports and imports would not be tied to the seaports served by the British shipping lines. With the help of the Israeli government, the Black Star shipping line was started— the first nationally-owned line in independent Africa.

As trade grew, it became clear that the seaport of Takoradi was no longer large enough, especially since Ghana had its own shipping line. An entirely new seaport and

industrial area were created at Tema, a few miles to the east of Accra, the capital city.

Questions
1. From a study of the plan of the port, name one of the most important exports of Ghana.
2. What are marshalling yards?
3. Since 1961 a loading berth for alumina (refined bauxite used for aluminum) has been built near the dry dock. Why might special berths speed up the loading and unloading of different cargoes?

(Left) Figure 4.36

(Right) The *Uti River,* a Black Star Line cocoa boat is moored alongside the wharf at Tema, along with boats from Poland, Bulgaria and the United States.

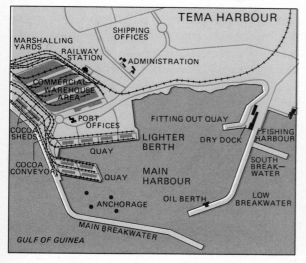

PORT OF TEMA ANNUAL FIGURES*
(10^3 t)

	1962	1963	1964	1965	1966	1967	1968	1969
Imports	727	1120	1738	1891	1511	1373	1461	1663
Exports	190	272	511	605	536	507	590	665
Total	917	1392	2249	2496	2047	1880	2142	2327
Cocoa	175	172	175	268	199	164	182	161
Cement Clinker	—	—	—	44	58	115	175	184
Aluminum Ingot	—	—	—	—	—	15	50	108
Number of vessels cleared	867	910	996	998	856	877	871	877

*From: *Ghana Railway & Ports*, Port Manager's Office, Tema, Ghana

Figure 4.37

4. When was Tema's busiest year?
5. What was the average number of ships per day docking at Tema in 1969?
6. Why was it a good idea to locate the new port near to Accra?
7. The region adjacent to a port, and whose trade is carried on through that port, is known as the *hinterland*. Describe the hinterland of Tema.

Independence has meant that the African countries can try to find the best prices for their goods on the world market instead of being tied to one or other West European country. In spite of this, prices for African agricultural commodities fluctuate wildly, and for most commodities there has been a steady downward movement since World War II. This means that African farmers are discouraged from growing export crops. It also means that African countries find it difficult to plan for development, when they do not know what the prices of their exports will be from one year to the next.

Independence also means that the African countries can buy their imports at the lowest prices they can find in the world market. However, aid programs from the West European countries often include a requirement that the African countries must promise to buy their imports from the same European country that gave them aid. In this way, the change from the *colonial pattern of trade* (in which almost all trade was to and from one or other European country) is breaking down slowly.

North America, which did not have African colonies, is gradually increasing its share of African trade. Both Canada and the United States are trying to sell more goods to Africa, and are buying more African products.

Just as African villages are gradually being linked more closely to the towns and cities through the marketing network, so the African countries are gradually increasing their contacts with the rest of the world through trade. The change from colonial trade to world trade means that Africans are more and more interested in new trading partners such as North America, Japan, Eastern Europe, India, and other parts of the world.

RESOURCES AND INDUSTRIES

Africa is a continent rich in natural resources, such as iron ore, oil, diamonds, and other mineral deposits, as well as sizeable forests. Its great rivers provide water for irrigation, and are sources of hydroelectric power.

(Top) The Volta River, about 1600 km long, is the power behind Ghana's hydroelectric project.

(Bottom) Figure 4.38

Minerals

Gold, the precious metal that spurred on Europeans to invade South America and settle in Australia, also led them to penetrate the interior of Africa. The discovery of gold in South Africa brought thousands of English immigrants to areas previously controlled by Dutch cattlemen. The Portuguese explorers of present-day Angola and Mozambique were also looking for gold.

With the growth of industry in Europe and America, however, many other minerals became important, and the gold-mining companies switched their interests to copper, lead, zinc, chrome, and other minerals. In more recent years, the iron and steel industries of Europe, North America, and Japan have exhausted many of their old sources of iron ore, and have begun to look to Africa for supplies. Huge new iron ore mines have been opened in Mauritania, Swaziland, Liberia, and the Ivory Coast. The worldwide demand for fertilizers has also grown, as farming in the richer countries of the world has become more and more modernized. Thus, phosphate deposits in North Africa, along the Red Sea, and in West Africa, are being worked to supply material for superphosphate fertilizers.

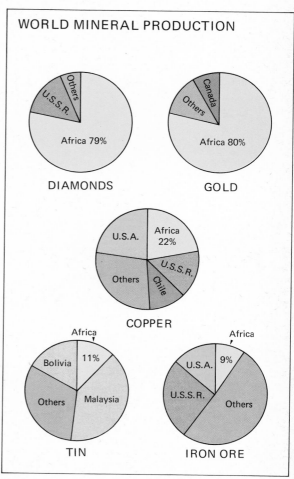

WORLD MINERAL PRODUCTION

141

Questions
1. In which minerals does Africa lead world production? Account for the importance of these minerals in world markets.

2. What uses are made of copper and tin today?

3. Draw a graph similar to the ones here, showing Africa's share of the world production of cobalt. Production, 1969 (in 10^3 kg): Canada 1473; U.S.S.R. 1500; Africa 13 045; Total 20 178.

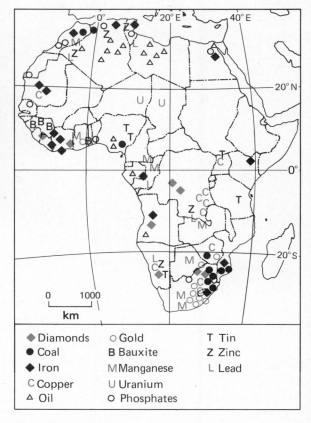

Figure 4.39 Map showing the main mineral deposits of Africa.

The map shows the main mineral deposits presently being worked. There are many more deposits that companies are keeping in reserve, and many parts of Africa have not yet been thoroughly prospected.

Modern mining operations are costly, especially when the ore bodies are located in deserts or swamplands. Because few African governments have sufficient money to launch large mining operations, they often grant *concessions* to large foreign-owned companies to establish mines. In return for their concessions, the mining and oil companies pay company taxes to the government, as well as *royalties*, which are a special tax on the amount they produce.

Most of the companies that operate mines and oil wells in Africa are international companies which have operations all over the world. Three examples are the *Rio Tinto* company, the *Anglo-American* group of companies, and *Union Minière*. To these companies, Central and South Africa are the most important part of their worldwide operations, and they are involved in mining diamonds, gold, copper, lead, zinc, iron ore, uranium, and many more minerals. *De Beers,* a subsidiary company of Anglo-American, is so powerful in the world production and marketing of diamonds that even the U.S.S.R. (where foreign companies do not operate) must market its diamonds through De Beers' outlets.

Questions
1. Compare the minerals map with a political map of Africa.
2. Where are the major oil fields, coalfields, goldfields, and diamond mines?
3. What are the uses of bauxite and manganese?
4. Locate the iron ore deposits of Mauritania and the sources of uranium on the map. Why is uranium called a "strategic" metal?

Many African leaders complain that the international companies take too much of the profits, so that the African countries do not gain enough benefits from their local mineral wealth. As a result, several African countries have begun to either:
1. *increase the royalties* that the foreign companies must pay. Libya, for example, raised its oil royalties in 1970 and again in 1971.

2. *take over, or nationalize,* the mining operations. This is difficult to do successfully, as most African countries are still short of skilled technicians. In 1970, however, Zambia nationalized the copper mines, and Algeria nationalized the oil industry in the following year. Mauritania took over its iron mines in late 1974, in spite of the danger that the rich countries might take countermeasures, such as cutting off aid.

3. *insist that more processing* (i.e., smelting, refining, rolling, etc.) is done in their countries before the mineral is exported. This would mean more employment for Africans, and an increase in industrialization.

So far, only the North African countries and South Africa have big iron and steel plants. This means that industries in many other countries cannot be established, as they would have to import expensive iron and steel from countries outside Africa. It also means that even metal rods for building, rails for railroads, and girders for building bridges, pipes, etc. must be imported at high cost. A medium-sized plant, for example, which would satisfy the needs of Ethiopia, Somalia, and the Sudan would cost

over $750 000 000. Until the African countries are able to obtain finances on this scale, many of their coal, iron ore, and limestone deposits will not be used, unless they are mined and exported for use in the industries of Europe, North America, and Japan.

As noted earlier, Africa produces about eighty percent of the world's gold and diamonds, and much of these are mined in the Republic of South Africa.

Gold was first discovered in South Africa in 1886 when a farmer discovered a nugget of gold on a *rand* or stony ridge. This ridge, named by the Dutch settlers as Witwatersrand or White Water Ridge, was to become world famous. The discovery brought thousands of prospectors to the area, and Johannesburg grew from a camping site to become the world's major gold-mining city.

The Rand, approximately 160 km in length, is the richest gold-mining area in the world. Its mines reach depths of 1830 m and three of them touch 2744 m. They are equipped with air conditioning, as the normal temperature at such depths would be 43°C even without the further heat generated by machinery and workers.

(Left) Figure 4.40 A map showing the extent of the rich gold-bearing Witwatersrand. Note the positions of Johannesburg and Pretoria.

(Right) Figure 4.41 Diagrammatic section of a gold mine. *Banket* is the term used for the ore-bearing rock. The liquid gold extracted from the ores is finally cooled into bars the size of small bricks and stamped.

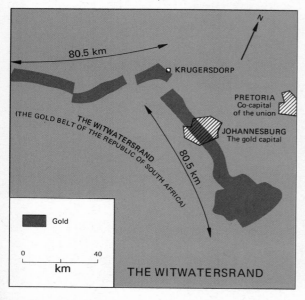

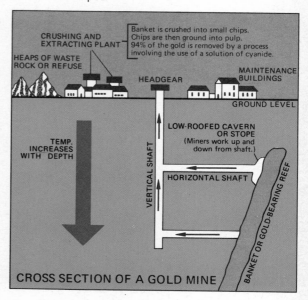

143

(Top) Only in a few parts of Africa can ordinary people try their luck at mining. The Sierra Leone government has kept part of their diamond fields for local prospectors, and crowds of Africans try their luck, in scenes reminiscent of the California gold rush.

(Bottom left and right) Two scenes of salt production in Africa illustrate the contrast between old and new methods. The salt puddles on the left are in Niger. Reddish, salt-rich earth is stirred up in the larger pools and the layers of salt are then skimmed off into smaller pans to complete the evaporation process. The picture on the right shows a modern salt mine in Senegal where the mines produce much larger quantities and better grade salt.

Page 144

The "Big Hole" Kimberley, is the deepest pit dug by man. Discovered in 1871 and worked until 1914, this was the richest diamond mine in the world. It is estimated that, in its time, this mine alone yielded 240 000 000 dollars worth of diamonds.

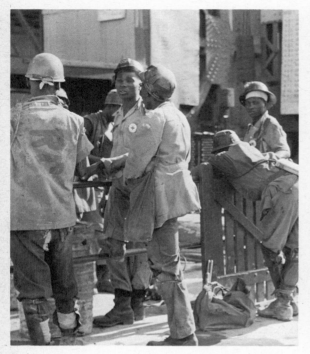

(Left) Miners waiting to go underground at a gold mine in South Africa come from all parts of the Republic as well as from neighbouring countries. A mine employes hundreds of miners. During their period of contract, usually a year, they live in compounds near the mines. The compounds are owned by the mining companies.

(Right) African miners use modern equipment. Miners feel bitter because they do not get the same wages as European miners working in Africa. The miner's chief aim is to save money in order to return to his family. They are generally flown into the mining regions from their Bantu Reserves or from independent neighbouring countries for their period of contract.

Diamonds are second to gold in the export trade of South Africa. Discovered before gold, the first recorded diamond find was by a young girl on the banks of the Orange River. Two years later a young boy found one which was to become the famous Star of Africa. He, however, exchanged his find for a few oxen, sheep, and a horse.

Diamonds consist of pure carbon and are found in *pipes* or cylindrical veins where they had been crystallized by volcanic heat in earlier geological times. In Kimberley the diamond miners dug down thousands of metres until it was not safe to dig further. This mine became known as the Big Hole because of its depth of 427 m.

Although South Africa produces the purest and therefore the most expensive diamonds, most of Africa's diamonds are mined in Zaïre and neighbouring areas of Central Africa. Being of poor quality and colour, these diamonds are used for indus-

trial purposes such as rock-boring drill bits, precision tools, and glass cutters.

Side by side with modern mining operations, a few traditional methods survive, such as salt puddling. Traditional ironworkers still work at their forges in many African towns and villages. The quality of their products, however, is not good enough for export— neither could they fill large orders.

Much of Africa's mineral wealth is still unknown. In Kenya, for example, only seventy-five percent of the country has been geologically surveyed. Upper Volta, a country which exports no minerals, has already reported finds of manganese, gold, and diamonds. Since independence, there has been a boom in prospecting in the African countries, usually supported by the governments. This is because each country is in need of sources of money to pay for its health, education, and industrialization programs.

Forests

Minerals are not the only natural resource that gives Africa hope for the future. The soil itself is rich, and farming is important. The lakes and rivers are a source of fish as well as hydroelectric power. The forests of West Africa, the Congo, and Madagascar together form a natural resource that has been badly misused in recent years.

Heavy lumbering, without replanting or care over the destruction of other trees and plants, has led to a shrinkage of most of the once-vast forests. The lumber companies, mostly foreign-owned, were interested in supplying the European and American markets with certain well-known woods for furniture and panelling. Mahogany is perhaps the best known of these. Thus, almost all the mahogany trees within reach of roads or streams have been removed, while other kinds of timber have been left untouched. Part of the problem of proper use of African forests, therefore, is to encourage the use of other kinds of wood.

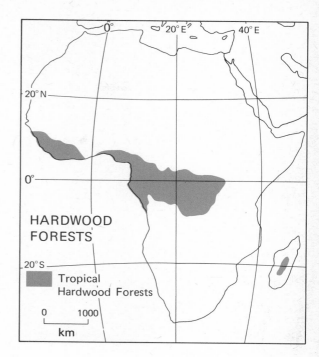

(Top) Figure 4.42

(Bottom) Timber ready for export from Ghana.

Valuable hardwood trees are scattered throughout the forests. It is difficult to bring in heavy equipment, so the trees must be felled by hand. Because of lack of money, good forest roads are lacking in Africa. Logs must be sawn where the trees are cut down. If there is any delay in getting them out, the lumber will begin to rot in the poor storage conditions of a pit in the forest. Many cubic metres of hardwood are lost in this way. It is also expensive to use handsaws when mechanical saws could be used if the logs could first be taken to a lumber mill.

Questions
1. Some of the tropical hardwoods are: limba, iroko, sipo, azobe, mahogany, tola, makore, and aboura. Which one is best known to you? What uses are made of these valuable hardwoods?

2. What is one of the major dangers to North American forests that would not face wet tropical African forests?

The forests are also rich in gums, resins, rubber, nuts, e.g., palm nuts from which oil is extracted, barks, and dyes. worthwhile for people to search the forests for these products. Probably the only answer will be to create forest plantations of valuable trees, such as the Firestone rubber plantation in Liberia, or the palm oil plantations of Cameroon and the Ivory Coast.

Water and Power

As already stated, the availability of water is a continual problem throughout most of the African continent.

There are serious water shortages in most African cities, because the colonial powers did not install adequate water supply systems, and also because the cities are now growing very rapidly. The new African governments are trying to solve their water problems as fast as their limited money allows.

The new generation of African planners is trying to harness the continent's rivers and streams. In one sense, a river that runs its course to the sea without interruption is really "wasted water". To a planner, a properly managed river should provide electric power, irrigation water, drinking water, water for industry, supplies of fish, and a good transport route, all of which were in short supply in most newly independent African countries. It is not surprising, then, that the planners began to dream up enormous dam-building projects, of which the biggest was the Aswan Dam project in Egypt.

The building of the Aswan High Dam means (a) more water for irrigation and therefore more available land area for cultivation, (b) better drainage, (c) the farmers no longer have to be dependent on the water levels of the Nile at various seasons, and (d) hydroelectric power for homes and industries.

The building of the High Dam necessitated:
(a) the creation of a new lake stretching into the Sudan and flooding the Sudanese town of Wadi Halfa,
(b) removing huge ancient Egyptian monuments, and
(c) financial aid and expertise.

These problems were overcome and the Aswan High Dam was completed in 1971. Africa's biggest dam, it is 3.2 km wide and 1.6 km broad at its base. It is thirty-six storeys high.

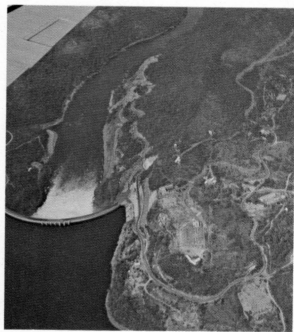

A giant new steel plant is under construction near Cairo. This will make Egypt an important steel-producing country, able to export steel to other Middle Eastern and African countries. Many more factories are planned in the Nile Delta, which is the most important industrial complex in Africa.

Dams have been built in several African countries, and many more are planned. Ghana's Akosombo Dam is intended to provide electricity for an industrial complex based on the port of Tema, and Zambia and Rhodesia share power from the Kariba Dam on the River Zambezi. Morocco has built medium-sized and small dams on the torrents that rush down from the Atlas Mountains. Nigeria has built the Kainji Dam, and will provide power to neighbouring Dahomey and to the industries of Lagos and Ibadan.

Soon electric power lines will snake out across most of the African countryside. This is perhaps the most important thing that is happening, for without power there can be no real economic development, and without economic development people's lives cannot be made richer.

(Top left)   The Akosombo Dam.

(Top right)   Aerial view of the Kariba Dam.

(Bottom)   An Egyptian farmer using the primitive Archimedes' screw to irrigate his land. Other primitive methods used even today, include the ancient water wheel, or the *sakia* and the *shaduf* (a bucket at the end of a long pole and worked on the lever system). With modern irrigation methods controlled by the Aswan Dam, these ancient laborious methods will become less prevalent. Besides supplying adequate water for irrigation, the huge turbines of the High Dam's power plant bring electricity to each of Egypt's 5000 villages.

Industrial Development

Modern industry destroys traditional crafts and industries, just as the invention of the automobile led to the disappearance of the horse and buggy. The years of European occupation meant a vast inflow of cheap factory-made clothes, pots, knives, rope, tools, weapons, and even furniture. This, in turn, meant the decline of African cloth-making, pottery, ironworking, and other traditional industries. Even today, however, many craftsmen still survive, in places where the Africans are either too poor even to buy cheap imported goods, or where they prefer the styles and patterns of their own craftsmen.

People in every country are now becoming interested in traditional art and handicrafts. Exports of handicrafts are already important from some countries— Morocco, Tunisia, and Kenya— where the governments encourage the craftsmen. United Nations' experts have helped to improve the quality of dyes and leather-tanning materials so that the goods meet international standards. Many countries have a Ministry of Small Industries, which lends money to small, local workshops in the hope that they will develop and expand.

African governments are trying to encourage the production of goods which they presently buy from overseas, such as matches, glassware, cloth, cutlery, string, and shoes. Special encouragement is given to factories producing such goods, and the owners of these factories receive large government grants. It is also common for

(Top) This Nigerian leatherworker is making a contribution to Nigeria's economic development by producing handicrafts for export.

(Bottom) Leaving for home after a day's work in the Uganda Rayon Textile Manufacturing. This plant produces about 14 000 m of cloth per day and employs 1000 workers.

high taxes to be imposed on imported goods, as another way of protecting and encouraging local production.

Most of the African cotton-producing countries have opened textile factories. The problem is that none of them can hope to export textiles to neighbouring countries, because they, too, have their own factories.

This problem also affects industries using imported materials. The Uganda Rayon

150

Textile plant, for example, is sure of a good market for its cloth inside Uganda. However, it would be difficult to export rayon cloth to Egypt, for example, which also has rayon textile plants, so its chances of expansion are limited.

Another way to develop industries in Africa is to encourage large foreign companies to build plants as part of their international operations. The attractions are the low wages that most Africans receive, as well as special *incentives* offered by the interested African governments. These incentives include low taxes, free land, government loans, cheap power, and cheap factory buildings. So far, very few examples of this type of industry have been located in Africa. The international companies prefer to locate as near as possible to the big markets of North America and Western Europe so that transportation costs from factory to market will be low. Thus, the states of Mexico, Puerto Rico, Greece, and Spain have all enjoyed a rapid industrial expansion in recent years. While low wages do, indeed, attract international companies, the low wage situation creates other unhappy social problems.

Other African economists believe that the road to industrialization is through developing *forward linkages*. They feel that it is dangerous to allow African raw materials to be exported. Instead, they would like to see them processed first, and are beginning to study the type of laws passed in Latin American nations. Nicaragua, for example, does not permit the export of raw lumber. It must be sawn in Nicaragua first. Even the Canadian government finds it necessary from time to time to insist that certain raw materials are processed in Canada before being exported.

Multiple linkages, in which plants provide the materials for other factories, which in turn feed other plants with materials, are considered to be the best sign of a healthy industrial growth. To achieve this, some African governments feel that they must

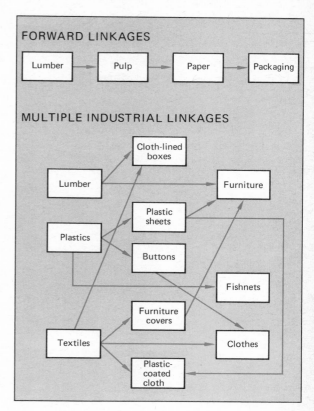

Figure 4.43

borrow millions of dollars from richer countries in order to construct *basic industrial complexes*. A basic industrial complex is a group of factories. Products such as sheet steel, sulphuric acid, copper wire, raw plastics, glue, and metal rods are basic needs for a wide variety of industries. Egypt, Algeria, Ghana, and Tunisia are countries which have started to create basic chemical and metallurgical complexes. Because of the loans they must raise, their countries run into debt, and the present generation must make sacrifices so that their children may enjoy the benefits of living in a highly industrialized country.

The main problem facing the growth of industry in Africa is that it is difficult to break into the world markets. Customers in North America, Europe, and elsewhere are slow to change to new products in new countries.

151

In spite of problems such as the shortage of *capital* (money for machines and factories), the difficulty of finding export markets, and disagreements over the best economic policies to follow, Africa is making progress. All over the continent, African workers are learning new skills, which will be useful as Africa's industries grow.

> *Questions*
> 1. Why could we say that nationalism often reduces international trade?
> 2. What kind of social problems are caused by low wages?
> 3. Why would low wages attract international companies?

PRESENT-DAY PROBLEMS AND THE FUTURE

The Problems of the Republic of South Africa

The Republic of South Africa is rich. It leads the world in the production of diamonds and gold, and the South African mining companies have become so powerful that they now control mines and factories in other parts of the world, including Canada and Latin America. It is already an important industrial country, and contains more than half of all the factories in Africa. Large amounts of capital invested in farming have made South Africa's farms and orchards world-famous, and the country exports high quality fruit and wines. In spite of this wealth, South Africa is not a happy country, and the roots of its present-day problems lie in the past.

Workers in a cigarette factory *(Top),* spinners in a textile mill *(Centre),* and mechanics in a railway repair and service shop *(Bottom).* Throughout modern Africa, thousands of workers are learning the skills needed to help their countries become industrialized.

The first European settlers were from Holland. They rapidly grew in number and pushed inland, carving out large farms and cattle ranches. They soon clashed with the African peoples, and South African history is a long series of land wars. In the nineteenth century, English settlers arrived in large numbers and were interested mainly in mining and trade. Other European countries, particularly Germany, provided small but important additions to the white minority in South Africa, which today numbers over 3 000 000.

Many of the European settlers came to South Africa with already fixed ideas of their own racial superiority. These feelings of superiority had developed during the years of colonization in other parts of the world. Since the first Africans they met were poor cattle herders, with no modern weapons or machinery, there seemed no reason for the Europeans to change their ideas. The Africans, they decided, were an inferior kind of people fit only to "hew wood and draw water". Even many of the religious settlers managed to justify this attitude.

The present South African government continues the policy of separating people rigidly according to their "race", using a classification system which includes *White, Asian, Colored,* and *African.* People classified as different are not allowed to marry, to live in the same part of town, to go to the same schools, to sit on the same park benches, or even to play together.

Everywhere "Whites Only" notices, written in Afrikaans and English, hit a "nonwhite" South African in the face. He must use separate drinking fountains, restaurants, hotels, movie theatres, elevators, and even public conveniences.

In order to carry out its policy, the South African government issues everyone with special identity cards, called *reference books* or passbooks. Failure to produce one when asked can mean a fine or imprisonment, even if the book was only accidentally left at home.

Signs such as seen in these pictures appear in all the cities and towns of the Republic of South Africa. Notice the use of the English language and Afrikaans. Afrikaans is one of the two official languages. It is a Dutch dialect spoken by the Afrikaaners — descendants of the original Dutch settlers.

153

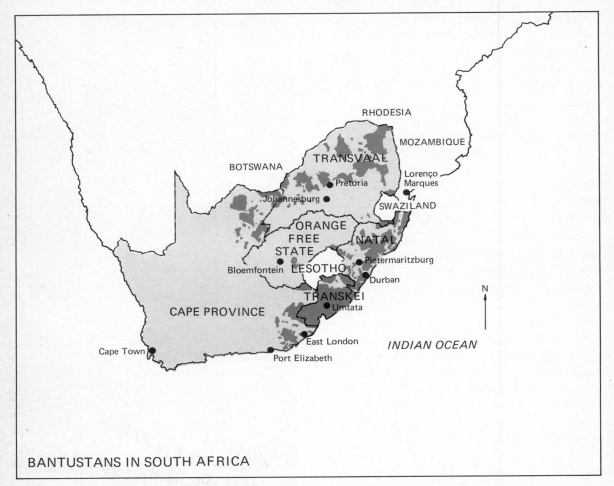

Figure 4.44 Map showing the Butustans (Bantu Reservations) of the Republic. Most of the farmland they contain is poor, and making a living is difficult. The largest Bantustan is known as the Transkei.

The South African government's policy of *apartheid* is to let each race develop at its own speed without interference from the others. Opponents of this policy, however, say that it is evil, designed to make sure that white people continue to enjoy a very high standard of living at the expense of everybody else.

Africans may only own land and farms in reserves, called *Bantustans,* which are similar to Indian reserves in North America. These total less than fourteen percent of South Africa's total area, and less than fourteen percent of its good farmland, although the Africans make up over seventy percent of the country's total population. Overcrowding and unemployment mean that many Africans must leave the Bantustans to look for work in European-owned mines or on European-owned farms.

Africans who leave the Bantustans are crowded into special housing areas outside the city limits, where living conditions are poor. Bad water supplies cause dysentery and other stomach complaints, and many people live in shacks. Medical facilities for Africans are limited, and schools are overcrowded and short of equipment. Africans who are out of work or are called "troublemakers" are always in danger of being sent back to the Bantustans.

Poor food, poor medical service, and poor housing are fatal to many young children. The total of all children who die before reaching one year of age is usually called *infant mortality*. When this total is expressed as the number of deaths per thousand births, it is called the infant mortality *rate*. It is one of the best ways to make quick comparisons between living conditions. The infant mortality rate for Africans in the cities is about 200 per 1000, and in the reserves it can reach 400 per 1000. For white South African babies the figure is 27 per 1000, one of the lowest rates in the world.

African wages are generally very low as it is difficult for the African Trade Unions to fight for higher wages and better working conditions. This is partly because Trade Unions for African workers are discouraged and are often illegal, and partly because there are over 1 000 000 unskilled workers from other African countries looking for jobs in South Africa. These men come from desperately poor countries like Malawi and Angola, and are willing to work for very low wages rather than starve.

(Top) Facilities provided for non-white South Africans are never as good as those for whites. This is a crowded commuter train on the way to Johannesburg.

(Bottom) Basuto shepherds riding past a recruiting station. South Africa's mines and farms depend on immigrant labour.

Questions
1. Why would very young children be more likely than adults to die from poor living conditions?
2. How many times less likely is a newborn baby in a Bantustan to reach his first birthday than a white South African baby?
3. Why are living conditions better in the Bantustans than in the African settlements outside the big cities?
4. Make a rough count of the number of separate Bantustans.
5. Research and compare the living and working conditions of the native peoples in South Africa with those in other African countries, for example, Rhodesia, Kenya, Ghana, Ethiopia.

6. What is being done in Canada today to improve the living conditions of the native peoples?
7. Why does Canada maintain Indian Reserves?

Horse-racing attracts huge crowds in South African cities. Study this picture and note the different locations of the white people and the nonwhite people.

The nonwhite people of South Africa have tried many peaceful means of improving their conditions, and there are still many people who believe that change will come about gradually and peacefully. But more and more South Africans are beginning to feel that more drastic measures will have to be taken. The situation is made more explosive by the fact that every other African government except Rhodesia would like to see the apartheid system done away with. The few white South Africans and Rhodesians who believe in equal rights have been swamped by a rising tide of racism in the rest of the white minority population. Unhappy and unsettling conditions prevail in these two countries, and solutions to many problems will have to be found soon in order to avoid further conflict.

The Future

Outside South Africa, there are only a few countries which are not ruled by black Africans. These are: Rhodesia, Spanish Sahara, French Somaliland (Territoire des Afars et Issas), São Tomé e Principe, Comoro Islands, and South West Africa (Namibia).

Questions
1. Locate these countries, and check if any of them have recently become independent.
2. If you can find an old map or atlas, check which countries were independent in 1930. Which European countries had colonies in Africa at that time?
3. What is the present situation in Rhodesia?

It is one thing, however, to fight for freedom, but it is quite another to know what to do with it afterwards. Soon after Kenya's independence, for example, Jomo Kenyatta sounded a note of warning:

> "... many people may think that, now there is *Uhuru* (independence), now I can see the sun of Freedom shining, richness will pour down like manna from Heaven. I tell you there will be nothing from Heaven. We must all work hard, with our hands, to save ourselves from poverty, ignorance and disease ..."

From: Jomo Kenyatta, *Harambee: The Prime Minister of Kenya's Speeches, 1963-1964,* Oxford University Press, 1964, pages 18-19.

Every independent African country agrees that it is necessary to:
— build schools, training colleges, and universities,
— modernize farming,
— improve health,
— build factories,
— build playing fields, swimming pools, and other sports facilities,
— improve housing,
— build good roads and seaports.

It is difficult to agree, however, on which of these things to do first. Who will be the first to benefit and how is the limited amount of money to be divided? Are the sports facilities more important than modernized farming? Should good roads be built before or after factories are opened? Should factories be left to private enterprise, or should the state finance industry or even run factories itself? These are just a few of the questions to be answered, in different ways for different countries.

Julius Nyerere of Tanzania once said:

> "No blueprint can be drawn up, and no one can accurately foretell how all the different pressures will reveal themselves in the Africa of the year 2000 ..."

Gamal Abdel Nasser, who led Egypt from 1954 to 1970, hinted nearly twenty years ago that such disagreements over how to build modern countries could become serious and even lead to bloodshed.

> "Every man we questioned had nothing to recommend except to kill someone else. Every idea we listened to was nothing but an attack on some other idea. If we had gone along with everything we heard, we would have killed off all the people and torn down every idea, and there would have been nothing left to do but sit down among the corpses and ruins, bewailing our evil fortune and cursing our wretched fate."

From: Gamal Abdel Nasser, *The philosophy of the Revolution,* Public Affairs Press, Washington, 1955, pages 34-35.

The best way to spend money wisely is to plan. Almost all of the developing countries in the world now produce National Development Plans, in which they set down their *priorities* and *objectives*. They also have a planning organization. Large projects, like the Aswan Dam and the Akosombo Dam, and Tema seaport, are usually assigned to special government agencies, as they are too big for an ordinary Ministry to handle. The Ministries, however, organize their own lists of suggested projects, and make suggestions as to how they could be financed.

For example, Nigeria's 1971-1974 Development Plan set out the first five industrial priorities as:
(a) iron and steel basic complex,
(b) petrochemical industries,
(c) fertilizer production,
(d) petroleum products (especially for local distribution),
(e) a passenger vehicle assembly plant.

From: Julius Nyerere, *Freedom and Unity / Uhun na Umoja,* Oxford University Press, London, 1967, page 116.

In addition, three lists of proposed new industries were given:

> 1. "proposals for new industries already submitted (by private enterprise):
> synthetic filaments and yarn going back to polymerization and polycondensation stage, fishing nets, insulated cables, bicycles, printing ink, electrical fittings and pharmaceuticals
> 2. other projects:
> assembly and partial manufacture of air conditioners and refrigerators, melting scrap iron, re-rolling mills, ferrous and nonferrous foundries, and alcohol and yeasts
> 3. projects which are likely to be ready for implementation during the plan period:
> rubber items, glass windows, exhaust pipes, radiators, interior upholstery, springs, etc. for the motor vehicle assembly; bottles and household glassware, livestock feeds (maize, cassava, fishmeal), plywood and veneers, chipboard, industrial yarns and surgical dressings from textile wastes, spools and shuttles for textile industries, cutlery, vegetable oil from ground nuts and cottonseed and shea nut"

From: *Second National Development Plan, 1970-1974,* Ministry of Information of the Federal Republic of Nigeria, Lagos, 1970, pages 145 and 150.

In some African countries, the military play a part in political affairs. Governments in Nigeria, the Congo, Dahomey, Algeria, Libya, the Sudan, Upper Volta, Mali, Ethiopia, and many other countries have been overthrown by army officers. This usually happens suddenly, and is called a *coup*. It is not the same as a revolution, which takes time and involves large numbers of people from all walks of life. The army officers involved in a coup often claim that they are acting because the politicians are corrupt, or inefficient. The problem is that army officers can also become corrupt and inefficient.

To develop rapidly, as well as to defend itself, Africa needs many kinds of help from richer parts of the world. The list of other countries providing help is already very long. These are just a few: Canada, United States, U.S.S.R., Czechoslovakia, West Germany, East Germany, China, Denmark, Poland, Japan, Hungary, France, Italy, and Rumania.

Some of the "aid" is in the form of loans which must later be repaid. Perhaps this should be called "finance" rather than aid. Some of the aid is also in the form of gifts, or the loan of experts, or the loan of machinery.

There are advantages to be gained from supplying aid to African countries. If France, for example, provides most of the aid to one country, such as the Ivory Coast, that means that the Ivory Coast will then buy a lot of French exports, and also that it will support France in the United Nations and elsewhere. Many contracts for building roads, ports, cities, factories, and dams will go to French

A Zanzibari tank crew. African countries wish to spend their precious finances on development projects rather than weapons and armies. The possibility of war, however, is a constant worry.

companies. There is a great deal of competition, therefore, to *give* aid to African countries, as part of larger economic and political sturggles.

A change in government in an African country often means that the new government will rely on different sources of aid. In this way, the military coups in Ghana, Mali, and Uganda meant that less aid was received from the U.S.S.R. and Eastern Europe and more from the U.S.A. and Western Europe. The reverse happened with the military coups in Somalia, Egypt, and Congo (Brazzaville).

Africa's history contains many tragedies, and there will be many struggles in the future. But the independent African countries are standing on their own feet and we should learn to understand and welcome our new colleagues in the family of nations.

A military coup in Ethiopia in 1974 ended the rule of Emperor Haile Selassie. The picture shows a poor Ethiopian farmer who knows little about coups and revolutions. His main concern is peace and plenty, if not in his lifetime, then at least for his children.

5. THE SOUTH AMERICAN CONTINENT

INTRODUCTION

With a land area of approximately twenty million square kilometres, South America is only slightly smaller than the combined areas of Canada and the United States.

This great, pear-shaped landmass looks like an inverted triangle with its base bordering the Caribbean Sea and the Atlantic Ocean and its apex at Tierra del Fuego, far to the south.

South America projects so much further eastward into the Atlantic Ocean than does North America, that no part of it lies directly south of Windsor, Ontario.

Atlas Exercise

1. Name the large bodies of water which surround South America.
2. Locate the equator and the Tropic of Capricorn. Why do you think Ecuador is so named?
3. Approximately how much of the continent lies within the tropics?
4. South America is linked to North America by the narrow Isthmus of Panama. What is an isthmus? Why do you think this isthmus was chosen for a canal?
5. What is the approximate north-south length of South America, between Panama and Tierra del Fuego?

THE PHYSICAL ENVIRONMENT

Landforms

Dominating the physical environment of the South American continent is the Andean mountain chain or *cordillera* (backbone or cord). Like an immense curved spine, the Andes run the whole length of South America. This mountain chain continues north through Central America, Mexico, the United States, and Canada, and into Alaska. These enormous folds in the earth's surface can even be traced through the Aleutian Islands towards Japan. Like all the very high mountain ranges in the world, they are quite "young", that is, there has not been time for wind and rain and frost to wear them down like the Appalachians or the Laurentian Shield.

A general view of the Andes.

Figure 5.1

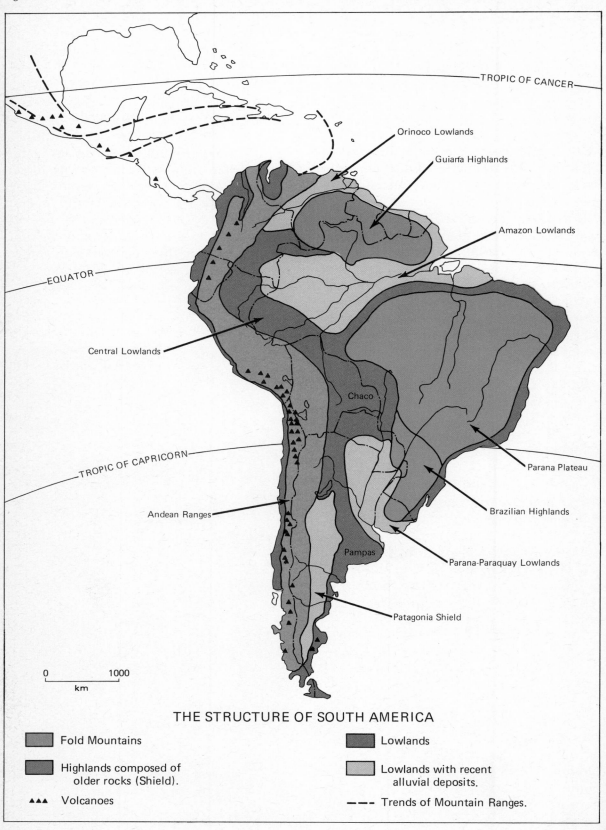

TROPIC OF CANCER

Orinoco Lowlands

Guiarfa Highlands

Amazon Lowlands

EQUATOR

Central Lowlands

Chaco

TROPIC OF CAPRICORN

Parana Plateau

Andean Ranges

Brazilian Highlands

Pampas

Parana-Paraquay Lowlands

Patagonia Shield

THE STRUCTURE OF SOUTH AMERICA

0   1000
      km

Fold Mountains

Highlands composed of
older rocks (Shield).

▲▲▲ Volcanoes

Lowlands

Lowlands with recent
alluvial deposits.

––– Trends of Mountain Ranges.

Questions
1. Name three separate highland areas and three great rivers.
2. The Andes and the Rockies are, in fact, made up of numerous ranges or *sierras*. In your atlas, locate the Kootenays, in British Columbia, and the Sierra Madre, in Mexico. Find and name three Andean ranges in South America.
3. Locate some of the highest peaks in the Andes, for example, Aconcagua, Cotopaxi, and Chimborazo.
4. The world's highest ski lodge is at Chaclataya, near La Paz in Bolivia. It is built at 5335 m above sea level, and the ski lift ascends to 5580 m. Compare this elevation with a ski resort in Canada. What would be the biggest problem faced by a European or North American skier at this Bolivian ski lodge?
5. In an atlas, locate the three major lakes of the continent. Name the two situated on the lofty Bolivian Plateau, over 3 km above sea level.

The mountains are not just made up of steep peaks and ranges. Nestled between the summits are a series of basins or depressions and high plateaus. The largest of these *intermontane* depressions are in Peru, Bolivia, Ecuador, and southern Colombia. The biggest of all is called the *altiplano,* and contains Lake Titicaca, between Bolivia and Peru. It is a harsh land, suffering from severe droughts in the dry season, floods in the rainy season, intense cold except when the sun shines, strong winds, and isolation. Only in Tibet can we find a similar environment. In spite of all this, the altiplano was the cradle of one of the most powerful and ancient civilizations in the Americas. The Aymara and Quechua peoples, who still live there raising sheep, alpacas, and llamas, and growing potatoes, corn, and peppers, created several important civilizations. The last of these was the great Inca Empire that was destroyed by the Spaniards in the sixteenth century.

Sheep herders on the altiplano in Bolivia.

In addition to the Andes, there are also highland areas made of older rocks in South America. These are areas of shield, similar to those in Canada and in Africa. The Brazilian Highlands, for example, have a fairly steep slope facing the Atlantic, and then slope gently down into the Amazon Basin and the region to the south of it, known as the Mato Grosso. The Guiana Highlands in Venezuela were, in some places, thrust upwards by sharp *faults* in the earth's crust, giving them dizzying precipices instead of gentle slopes. Over these fall two of the highest waterfalls in the world: Angel Falls (highest in the world), in Venezuela, and the Kaieteur Falls, in Guyana. The roaring Iguassu Falls, between Argentina and Brazil, are formed by a river plunging off the edge of the Brazilian Highlands.

The Andes, Guiana Highlands, and Brazilian Highlands together form the rim of the immense Amazon Basin. The Amazon, which has a length of 6300 km, is navigable to Iquitos, Peru — 3700 km inland. No other river in the world drains as large an area as the Amazon or carries as much water to the sea. From the air the endless jungle of the Amazon Lowland looks like a huge green carpet with no pattern, broken only by scattered red or purple flowering trees and the occasional river.

The most important farmland for the natives of the Amazon Basin exists for only part of each year; it is formed of the *chacras*, or flooded islands in the river. Much of the land is waterlogged in the rainy season, so that the rivers are the only means of transportation. The fine new highways being built by the Brazilian Government must

The destruction in the main square of the city of Huarez, caused by the earthquake of May 31, 1970.

follow the higher ridges along the watersheds separating the various tributary rivers.

Both the Andean and Caribbean regions are subject to frequent and often severe *seismic movements* or earthquakes. In 1970, for example, the entire Huaraz Valley of Peru, a rich farming area, was destroyed, along with much of the main coastal highway. Gigantic mud slides accompanied the earthquake, burying whole villages. Another recent, disastrous earthquake destroyed the city of Managua in Central America.

Central and South America are also a paradise for *vulcanologists,* as a string of active, inactive, and extinct volcanoes stretches all the way from Mexico to Chile. Their cones occasionally reach 6100 m, and they form beautiful landscapes just as in Japan, Washington State, and Armenia. When they do erupt, however, they can cause great damage. The worst disaster ever recorded took place in 1902, on the island of Martinique in the Caribbean, when the volcano Mont Pelée erupted, destroying the city of Saint Pierre and killing about 38 000 people.

In conclusion, three main island groups must be noted during this physical study of South America. These islands are the tops of undersea mountains which protrude above the ocean's surface. To the west of the

(Top) The Iguassu Falls are really a whole complex of waterfalls, each one different in size and shape, formed by the river cascading over the edge of the Brazilian Plateau. They are far more beautiful than any other waterfall in the world, mainly because of their variety. Which two countries meet at the Iguassu Falls?

(Bottom) The River Amazon from the air. For the air passenger the river provides light relief from the never-ending Amazon jungle. For the people who live there, it provides the only way of getting around. It also provides fish, the main source of protein.

A view across an Andean Valley towards the volcano Cotopaxi, in Ecuador. The snowline in this photograph is at an altitude of 4300 m above sea leve

Page 167

Figure 5.2 Map showing prevailing winds and the ocean currents that influence the climate of South America. Also the main types of vegetation found on the continent.

A tourist resort near Mount Cotopaxi, Ecuador. The waters of this pool are fed by warm underground waters in this volcanic area. Name another volcanic region you have studied where the local communities make use of warm underground waters. Locate Mount Cotopaxi on a map. In which large mountain chain is it located?

continent lie the volcanic Galapagos Islands, home of the gigantic Galapagos tortoise; to the south are the islands of Tierra del Fuego — Magellan's *Land of Fires;* and to the east are the rugged, bleak Falkland Islands.

Questions
1. What is the difference between inactive and extinct volcanoes?
2. What do you think a *seismologist* studies?
3. Why might the Iguassu Falls be *less* useful for hydro power than Niagara?
4. Would a *chacra* be formed in the wet season or the dry season?

Climate

Because of its vastness and its variety of landforms, and because it stretches from the tropics to extreme southerly latitudes, we can expect to find many different types of climate in South America. The extensive northern part of the continent lies within the tropics, where high temperatures encourage rich, tropical vegetation. It is only at the higher altitudes in the Andes that lower temperatures produce alpine grass-lands. Some of the higher mountains are

166

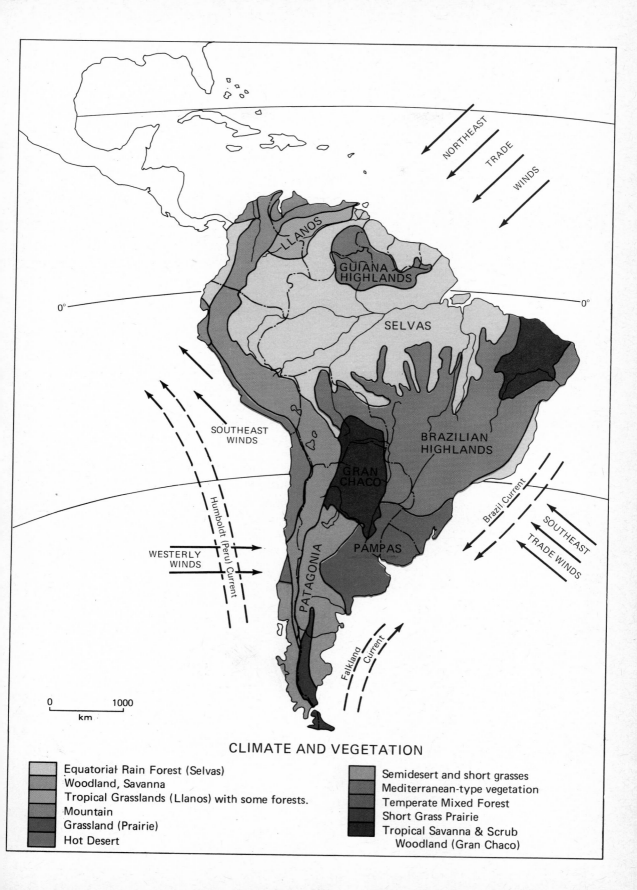

CLIMATE AND VEGETATION

Equatorial Rain Forest (Selvas)
Woodland, Savanna
Tropical Grasslands (Llanos) with some forests.
Mountain
Grassland (Prairie)
Hot Desert

Semidesert and short grasses
Mediterranean-type vegetation
Temperate Mixed Forest
Short Grass Prairie
Tropical Savanna & Scrub
Woodland (Gran Chaco)

barren and their peaks remain snow-capped all year round. The southern region of the continent, however, lies within cooler, temperate latitudes and the climate is further influenced by the two cold ocean currents that flow along the east and west coasts. Even in summer there are few really warm days in Patagonia.

Questions
From Figure 5.2:
1. Name the winds that blow towards the east coast, both north and south of the equator. Explain why these would be rainbearing winds.
2. Which are the two cold ocean currents that flow parallel to the coasts?
3. The Amazon jungle is sometimes called the *selva*. What does this mean?
4. What type of vegetation grows on the Pampas of Argentina? Which part of Canada would resemble this region?

Two areas of interest shown on Figure 5.2 are the *llanos* and the *Gran Chaco*. The llanos are tropical grasslands in the Orinoco Basin and the Guiana Highlands. They are suitable for cattle rearing, but the lower lands are often flooded in the rainy season. Then the *llaneros,* Venezuelan cowboys, must round up their cattle and herd them onto higher ground. The Gran Chaco, which means Great Forest or Great Hunting Field, was once covered with scrub woodland, but today most of the trees are gone. The region is famous for its quebracho trees. Quebracho means "axebraker", which aptly describes its tough wood, and it is the main source of tannin, used in curing leather. Cotton is grown in the cleared areas of the Chaco, but most of the region is very poor pastureland, where cattle struggle for survival, often dying for lack of water.

The Andes have a tremendous effect on climate — an effect that varies according to latitude. In the extreme south, westerly winds blow, almost without interruption, from the Pacific onto the rugged coast of

Chile, bringing heavy rains and sleet. The result is a dense, fog-shrouded forest that is only partially explored. Once across the snow-covered mountains, however, the winds bring no more rain, so that the Patagonian Plateau is dry and windswept, fit only for sheep and a few hardy shepherds. Even they spend much of the year sheltering in the broad, dried-out river valleys.

Questions
1. On the altiplano, the sun seems to shine more brightly than anywhere else in the world, giving a strange brightness to the sky. Why might this be?
2. Check in your atlas to review which other parts of the southern continents are affected by the westerly wind belts.
3. How do the cattlemen's problems differ on the llanos and the Chaco?

Further north, a cold sea current (named after Alexander von Humboldt, a famous naturalist) means that cold air masses reaching the coast of Chile and Peru warm up as they blow over the land, thus absorbing moisture rather than depositing rain. This region also has very few westerly winds. The result is the driest strip of desert in the world, the Atacama Desert.

This archaeologist is working in the Atacama Desert. The air and ground are so dry that some skeletons still have bits of dried skin attached to them even though they are thousands of years old.

(Top)　A typical scene of the Gran Chaco in Paraguay.

(Bottom)　Most of the Patagonia Plateau is suitable for the rearing of sheep. Here the ground is high and arid with the occasional fertile valley intruding into the Andes. In the background can be seen the foothills of the great Andean "backbone" of South America.

Figure 5.3

MEXICO CITY (2278 m above sea level; Latitude 19°N)

	J	F	M	A	M	J	J	A	S	O	N	D
Temp. (°C)	12	13	16	18	18	18	17	17	16	14	13	12
Precip. (mm)	5	5	15	15	48	99	104	119	104	46	13	5

COLON, PANAMA (11 m above sea level; Latitude 9°N)

	J	F	M	A	M	J	J	A	S	O	N	D
Temp. (°C)	27	27	27	27	27	27	27	27	27	27	27	26
Percip. (mm)	94	41	41	109	315	338	406	376	318	384	526	290

BOGOTA (2660 m above sea level; Latitude 4°N)

	J	F	M	A	M	J	J	A	S	O	N	D
Temp. (°C)	14	14	15	15	15	15	14	14	14	14	15	15
Precip. (mm)	58	61	104	145	114	61	51	56	61	163	117	66

QUITO (2850 m above sea level; Latitude 0°)

	J	F	M	A	M	J	J	A	S	O	N	D
Temp. (°C)	13	13	12	13	13	13	13	13	13	13	12	13
Precip. (mm)	102	112	122	178	122	38	18	38	71	81	86	86

IQUITOS (100 m above sea level; Latitude 4°S)

	J	F	M	A	M	J	J	A	S	O	N	D
Temp. (°C)	26	26	24	25	24	23	23	24	24	25	26	26
Precip. (mm)	259	269	305	168	254	185	165	114	224	180	216	287

LA PAZ (3632 m above sea level; Latitude 16°S)

	J	F	M	A	M	J	J	A	S	O	N	D
Temp. (°C)	11	12	12	11	9	8	8	8	9	11	11	11
Precip. (mm)	178	168	155	56	15	13	8	8	13	56	97	147

On the eastern slopes of the mountains, however, there is some rain. This has produced the rolling pastures of Paraguay, the pampas grasslands of Argentina, and, further north towards the equator, the tropical forests of the Mato Grosso and the Amazon Basin.

In central Chile, where the westerly wind belt moves north in winter, the combination of hot, dry summers and mild, wet winters has produced a Mediterranean type of climate. This area is famous for its wines, which are the best in South America.

In Ecuador, on the equator, heavy tropical rains make almost all the lowlands into forests and jungle, so that the effect of the Andes as a *climatic barrier* disappears. Instead, the climate changes dramatically with altitude — from thick, equatorial forests at the base of the Andes to icy plateaus and snow-covered peaks at the summits. The South Americans grow quite different crops according to altitude above the sea. Thus, on a journey in a rickety bus down into a typical Colombian valley, say the Magdalena, you would first pass fields of potatoes, oats, and rye, then fields of corn lower down. Still lower you might see coffee plantations, oranges, and more corn. In the valley bottom you would find bananas, sugar cane, and tropical fruits.

The Spanish settlers preferred to build their towns and start their farms high up in the mountains. Mexico City, San Jose (Costa Rica), Bogota, Quito, Cajamarca, and La Paz are just a few of the cities where a North American might complain of the cold!

Questions
1. In an atlas, locate the cities in the climate statistics on Figure 5.3. Which are in South America proper? Which are in Central America or the Caribbean?
2. Where is the heaviest rainfall (a) in December and (b) in June?
3. Why did the Spanish settlers prefer to live higher up in the mountains rather than in the valleys?

4. Which cities show lengthy periods of drought?
5. Which cities are in areas where you probably could not farm at all without irrigation?
6. Which city has the heaviest rainfall?

The Brazilian Highlands become drier from south to north. In the south, the rich farms of Uruguay and Rio Grande de Sul have flourishing herds of dairy cattle and beef cattle, and grow excellent wheat. The northern states of Ceara, Pernambuco, and Paraiba, on the other hand, suffer from terrible droughts that may last for years. Josue de Castro, a great Brazilian geographer, says of the area (called *sertao*) that:

"... its greatest fruit has been suffering; the principal legacy of the Northeast is the wretchedness that has been handed down from generation. And no land gives a stronger impression of suffering than the sertao, with its skin baked and corroded by the rigors of the climate. The sandstone cover is so heavily eroded and denuded that in places crystalline rock shows through the granitic surface, and the soil is a thin and meager layer, with outcroppings of jagged rock protruding like bare bones. There is a deep poignancy, and air of desolate suffering, in this wounded land, its sides riven by flash floods."

From: Josue de Castro, *Death in the Northeast*, Random House, Vintage Books Edition, 1969, pages 23-24.

Questions
1. Why does thin soil usually mean poor crops?
2. Why would rainstorms cause more erosion in areas that are often very dry than in fairly wet areas?

Besides such terrifying, natural disasters as earthquakes, the people of South America have to face the hazards of floods, droughts, and hurricanes.

The year 1974 saw the worst floods in South America for many years. The town of Trinidad, in Bolivia, was completely cut off for weeks, and only a few hummocks of higher ground remained above the water. On these crowded the survivors, their animals, and snakes. Families caught by the rising waters outside the town climbed the highest trees, and some of them were lucky enough to be rescued by boats and army helicopters. The highway from La Paz to Puno, in Peru, was cut off for almost a month, the railway lines were washed out, and it was almost impossible to travel from one highland town to another. The waters of Lake Poopo crept up on the city of Oruro, but stopped advancing just before they reached the city. The road and rail links to Argentina were cut off, and northern Argentina was severely flooded. Much of the Amazon Basin was under water, and Brazil lost a major part of its crops. In Peru there were severe landslides. For poor farmers all over the continent, one year of bad weather like this can mean being in debt for the next ten.

Droughts affect the interior plateaus of the Brazilian northeast, and also the Chaco — the lowland area between Argentina and Paraguay. There, surface lakes, water holes, and wells dry up in bad years. Even today, the lack of reliable water supplies means that the rich pasturelands are hardly used. Irrigation has provided a solution only in a few parts of South America, for it is costly and the continent lacks capital to invest in its farmland. Along the Peruvian coast, even the pre-Inca civilizations used the water of the few rivers that tumble down from the Andes, and in Argentina, irrigation has turned the city of Mendoza into an oasis.

The most dramatic natural hazard in the Caribbean is a hurricane. Today, with satellite observation, advance warning is usually available, and most people in the Caribbean listen carefully to their radios during the hurricane "season".

In the past, people have tried to guess the likelihood of a hurricane by carefully studying the weather every day. As with rain, a host of superstitions grew up. Even today, the people of Belize, in Central America, have a short poem:

"June too soon.
July, stand by.
August, it must.
September, remember.
October, all over."

A satellite photograph of a hurricane over the Caribbean Sea. The island of Cuba can be seen in the background.

Unfortunately, hurricanes can change direction quite suddenly, and can alter their speed. Thus, if everyone on the north coast of Yucatan, for example, is preparing for a hurricane, the people further south may not be worried. But in a matter of hours the storm could crash into the coast much further south, catching people unawares. Such a change in path and people being unprepared were the reasons why hurricane Fifi caused so much damage and 10 000 deaths in Honduras in 1974.

Ordinary storms also occur, making life hazardous for fishermen and travellers. The worst sea storms blow up in the extreme southerly latitudes of South America, around Tierra del Fuego and the Straits of Magellan. This used to be the main route from Europe to the South Pacific, to Chile and Peru, and even from the Eastern U.S. seaboard to California and Vancouver. Shipwrecks were very common, and storm-battered ships often limped into the Falkland Islands, where many of them were declared unfit for further sailing and beached by order of the Governor.

Thus South America's physical environment is immensely varied. It can be lush and kind to man, but also harsh and merciless. Disasters can wipe out years of work.

173

Vegetation

Every living plant is marvellously adapted to its environment: temperature, rainfall, frosts, minerals in the soil, soil moisture, humidity, winds, sunlight, and competition from other plants. As we might expect in a continent with so many different climates and altitudes, South America supports a richly varied plant life, which is quite different from the other southern continents.

The Amazon Forests

The taller trees are the first things that strike the visitor to the Amazon jungle. They rise to an average height of 30 m and are impossible to climb, having tall, thick trunks that shoot up 15 m or more without a branch or a toehold. Even the thin bark is smooth. At the top they open out like huge, green umbrellas, and although there are over 2500 species of "tall tree", they all look alike, with large leathery leaves shaped something like laurel leaves. Together they form an almost continuous canopy above the forest that looks like a gently undulating, bumpy green mat from the air.

Below this canopy, sunlight only filters through in flecks and spots for an hour or two each day, and very little wind can find its way into the "under-forest". This means that the climate for smaller trees is quite different, and they are very rarely able to grow to their full height. Even lower down towards the forest floor, the light is only one percent as strong as outside the forest, so that only a few mosses and fungi are able to grow. There are very few bushes and small shrubs such as abound in the more temperate forests such as those of North America.

Although the forest looks like a hopeless jumble from inside, it is possible, by carefully measuring the height of each tree, to pick out three "layers". The tall trees generally rise to 30 m, the second layer to 18 m, and the lower layer to 9 m. The trees in the lower layers tend to have cone-shaped crowns rather than the umbrella shapes of the tall trees. Altogether, there are thousands of species, and only a few are used by man, and even fewer are exported to North America for use in furniture making and construction.

The taller trees are covered with *lianas* and *epiphytes*. Some of the lianas, or creepers, are thicker than a wrestler's biceps, and in the more open forests of the Venezuelan llanos and the Brazilian Mato Grosso, may eventually strangle their host tree to death. The most famous of the epiphytes are the *orchids*. These favour dead trees that have not been able to fall down, and flourish in the crooks of the branches, trailing their roots downwards. The orchids draw their sustenance not from the soil but from the rotting vegetation in the trees.

Two other characteristics of Amazonia's tall trees that impress visitors are (a) their buttresses, which flank and support the tall trunks, and (b) their tendency to grow fruit

Figure 5.4

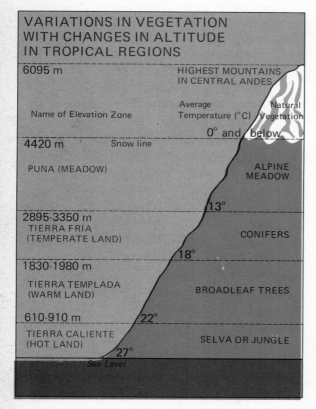

VARIATIONS IN VEGETATION WITH CHANGES IN ALTITUDE IN TROPICAL REGIONS

Name of Elevation Zone	Average Temperature (°C)	Natural Vegetation
6095 m		HIGHEST MOUNTAINS IN CENTRAL ANDES
	0° and below	
4420 m Snow line		
PUNA (MEADOW)		ALPINE MEADOW
	13°	
2895-3350 m TIERRA FRIA (TEMPERATE LAND)		CONIFERS
	18°	
1830-1980 m TIERRA TEMPLADA (WARM LAND)		BROADLEAF TREES
610-910 m	22°	
TIERRA CALIENTE (HOT LAND)		SELVA OR JUNGLE
	27°	
Sea Level		

from the trunk (called *cauliflory* by botanists). Cocoa pods are harvested from the trunk, for example.

The Grasslands

There are really three kinds of grassland in South America:
1. The temperate grasslands of Argentina and Southern Chile.
2. The mountain grasslands of the altiplano and mountain slopes.
3. The tropical "savannas" of Venezuela, the Guyanas, parts of Brazil, and the Chaco.

The temperate grasslands: The greatest area known as the Pampas, lies in Argentina, and supports vast herds of cattle. In recent years range improvement has included the introduction of grass types from other countries to enrich the grazing.

The mountain grasslands: Above the forest zone in the Andes lies a narrow belt of mountain grassland — the home of such animals as the vicuña, llama, and alpaca. Tufty and rather coarse, a great deal of improvement is needed to make them into really rich pastures.

The savannas: Most botanists agree that the savannas are not natural grasslands. The use of fire seems to have driven back the forest so that, particularly in drier areas, it has never been able to grow back. The number of grass species is small in comparison to the number in the mountains or the Pampas, and they are not as nutritious for the cattle that graze them.

The Scrub and Thorn Forests

Fire has also played a big role in the dry scrublands, which are most common in northeast Brazil, the Chaco, and southern Ecuador. Such forests consist of short, tough, thorny trees, shrubs, and cacti. There may be occasional taller trees.

A few large trees have adapted to this dry, hostile environment by having thick, leathery leaves, bulbous, water-storing trunks,

A view of the llanos, the dry, grassy plains of Venezuela.

and thick, protected barks. Such water-storing species include the *barrigudos* or bottle trees of northeast Brazil.

Mangrove Forests

Mangrove forests thrive in tropical coastal areas, producing a tangled mass of growth. Thick, twisting roots grow down from the branches to support the trees, and when the tide is out the roots are exposed and help in obtaining air for the plant. These forests in South America are only important along the Pacific coast of Colombia, where the collection of mangrove bark for tannin provides a poor living for the local inhabitants. The bark collectors suffer terribly from fly bites.

175

Lotus flowers in the rain forest of Guyana.

Questions
1. Briefly list the ways in which Amazonian evergreen tall trees differ from the taller types of tree in your environment.
2. Why might a forest with 2500 species of tall trees be *less* interesting to a lumber company than one with only a dozen varieties?
3. Next time you are in a wood or forest, make a collection of ground plants to see how many varieties you can find. You can try the same exercise with shrubs and tall trees. To be more scientific, it is best to pace out a square of, say, forty square metres so that you know how many varieties you found in a given area.
4. If there is a knowledgeable furniture store salesman in your community, you might ask him to show you examples of some of the tropical hardwoods he has.
5. Why would savannas expand more rapidly in drier areas?

For the people who live in the forests or grasslands of South America, the natural environment provides a startling variety of foods. However, very few of the useful plants of South America have been *domesticated* and converted into modern crops. Four important exceptions are maize or corn, potatoes, squash, and peppers.

Animals, Birds, Fish, and Insects

Curiously, although South America has more varieties of plants than either North America or Africa, it has fewer varieties of mammals, snakes, and insects. However, it is always dangerous to make a generalized statement like this, because biologists have not fully explored South America or Africa, and it is not true of every family or genus of insect, mammal, bird, or snake.

Most animals and many insects, birds, fish, and snakes, can be eaten. Thus, to a very hungry man, anything can be a game animal. Generally, a society contents itself with those animals that yield the greatest amount of good-tasting flesh for the least effort on the part of the hunter. The early South American inhabitants, the Amerindians, found themselves fairly well-endowed with game animals, although not as richly as their cousins in Africa and Asia. The number of species of big game animals was few, but the actual animals were fairly plentiful. They included deer, peccaries, tapirs, and manatees or sea cows. To these could be added smaller game animals such as monkeys, armadillos, pacas, vicuñas, and turtles. The Indians of Patagonia and Tierra del Fuego could feast themselves on seals. The greatest gap in the zoogeography of South America is the total absence of representatives of the *bovine* and *equine* species, that is, there were no wild cattle, buffalo, or horses that could be domesticated.

Snakes are fairly common in the South American continent. They vary a great deal in size and colour, and include poisonous rattlesnakes, vipers, sea snakes, and boa constrictors.

Several species of rattlesnakes spread southwards through Mexico and the Central American highlands, since the Mexican desert was no barrier to them. They evolved new characteristics as they went. The wetter conditions in the lower mountains of Panama formed a barrier to all but one large, dangerous species, the *cascabel*. This may be 2 m long, and today inhabits South America.

The vipers, whose main habitat is in the upper Amazon, include the palm viper and

Milking a snake of its venom in the Butantan Institute in Brazil. Antivenins made by the Institute have greatly reduced snakebite deaths across South America. In the 1920's, probably as many as 8000 South Americans died every year from snakebites, but today the number is below 1000. The reason is not only the invention of antivenins and their production in Brazil's famous snake farm, but also the fact that all farmers kill snakes with an almost superstitious frenzy. It may soon become necessary to protect some varieties of snakes from extinction!

the jumping viper. Palm vipers live in trees, and have a nasty habit of curling around branches just about level with a human head; this makes them a threat to people cutting a path through the forest. Jumping vipers are highly aggressive, hog-nosed vipers that strike with such force that they actually throw themselves forward. Fortunately, their venom is not particularly strong.

The continent's most dangerous snake is the bushmaster, which has a nasty habit of sidling towards an intruder, ready to strike. Some grow to over 3.5 m, almost as long as the giant cobra of India. A bushmaster's victim suffers from paralysis, as the poison affects the nerves rather than the blood; bites from other species, on the other hand, cause serious bleeding, as they affect the blood stream. It is for this reason that clinics in South America are equipped with *polyvalent* anti-venins that will handle any type of snakebite.

Questions
1. How many species of poisonous snakes are found in Canada?
2. Why is it important not to let any kind of animal become completely extinct, even snakes?
3. Why are there so few snakes in colder countries?

A Galapagos tortoise. This one is in captivity, but it is hoped that one day, with careful breeding, these giant creatures will again populate the islands.

Turtles make interesting pets, and, except for snappers which occasionally take a bite from someone's finger, are harmless to man. Man, however, has been far from harmless to turtles. He has preyed on them for (a) their flesh and eggs for food, (b) their shells which were used for combs, ornaments, utensils, and especially the backs of musical instruments, before plastics were invented, and (c) their young for sale to pet shops. The Amerindians and early settlers were only interested in the first two uses, although later it was the third use that nearly wiped out turtle populations throughout the Americas, just as ivory hunting decimated the African and Asian elephant herds. Even today, the Miskito Indians of Cabo Gracias a Dios (Honduras and Nicaragua) drop all other activities for a week or two when it is turtle-egg gathering time (like penguin-egg time in the Falkland Islands), as do many of the Amazonian Indians.

The Miskito Indians became very skilled at "striking" or catching the green sea turtles, and when large numbers of European vessels began to haunt the Caribbean coast of Central America in the seventeenth and eighteenth centuries they hired themselves out as ship's turtle catchers. For meat-hungry ships' crews, turtles were especially valuable because they could be flipped over onto their backs and kept alive, and therefore fresh, for weeks at a time. It is reported that the giant Galapagos tortoises could be kept without feeding for almost a year before they died. Perhaps the demand from both the local inhabitants and the visiting ships' crews would not have been enough

to wipe out the Galapagos tortoise and the sea turtles, but when tortoise and turtle catchers began to send their catches back to the land-based North American markets, there was no hope. Today conservation laws protect these animals in the Galapagos Islands.

Lizards of many kinds abound throughout South and Central America, feeding on the rich insect life. A large lizard, the *iguana*, makes good eating, tasting something like chicken, but the largest lizards live, and are protected, on the Galapagos Islands.

Crocodiles and alligators are now almost extinct as a result of the international demand for their skins. However, recent laws in the United States prohibiting the import of crocodile skins have led to the closure of the big skinning factories in Manaus, and may give the animals a chance to replenish their numbers.

The Galapagos Islands

This rocky, dry group of volcanic islands, about 965 km off the coast of Ecuador, contains far fewer species than the South American mainland. However, their isola-

178

tion has made them of very special interest to naturalists, for the few animals and birds that did manage to reach the islands in sufficient numbers to start colonies have, over the centuries, gradually formed subspecies which are unique to the islands. A small, unremarkable bird, the finch, for example, settled into every nook and cranny of the islands, and gradually developed differences in the shape, size, and thickness of beak in order to find the different kinds of food found in each of the local environments. Today there are over fifteen varieties of what was once the same bird.

From his observations on the Galapagos finch, Charles Darwin, a great nineteenth-century naturalist, developed his theory of evolution, based on the development of several species from one common ancestor. Today these changes may be seen happening to the Gentoo penguins in the Antarctic; some of them have moved further south and are developing different characteristics from their fellow-Gentoo which remained in the north.

Isolation has also meant that the Galapagos are a last refuge for a number of species whose "parent colonies" on the mainland have died off. These rare species include the marine iguana, a huge sea-lizard that reaches 1.2 m in length, and a flightless cormorant that has "forgotten" how to fly. The Galapagos penguin, not to be outdone, is the only penguin in the world that jumps into the sea feet first.

South America's southern tip thrusts southward almost into the Antarctic, into the *habitat* of species of animals and birds, for example, seals and penguins, that were almost untroubled by man until the nineteenth century. The early Indian inhabitants of Patagonia and Tierra del Fuego killed the occasional seal for lunch, and enjoyed cooked goose, but the real tragedy began when the whalers, experienced from years of operating in the North Atlantic and the Arctic, descended on the Antarctic from

their bases in Boston, Halifax, and Liverpool. Within a few years they had practically wiped out the seal colonies of Patagonia and the Falkland Islands, for they would make up "short" cargoes of *whale* blubber and oil with the easily obtained *seal* blubber and oil; the seals seemed too friendly to run away, and had an unfortunate habit of congregating in large colonies. Even penguins were not exempt, and there are still ruined stone enclosures on the Falklands where penguins were driven to receive a fatal bang on the head and a dip in the oil vat.

Very strict conservation laws in recent years have enabled most kinds of seals to *regenerate*. Some modern world estimates are:

Weddell seals 500 000

Crabeaters 2 000 000

Elephant seals 750 000 (N.B. probably an overestimate)

Ross seals 50 000

Leopard seals 250 000

Elephant seals like this one live in Patagonia, on the Valdes Peninsula. Being the nearest colony to Buenos Aires, they have become a great tourist attraction.

Bird life in South America is equally rich and varied, from the condor, a majestic bald-headed vulture that lives in the high Andes, to the brightly-hued, darting kingfishers of the lowland riverbanks. Parrots, toucans, macaws, pelicans, owls, spoonbills, and many smaller birds make up the bird population of the continent.

The seas, lakes, and rivers of South America are still largely unexplored. Of course, we know *where* they are, but we do not really know *what is in them*. For example, the large shrimp beds of Nicaragua and Honduras, in Central America, were only discovered in the early 1960s. In the river systems that converge on the Amazon, we know that the *black rivers* (so-called because of their dark but fairly clear water) contain far fewer fish than the *white rivers* (which are actually brown and muddy). We also know that the varieties of fish increase as each river nears the sea. There is a need for many more fish collections, and for more *ichthyologists*.

Fish can be important to the international economy or to the local economy. Two examples of fish that are important in today's international trade are shrimps and anchovies.

Since 1960 there has been a huge expansion in the international demand for shrimps. In countries such as the United States and Canada, more recipes call for shrimps, and more and more people have begun to enjoy their taste. The big fishing fleets from Europe, Japan, and North America already catch shrimps off Panama, Guyana, Nicaragua, Mexico, and several other countries.

The Humboldt Current is rich in fish, including the tiny but numerous anchovy. With the world-wide demand for both animal feed and fertilizer in modern farming, fishmeal has become an important product, and the anchovies are an ideal source. Until recently, most of Peru's fishmeal industry was owned by U.S. companies. It is easy to recognize a fishmeal town along the Peruvian coast by the terrible smell. Scientists are still not sure why the anchovy shoals do not appear in some seasons. In 1972, for example, there were so few anchovies, that the pelicans were starving, and hung around the main towns like vultures feeding on scraps.

An interesting side product of the fish shoals, which provide food for vast numbers of birds, is *guano*, the thick deposit of bird lime that covers many of the small offshore islands of Peru and Chile.

Examples of the second category, that is, fish and marine animals that are used locally but not exported, include the paiche and the manatee.

The paiche can reach over 1.8 m in length and is the giant ""catfish" of the Amazon. Like many big fish, such as tuna and grouper, its flesh is delicious. The Indians of the Amazon use harpoons to catch paiche, but unfortunately for them it is a rather rare species.

(Top) Shrimp boats in the Gulf of Mexico. Their catch is destined for the United States. The shrimp beds were damaged by hurricane Fifi in 1974.

(Bottom left) Peru's incredible wealth of anchovies in her offshore waters, which extend 320 km seaward, has made her a top-ranking fishing nation and exporter of fishmeal.

(Bottom right) Vast numbers of birds, such as cormorants, pelicans, gannets, gulls, and terns, feed on the shoals of tiny anchovies that thrive in the cool waters of the Humboldt Current. The droppings of these birds accumulate to form guano, which is said to be the ideal fertilizer. It contains nitrogen, phosphorous, and potash — the three most important plant foods. In 1840, when the value of guano was little known, the thickness of the deposits on the offshore islands exceeded thirty metres. By 1874 the export of millions of tonnes almost completely exhausted the ancient deposits. The industry is now carefully controlled. Guano droppings dry quickly and in this dry desert region, will be preserved for centuries.

Manatees, often called sea cows, are mammals that live in the water, and have become rare except in the isolated streams of Guyana and northern Brazil. They can live in either fresh or brackish water. Unfortunately, they tend to be friendly, which is a fatal habit for any animal used by man as a source of food.

> Questions
> 1. What is brackish water? Where would you find it?
> 2. Why do you think some South American countries, such as Peru and Ecuador, have extended their territorial boundaries out to 320 km?

Electric eels can give an intruder a terrific shock or punch generated by "batteries" that take up most of the eels' length. They live in swamps in the Amazon Basin, especially in the shallow, curved lakes that used to be part of the main river course but have been left behind as the river meandered off in a different direction.

Piranas, although they taste good, especially when fried, are better known because they have, on occasion, eaten people. Like other carnivorous fish, they become excited by the "smell" of blood. There is some doubt, however, that they really hurl themselves on people or animals that fall into a river. Most observers suggest that they prefer dead meat and will not normally attack a living, moving animal (or man). The people in the Amazon and other tropical river basins swim quite happily in the rivers, and never seem to get eaten.

The diversity of landscapes, types of vegetation, climates, wildlife, and soils has given South America literally thousands of different physical environments. This forced its Amerindian inhabitants to devise countless different methods of fishing, hunting, farming, dressing, housebuilding, herding, and so on. In other words, man had to adapt and develop his cultures whenever he encountered a new environment.

THE HUMAN BACKGROUND — PAST AND PRESENT

Origins

The Americas appear to have been settled much later than Asia and most of Africa. Some archaeologists think that man first arrived at least 11 500 years ago across the Bering Strait from the Chukchi Peninsula in Asia. (Further research and new discoveries suggest that this date may be extended to some 20 000 and even 30 000 years ago.) From Alaska, each wave of new arrivals gradually made its way southwards, with some moving as far south as Tierra del Fuego.

As they migrated across endless plains, over high mountains, and through jungles and burning deserts, the people learned to adapt to all the natural environments they encountered, creating civilizations of their own.

Besides adapting their ways of living (food, shelter, clothing, customs, and so on) to the regions in which they settled, the early settlers developed basic differences in languages. By the time Christopher Columbus landed in the New World in 1492, some 1700 different languages and dialects were spoken in Middle and South America.

Linguistics, or the study of languages, is one method of tracing the movements of people. Many languages, which seem quite different from one another, are, in fact, closely related. Human groups, however, may, and sometimes do, discard their own language for another. For example, this has happened to most immigrants who came to North America. In the *altiplano* and mountain valleys of Colombia, Ecuador, Peru, and Bolivia, many people lost their own languages when the Inca Empire made *Quechua* the official language in the fifteenth century.

Questions
1. How far is it from Asia to America across the Bering Straits?
2. Look at Figure 5.2 showing the ocean currents. Why is it unlikely that people came to South America by sea? Why would it be easier to go from South America to Asia by sea? You might find it interesting to read about Thor Heyerdahl's Kon Tiki expedition.
3. Why are people in mountainous areas more likely to develop several different languages than people living on a grassy plain?

Very, very few Amerindians in South America today live by hunting and gathering, although this was once a way of life for most of the continent's peoples (as it was in Europe and everywhere else). Long before the invasions from Europe, the people of South America had learned to cultivate plants and domesticate animals.

The most important breakthrough was the domestication of maize or corn. Like all domesticated plants, corn comes from a wild ancestor. Both Mexico and Peru may have developed domesticated corn at about the same time. Potatoes, tomatoes, squash, beans, and melons were also developed in these two countries.

This Shipibo girl, who lives on the Ucayali River in Peru, is carrying a pot whose pattern immediately betrays the fact that she is a Shipibo. Throughout South America, each distinctive culture developed its own designs.

The Earliest Civilizations

Wherever conditions made it possible, that is, wherever farming, stock-rearing, or commerce produced a sufficient surplus above the daily needs of the people, small states appeared. Each state grew and developed its own distinctive styles in pottery, textile patterns, and sculpture. Each state would also develop its own system of laws, government, and religion.

The main concerns of the early Americans were over death, illness, success in war, and food supplies; naturally, these concerns found expression in their religions. It seems that every group of people in the Americas believed in a life after death, and conceived of it as very pleasant but not much different from life before death.

Illness was seen as being the result of evil influences, as was also the case in so many African, European, and Asian religions. However, many of the Amerindians were skilled in more practical methods of curing disease and illness. Success in war or other risky undertakings could, they believed, be foretold by correctly reading omens. Success in farming came from carefully studying the stars, sun, and moon. As may be imagined, all of these complex calculations led to the rise of specialists, or priests, who acquired more and more power in their communities.

When the Spaniards first landed in the New World there were many distinct cultures in existence in Middle and South

America. These varied from small groups of nomadic hunters to important states based on an agricultural economy. Some, such as the Araucanians of Chile, were sufficiently warlike to be able to resist the Spanish invaders, while other were soon overwhelmed. Thus the complex civilization of the Chibchas, in Colombia, who produced fine jewellery, was defeated in a few years. Other native peoples, such as the Guarani of Paraguay, intermingled readily with the Spaniards, while others, such as the Aymaras of the altiplano, tended to keep to themselves as much as possible. In some areas the Europeans killed off the native population, as in Argentina, but in other countries, such as Guatemala and Bolivia, the native peoples are still in a majority.

It is worthwhile to take a closer look at three of the highly developed civilizations that existed in Middle and South America before the Spanish invasions of the sixteenth century — the Mayan, Aztec, and Inca empires.

The Mayan Empire

These people first arrived in Guatemala about 2000 years ago and spread into the Yucatan Peninsula. They were basically a farming people, and reached the peak of their culture between 300 and 900 A.D. Excavations have shown that they built magnificent pyramids and temples, and that they were skilled in astronomy, mathematics, and picture-writing. The collapse of the Mayan Empire remains a mystery. Some archaeologists suggest that the increasing population could not grow enough corn to sustain itself and its priests and soliders; others suggest that the Mayan farmers rebelled and overthrew their rulers. There are several other theories to explain the sudden abandonment of the religious centres. Today the Mayan people survive as industrious farmers in Mexico, Guatemala, and Belize.

These pillars are the remains of the Mayan "Temple of Warriors" at Chichen Ltza, Mexico.

The Aztec Empire

It is believed that the Aztecs occupied the Mexican Plateau around 1200 A.D. They, like the Mayas, had a 365 d round calendar and were gifted in the arts — architecture, pottery, textiles, and carving. At first they were farmers, miners, workers in precious metals such as gold and silver, traders, and weavers. Later, as their empire grew, most of them became soldiers and administrators. The tribute they demanded from conquered peoples, such as the Tlaxcalans, made the Aztecs increasingly unpopular. Tenochtitlan, their capital city, was founded in about 1325 A.D. on an island in the middle of Lake Texcaco, near present-day Mexico City.

A painting showing the Spanish cavalry, led by Cortes, defeating Mexican foot soldiers at the Battle of Otumba.

Great causeways linked the shores of the lake and the city, which was described by the Spanish conqueror, Hernan Cortes, as one of the most beautiful cities he had ever seen. It consisted of temples, broad avenues, and huge public squares or plazas. When Cortes began his invasion of Mexico, many of the Aztecs' subject peoples joined him. Even so, it took several battles before the Aztec Empire was overthrown.

The Incas — Children of the Sun

The Inca Empire reached its peak about 1490 A.D., less than fifty years before its conquest by a Spanish force under Francisco Pizarro, in 1532.

Unlike the Mayans and the Aztecs, the Incas had no written language. However, they kept records by using a system of knotted cords called *quipus*. They built no pyramids, but rather used their energy to build temples, bridges, roads, terraced gardens for crop cultivation, and irrigation systems. Their highways, through mountains and canyons, linked the capital, Cuzco, with a vast empire which extended from present-day Colombia to Chile and Brazil and is estimated to have included a population of 16 000 000 people.

The vast empire was tightly controlled by a single divine ruler — the Son of the Sun. No private person was allowed to own land, which all belonged to the State. The State,

186

in turn, looked after the old and the infirm, and the families of those away on military service. Gold was reserved mainly for decorating the temples, and there appears to have been no form of money in use.

The empire was united by a system of laws and by a single language, *Quechua*, which is still spoken by many Andean Indians today.

Pizarro landed in Peru in 1532, which happened to be the year that civil war broke out between two Inca emperors, Atahualpa and his half-brother, Huascar. In spite of overtures of friendship and offerings of gold, Atahualpa was captured by Pizarro and was later cruelly murdered. Before his capture, however, Atahualpa had arranged to have his half-brother murdered, and so Pizarro had little difficulty in subduing a leaderless people. Some escaped to the city of Macchu Picchu, which appears to have been abandoned by its defenders only when all hope of expelling the Spaniards from Peru had gone.

> ## Questions
> 1. Why might the Mayan farmers have wished to overthrow their priests and soldiers?
> 2. Why do you think the Aztecs built their capital in the middle of a lake?
> 3. What might have been some of the reasons Cortes gave to *justify* his conquest of the Aztec Empire?
> 4. What military advantages would the Spaniards have enjoyed over the Aztecs and Incas?
> 5. Locate Cuzco, Yucatan, and Tlaxcala in an atlas.

Page 186

A silver llama, from the Inca culture of Cuzco, Peru. This figurine reveals the superb skill and craftsmanship of the Inca sculptor. The llama, a native animal of the Andes, is still used as a beast of burden. A tough, sure-footed animal, it is ideal for domestic purposes in such a rocky, mountainous environment.

Macchu Picchu, the last stronghold of the Incas. Terraces built at an elevation of 2590 m in the heart of the Peruvian jungle reveal the engineering skills of the Inca peoples. Cut into the mountainsides, these terraces provided valuable level ground for the cultivation of crops. An excellent system of irrigation using the waters of the mountain streams was also devised. After the conquest, these terraced slopes and the roadways and buildings fell into a state of decay.

European Penetration

The result of the conquest of Peru was that South America had lost its greatest native empire. Everywhere the Spanish priesthood ordered the destruction of the old religions, which was perhaps not a bad thing as they had become particularly bloodthirsty. The Indian farmers, however, found that they had merely exchanged one set of masters for another, in many ways even harsher.

Entire Indian villages were "granted" to Spanish soldiers, whose only interest lay in getting rich as quickly as possible. Gold and silver mines, such as the huge silver mine of Potosi in present-day Bolivia, were worked by thousands of Indian slaves. Taxes were extremely heavy, and the new masters did nothing to improve education, health, or social conditions. A great gap was opened up between the Spaniards and the Indians that has only recently begun to heal. Even today, countries such as Bolivia, Peru, Venezuela, Ecuador, and Guatemala have almost totally separate "Spanish" and Amerindian societies.

The riches of the Americas soon attracted people from other parts of Europe. Finding it impossible to share in the booty and the exploitation of the Indian farmers, they contented themselves with raiding the lumbering Spanish galleons that carried the treasure to Europe. Bases were set up on small islands and in hidden lagoons, where the raiders built up friendly relations with the local Indians who hated the Spaniards because of their constant slaving raids.

Real pirates, who preyed on any vessel or town, were fairly rare and seldom survived for long. However, some were supported by European governments provided they attacked and looted only Spanish ships and colonies. These semi-legal pirates, called *privateers,* attacked important cities such as Panama, Maracaibo, Vera Cruz, and Lima.

Many Spanish settlers objected to the high prices they were forced to pay for Spanish goods, and welcomed the arrival of English, Dutch, Danish, and other smugglers into the Caribbean. In addition, wars in Europe provided the European countries with excuses for seizing several islands and isolated strips of the mainland, such as Belize, Demerara (Guyana), Martinique, Jamaica, San Andres, and the Corn Islands. These rapidly became bases for smugglers and pirates, and remained so until the rich sugar plantations were established.

Portugal, like its neighbour, Spain, was also anxious to expand its colonies and its trade. Portuguese ships had reached the New World at the close of the fifteenth century, and the settlements were established along the Atlantic coast. The colony of Brazil became famous for its Brazil wood — a source of dye. From 1532 to 1536 the woodcutters were joined by military men and settlers. The settlers had been familiar with sugar-cane cultivation in southern Portugal, where African slaves had been used for nearly eighty years. Furthermore, the ships which brought out supplies often returned to Portugal with empty holds. Thus, it was only to be expected that the early settlers in Brazil should begin producing sugar, importing African slaves, and building sugar mills to process sugar for export.

This emphasis on farming made the Portuguese colonies very different from those of Spain. Men struck out for the interior not so much to look for mines and empires to conquer, but to carve out ranches and plantations. Also, the settlers had usually come to stay in the new colony, rather than to get rich and then return home. They tended to take Indian or African wives, settle down, and look after their farms and businesses. Perhaps even more important, the Portuguese government did not attempt to impose strict controls, and simply expected its colonies to be self-sufficient.

Land-hungry settlers formed armed bands and called themselves *bandeirantes* after the flags they carried. They pushed westwards and southwards, far beyond the limits of territory Portugal was supposed to occupy under the 1494 treaty between Spain and Portugal. By the time new peace treaties were signed, Brazil's boundaries were pressing hard on the Andes and the River Plate, and the country covered almost half the entire continent.

Over the years conditions in Spanish South America changed. The gap which existed between the rich Spanish landowners and the poor Indian labourers became greater. Furthermore, there was friction between "Europeans" born in the South American colonies, who were usually called *creoles,* and those born in Spain or Portugal, who had emigrated to the New World as officials and administrators. The creoles naturally resented the superior attitudes of the more recent arrivals. Taking advantage of Napoleon's occupation of Spain and Portugal in the early 1800's, and inspired by the American and French revolutions, the colonists of Spanish South America staged a series of riots and rebellions against Spain. A number of great leaders, such as Simon Bolivar, Sucre, and San Martin, led powerful armies of creoles, Indians, Africans, and volunteers from European countries, such as Ireland, England, and Italy. The last Spanish garrison in mainland South America at Callao surrendered to Bolivar in 1826, and Spanish rule was over.

Brazil obtained its independence in a much more peaceful manner. The Portuguese king, John VI, had fled to Brazil when Napoleon attacked Spain and Portugal in 1807-1808, and on returning to Portugal had left his son, Dom Pedro, in control of Brazil. In 1822, encouraged by the collapse of Spain in the rest of South America, Dom Pedro proclaimed himself the king of an independent Brazil. Portugal made no attempt to reimpose its will.

Thus by 1829, while European powers were still busy conquering African and Asian states, the South American empires had already fallen apart and were now a series of creole republics. Only in the Caribbean

(Top) A colonial-style theatre in Rio de Janeiro. The Spanish and Portuguese settlers tried, successfully, to create imitations of the "good life" they had not been able to enjoy in Europe. Balls, operas, expensive clothes, and even fox hunting were introduced, as were skilled artists, dressmakers, architects, and jewellers.

(Bottom) A statue of Simon Bolivar.

189

were there still European colonies, some of which have still to achieve their independence.

Later Colonization

Independence meant that the old colonial restrictions on non-Spanish immigration had gone. South America became a paradise in the minds of many Europeans, for Europe was wracked by wars, social revolutions, and the expulsion of small farmers from their holdings. A wave of immigrants, therefore, built up during the nineteenth century, aimed at both North and South America.

The Industrial Revolution in Europe led to a great demand for raw materials such as sugar, wool, beef, cotton, coffee, minerals, rubber, timber, and sisal. This meant that there were jobs in South America, even if rates of pay were poor, and that there was always a chance of owning a small farm.

Usually an emigrant would choose to go where he already had friends or relatives, or at least could find people from the same village or part of the country. He was more likely to find a job and to get help during his first difficult years. In this way, distinct colonies of Germans, Italians, Basques, Greeks, Yugoslavs, Welshmen, Poles, and Syrians were established all over Latin America. Most of the immigrants, however, moved to the rapidly growing cities, where they formed a huge new addition to the work force.

Only the more successful of the recent immigrants were able to mingle socially with the "old colonial" society of creole families, and very few of the new immigrants chose to mingle with the already depressed societies of Amerindians and Africans. They thus created a fourth social group in an already very mixed continent.

Questions
1. Why do you think that very few English migrants chose South America as a new home?

2. Why might it have been difficult for an immigrant to obtain a piece of good farmland in spite of South America's size?
3. Why do you think some people emigrate while others stay at home?

South America Today

South America is a continent of contrasts. Isolated Indians live by hunting and fishing in the upper reaches of the Amazon forests, while the urban dwellers of such cities as Rio de Janeiro, Buenos Aires, and Santiago are, in many ways, more sophisticated than people in North American cities. Decrepit shacks adjoin luxurious high-rise apartments in the large coastal cities. In many countries, military governments try to contain the explosive unrest that simmers just below the surface.

South America is changing rapidly. All over the continent people are demanding a better life, and old social rules and customs are crumbling.

The Boro

When the Portuguese arrived in Brazil about 1500 A.D., it is estimated that there were about four million Indians, some one million of whom lived in the Amazon Basin. Slavery, senseless killing, and illnesses, such as influenza, smallpox, and measles combined to completely wipe out eighty-seven tribes and only about 100 000 Amerindians remain in Amazonia today. One of the smallest of these tribes is the Boro.

The Boro live an isolated existence in the upper reaches of the Amazon, where about a thousand live in scattered communities in the region between the rivers Japura and Putumayo.

A typical Boro house accommodates several families. The men are cultivators and hunters, and their implements include an axe, long hunting spears, and blowpipes. They tip their darts with *curare* which is obtained from the juice of a certain forest

(Top) A scene in the rain forest of the Amazon Basin. What materials would be used for building houses in this region? Compare this with the photograph (Bottom) of São Paulo, in Brazil — a "concrete jungle" of skyscrapers, high-rise buildings, and highways.

Figure 5.5

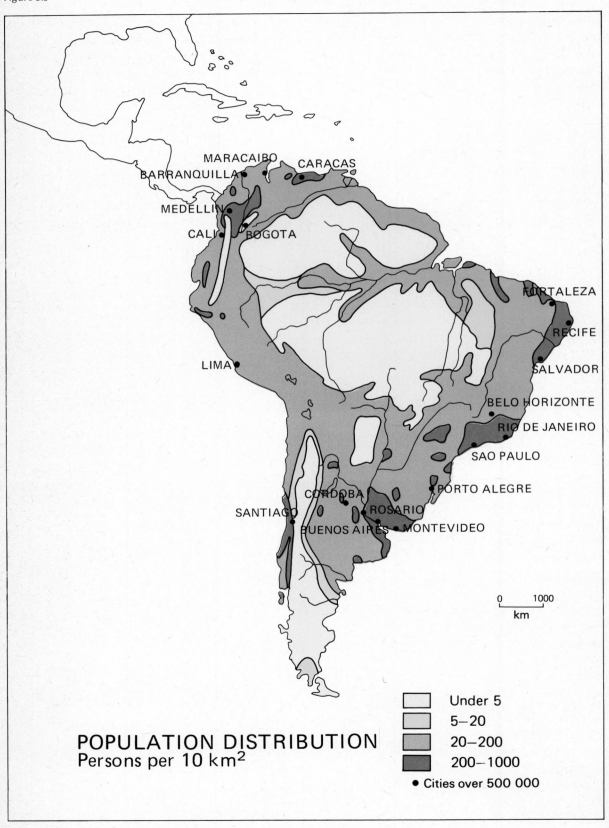

POPULATION DISTRIBUTION
Persons per 10 km²

	Under 5
	5–20
	20–200
	200–1000
●	Cities over 500 000

0   1000
km

vine. The juice paralyses the animal but does not make the meat poisonous. The Boro also catch animals by digging traps, and fish by means of long straw, basket-like nets. Today, many Boro have shotguns. The Boro eat most forest animals, especially iguanas, tapirs, monkeys, peccaries (wild pigs), armadilloes, and birds.

The potato-like, tuberous root of the manioc plant is the staple food. The trees are cut into to prevent the flow of sap, left to dry out, and then burnt. This is known as the "slash and burn" method of forest clearance. The larger stumps are left, and manioc, beans, and corn are cultivated around them. The ash from the burnt trees helps to enrich the soil, but after two or three years of cultivation the soil loses its nutrients and crop yields decline. The Boro then clear new fields. This constant movement of fields has given rise to the term *shifting cultivation*.

Population

The population of most South American countries has been increasing rapidly in recent years, although in the Amazon, northeast Brazil, and other isolated areas there are still some groups of people whose numbers are declining. While birth rates have levelled off in the richer countries of the world, they are still rising in Latin America.

Questions
1. Explain why some areas have a very sparse population.
2. Where are the areas of densest population?
3. Compare this map with a vegetation map and a map showing the landforms. What conclusions may be established?

Within each country there are areas of high population density and areas of very low population density. Sometimes the low densities coincide with areas that could not support more people (for example, the *tierra fria* in Colombia), but South America still has vast areas of land that could support many more people than presently live there.

There are also areas where people cannot find jobs or land to work. Here it is easier to talk about *overpopulation*, but one must be careful not to assume that this is always the real problem. *Apparent overpopulation* may be caused because a few people own too much land, or because crop yields are very low, or because not enough capital has been invested in industry.

Migration of people within South America is very common, and is made easier by the

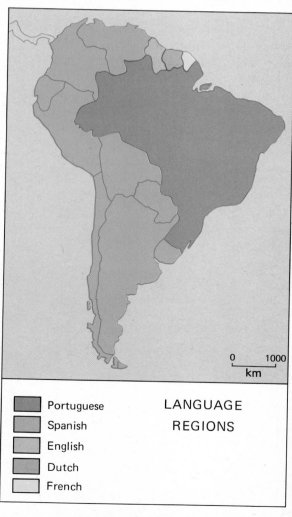

Figure 5.6 The language regions of South America. The major languages spoken in South America today were introduced by the early European invaders and settlers. The dividing line between Spanish and Portuguese is almost unimportant, because the two are so similar. They are both "Latin" or "Romance" languages. People who speak Spanish can usually understand Portuguese and vice versa.

LANGUAGE REGIONS

- Portuguese
- Spanish
- English
- Dutch
- French

0   1000
km

193

common use of Spanish and Portuguese, two very similar languages.

In Mexico, Argentina, Brazil, and the banana plantations of Central America, some of the large farms must search far beyond their own neighbourhoods and national boundaries for *seasonal workers.* Thus, it is quite common to meet truckloads of workers from Bolivia, Chile, and Paraguay travelling to Argentina, for example, to look for seasonal work. They are usually poorly paid and must spend much of their lives in miserable huts and barracks put up on the big farms, ranches, and plantations. Because they are migratory and only temporarily employed, they find it difficult to organize themselves into trade unions.

Housing Conditions

Millions of South Americans live in comfortable, spacious homes with running water, electricity, and pleasant gardens. In the cities it is common to find new apartment blocks as well designed as those in North America.

However, millions more live in shanty-type homes around the edges of the cities or in overcrowded slums in the city centres.

Unemployment, poor wages, and uncertain employment make life very difficult for millions of city dwellers, so that they cannot afford good homes or apartments. For this reason, a number of governments, such as those of El Salvador, Guyana, Peru, and Argentina, have created housing estates built with government money for working people. In fact, in the field of *public housing,* South America is probably more advanced than North America.

Health and Sanitation

Most South American countries are poor and so cannot afford adequate health and sanitation services. They are short of doctors, nurses, hospitals, clinics, and workers to visit communities to teach better health and hygiene practices. However, progress is now being made, in spite of the shortage of money, and one of the reasons for the population increase in recent years has been the defeat of the great killer diseases, such as yellow fever, and the control of weakening diseases, such as malaria. The child-killers, such as dysentery and enteritis, are still responsible for the deaths of millions of children every year, but even they are gradually being brought under control.

Prefabricated low-income housing in Guyana. Built for working people, these houses provide the bare necessities, including running water and sanitation. Such houses are in great demand because they are cheap. The people could not afford a home of their own without this kind of government help.

Sanitation problems are common in many South American towns and cities. The average North American householder's garbage is collected and taken to the local dump, and most homes are connected to a central water-borne, sewage-disposal system. Garbage and sewage disposal services cost money and are financed through property and other taxes. The problem in most South American cities is that the *tax base* is too low and many people avoid paying their taxes. The result is that there are insufficient funds to maintain efficient sewage collection and disposal systems.

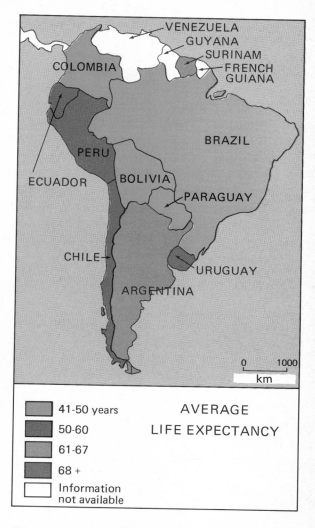

AVERAGE LIFE EXPECTANCY

▨	41-50 years
▨	50-60
▨	61-67
▨	68 +
☐	Information not available

Questions
1. How would child mortality affect a life expectancy table?
2. Why do you think some geographers use life expectancy as a guide when comparing living standards?
3. What is the level of life expectancy in Canada?

(Top right) Figure 5.7 Map showing average life expectancy figures for South American countries. Although life expectancy means the average number of years an individual may expect to live in a certain country or region, it is mainly the number of children who die that determines whether life expectancy will appear to be high or low. Child mortality can be reduced by providing better food, better medical and nursing services, better education, and better sanitation.

(Bottom left) These farmers in the Peruvian jungle are receiving shots from a foreign volunteer doctor. Almost all South American countries are still short of medical personnel, and in addition many of their doctors do not wish to work in the countryside or in the poorer parts of town.

(Bottom right) Sifting through garbage for anything worth saving is an activity still remembered by older Europeans; in South America it is still quite common. This picture, taken in Lima, also illustrates another common problem — that of garbage removal.

A good urban water supply system is also very expensive. Not only does it involve kilometres of piping that must be inspected and repaired from time to time, but also deep wells or reservoirs, filtration plants, and so on. Many cities have made this investment, and water is now safe to drink from the tap in almost every major Latin American city from Ushuaia, in Tierra del Fuego, to Panama. This, however, is not true in many of the smaller towns and in almost all of the villages. People who can afford it have filters or boil their water. The very poor cannot even afford these precautions, and water-borne diseases are still common.

Education

One of the main demands of people all over the world, and especially in the developing countries, is for a good education. Unfortunately, few countries in South America have

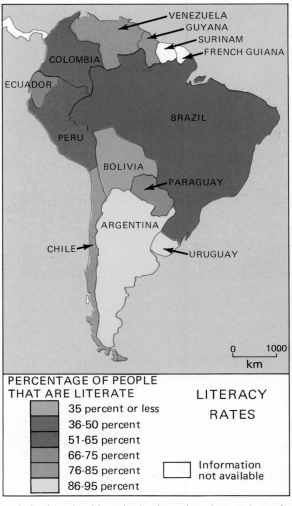

PERCENTAGE OF PEOPLE THAT ARE LITERATE

LITERACY RATES

- 35 percent or less
- 36-50 percent
- 51-65 percent
- 66-75 percent
- 76-85 percent
- 86-95 percent
- Information not available

(Top right) Figure 5.8 Map showing the literacy rates of South American countries, i.e., the percentage of people who have had at least a basic education and can read, write, and do simple calculations.

(Bottom left) The education system in Peru is improving rapidly with a new generation of teachers. Governments in most countries are endeavouring to improve old schools and build new ones but teachers often have to encourage parents to raise money to repair the school property and to provide teaching materials. Military governments, which exist in much of South America, provide a very strict and formal type of education. Rich parents send their children to private schools.

(Bottom right) The poor suburb of Belem (Bethlehem) in Iquitos. This is home to the children in the photograph on the left, and shows at a glance why the parents cannot afford

to help the school buy the books and equipment it needs. Clearly all children do not have an equal chance to get a good education. There are millions of children who drop out of elementary schools and millions who never get beyond Grade 1, either because they are needed for work or they become sick and fall too far behind.

been able to provide good, well-equipped schools, staffed by well-trained teachers. Education costs money and the money has not been available. Very poor families are often forced to keep their children out of school to help work on the farm, or to sell goods, or to generally try to help make money. This problem increases the drop-out rate.

The map illustrates the lack of education in many South American countries.

Questions
1. Name the countries where half the population is illiterate.
2. What steps might be taken, and are being taken, to improve these conditions in South American countries?
3. Why might poor health conditions be related to high drop-out rates?

As illiteracy is such an important problem in these developing nations of South America, several governments have launched adult education schemes. Brazil, for example, has introduced a project, known as MOBRAL (Movement for Brazilian Literacy), to reduce adult illiteracy. Cuba was able to wipe out illiteracy in six years by sending thousands of students from the cities into the countryside to teach people to read.

All over Latin America and the Caribbean, as in Africa, new universities and technical schools are training nurses, doctors, engineers, electricians, teachers, and other specialists. The main problem is that very few people want to work outside the capital city or the main towns. Most of the newly qualified people grew up in the cities, and are not prepared to face the shortages, difficulties, and isolation of living in the countryside. To solve this problem, it may become necessary to insist that newly qualified engineers, veterinarians, doctors, and so on, serve several years in small towns and

villages before they are allowed to take positions in the cities. Tanzania, in Africa, has already adopted this procedure.

Labour Conditions

Several problems face working people in South America today. These include (a) a high level of unemployment, (b) comparatively low wages, (c) too many unskilled workers, (d) a lack of capital to develop new and existing industries, and (e) a lack of job security.

Figure 5.9 Map showing per capita (per head or per person) annual incomes. A per capita income is obtained by dividing the total wealth produced or exchanged by a country in a single year (re GNP or Gross National Product) by the country's total population (men, women, and children). Remember that this gives an average figure, and so there are some people much richer or poorer than the figure indicated.

PER CAPITA
INCOMES
FIGURES IN U.S. DOLLARS

Note:
Canada $3500
U.S.A. $4400
Mexico $566

Many South American countries lack the financial resources to create industrial employment, and as a result, most of the people remain poor. This, in turn, means that there is little money in circulation, which discourages industrial investment, which means no new jobs, and so on, in a vicious circle.

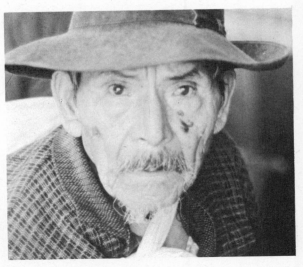

This old Brazilian field worker has suffered throughout his life from job insecurity, poor medical services, poor food, and low pay.

> **Questions**
>
> From Figure 5.9:
>
> 1. Which three countries have the highest per capita incomes in South America? Which has the lowest?
> 2. Venezuela has rich oil and tar reserves. How does this factor affect the per capita income of the country?
> 3. Why would industrialists be discouraged in countries where there is little money in circulation?

Many South American workers have never been able to learn job skills, either at school or at work. As a result, their wages are very low, and their situation is made more acute by having to compete for jobs with the farm families who are constantly moving to the cities to look for work.

The table shows the average weekly wages of workers in various countries in the southern continents in comparison to Canada. It must be remembered, however, that wages must be considered in terms of the cost of living in each country. As most things, such as food, clothing, and housing, cost almost the same as in Canada, people's living standards are often desperately low.

Cheap labour attracts large foreign investors, but the number of new jobs created by companies such as Volkswagen and Marconi in South America is quite small. The South American countries will have to rely mainly on their own resources to secure full employment and higher living standards.

Figure 5.10

Country	1970 Average Weekly Wages (in dollars)
Argentina	20
Brazil	20
Chile	20
Colombia	15
Ecuador	12
Peru	20
Venezuela	50
Mexico	35
Australia	50
New Zealand	70
Egypt	7
Ghana	16
Kenya	12
Tanzania	13
Zambia	22
Canada	120

From: *United Nations Statistical Year Book*, 1970.

Festivals, Sports, and the Arts

The South American countries have their own special festivals, sports, and artistic expression. Some of these are traditional, for example, the Indian dances and festivals, the early temples and carvings, and the ancient myths and legends. Other art forms, sports, festivals, and musical instruments were adapted from those introduced by the Spanish and Portuguese settlers.

South America, too, has produced some fine poets, writing mainly in Spanish. Although it is not as important as music in the daily lives of the South Americans, poetry is used much more than in North America. No Latin American love letter, for example, would be complete without at least one poem, and poetry books are passed from hand to hand even in the small villages.

The most popular sport in South America is, of course, soccer. Each city and small town has its own stadium, and immense crowds attend weekly football matches. Mexico, Brazil, Argentina, Uruguay, and Chile have all done well in World Cup competitions, and emotions can run high during an important soccer match.

Like North Americans, the South Americans enjoy getting out of the city at weekends and on holiday, but cannot afford to travel as far. Every city has its nearby picnic grounds or beaches, where people who have any money to spare at all will take their families. In many ways, it can be said that South Americans are more family-oriented than North Americans, and enjoy nothing better than to visit with relatives.

A soccer stadium in São Paulo, Brazil.

Music is an important element in South American life. Where people cannot afford to buy musical instruments, they will simply make their own. Weddings, christenings, funerals, and Saints' days all provide opportunities for fiestas, when music and dancing can enliven people's otherwise dreary lives.

Questions
1. Try to listen to some South American music; your local library may have a record-lending section. How does it differ from North American music?
2. What other forms of sport are enjoyed in South America?
3. Travellers often say that South America is "more alive" than North America. What do you think they mean?

AGRICULTURE

The two South American products with which people are most familiar are Brazilian coffee and canned beef from Argentina, which are the major exports. However, South America, with its variety of landforms, soils, and climates, produces a wide range of crops. These vary from tropical products, such as rubber, bananas, sugar cane, cocoa, and cotton, to more temperate crops, such as grapes, wheat, maize, flax, and vegetables. Tremendous numbers of cattle and sheep are raised on the grasslands.

It is a good idea to begin a study of South American agriculture by considering the size of farms and the types of farming practised, both of which vary a great deal.

A Variety of Farming Methods

Latifundia

Because of South America's colonial history, much of the farmland and pasture is still in the hands of a few very rich owners. Many large landholdings, or *latifundia* are managed as follows:

(a) The owner lives all, or most of the time, in the city or even in a foreign country.

(b) The land is not farmed intensively or scientifically, except in a few small areas.

(c) Thousands of peasants both work for the landowner and rent small parcels of their own.

(d) The landowner is more interested in obtaining rental income from his land than in investing new capital in it, in the form of

Figure 5.11   Diagram showing the variety of crops grown in South America in relation to altitude.

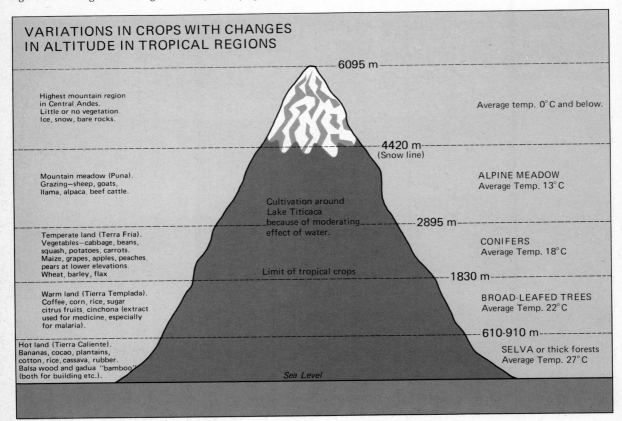

200

machinery, better seed, irrigation and drainage works, better livestock, and new fencing and buildings.

(e) The estate is run by a manager, who is often, trying to get rich himself.

(f) There is a preference for land use that requires little investment per hectare, that is, *extensive* farming, such as ranching.

(g) The estate is huge. One latifundia in Peru, which was taken over by the state in the early 1970's, was almost the same size as Switzerland!

Latifundia is one of the most wasteful kinds of *land-tenure* because it does not give any encouragement to the people who work on the land, and because the crops and animals are usually of poor quality. For these reasons, many Latin American governments and political movements have tried to take away some of these huge estates or *haciendas* from their owners and to re-divide the lands among those who work on them. Bolivia and Peru have had *land reforms* of this type.

A cowboy, or *vaqueros*, in Ecuador. Most South American cattle are of mixed stock, and of poor meat quality. The owner, a *latifundista*, does not want to invest his money into his ranching operation. The cowboys do not own the cattle and are paid low wages.

Plantations

Plantations, growing crops such as coffee, bananas, and sugar cane, are also huge, but differ from latifundia in that they are intensively farmed and usually have high yields. Large sums of money are invested in the land to make it more productive, and the

This plantation was largely destroyed by hurricane Fifi in 1974. It belongs to the United Fruit Company (United Brands) of Boston. The importance of bananas to the economies of several countries (47 percent of Honduranian exports by value in 1973) has led to them being called *banana republics*.

owners, who are often foreign companies, take a great interest in the management of the plantations. Like haciendas, they are run by managers, but these men must keep accurate accounts and are closely supervised by the owners.

Peasant Farming

This type of farming involves growing a variety of crops and raising sufficient numbers of domestic animals to supply the family's needs, while cultivating and selling one or more *commercial* crop in order to obtain the other necessities of life. There are many peasant farmers in South America, and their way of making a living is often precarious. Crops may fail, harvests may be poor, floods, droughts, fires, and insect pests may destroy a whole year's work, and crop prices may fluctuate. Very few Latin American peasants are able to make a good living from their farms. Many of them try to supplement their incomes by going to work on large farms or plantations. They also try to diversify their farming by growing a variety of crops in order to reduce the danger of total crop failure.

In an attempt to create areas of peasant or family farming, several Latin American governments have started settlement schemes in the still quite extensive areas of forest or swamp. There, however, the great distances from the main markets, the isolation, the poor quality of the soil, and the high cost of clearing the land have all too often combined to create poverty among the settlers. Some governments, for example, Peru, have tried to help even more by making grants available for clearing the bush, providing a few farm animals and implements, selling the land on an installment plan, and providing some medical and educational services.

Subsistence Farming

Subsistence farmers exist when city markets are too far away to make it possible to sell produce, and when nobody comes to their district to buy. Such farming is practised in the more isolated regions of the Andes or the upper Amazon Basin. True subsistence farming, where the farmers produce *everything* they need and sell nothing, probably does not really exist. Fishhooks, matches, kerosene, and cooking pots are some of the things they try to buy from traders, and they usually have a surplus of something — even a fish or two — to trade.

Of course, it is possible to make everything, such as medicines, clothes, utensils, twine, housing materials, and furniture. Near-subsistence farmers, who do make many of these things, have discovered that tourists are willing to pay high prices for some of them. For example, the Andean Indians used to colour their *ponchos* with vegetable dyes and *cochineal*. With the invention of cheap and fast *aniline* dyes, these skills almost died out. Today the demand for hand-made goods and for "natural" dyes has led to a recovery of cochineal bug collecting and vegetable dye-making.

Squatting

Poor peasants and subsistence farmers in Latin America often move onto land belonging to either the government or a big latifundia in order to carve out a family farm for themselves. It may be years before they are discovered. One reason for this squatting is that many villagers are not aware that uncultivated land belongs to anyone, and another reason is that they are often desperate for land. Some governments have recently legalized squatter farms of up to 42.5 ha (for example, in Panama), so long as the farmers register their "property" and pay taxes.

Subsistence agriculture is practised in the rain forest of Ecuador's Oriente Province.

Major Crops

The greatest variety of crops is usually grown by Amerindian subsistence farmers, because they have learned over the centuries how to make use of different kinds of plants. The next greatest variety is grown by the peasant farmers, both for their own use and for sale in the towns. The commercial farmers produce only a limited range of different crops because they concentrate on supplying the *staples* to the towns, such as beef, poultry, eggs, milk, corn, beans, sugar, and so on. Finally, the plantation owners grow only those crops that are sold on the world markets. Bananas, coffee, sugar, cotton, and cocoa are among the most important export crops.

Bananas

In the Caribbean countries and South America, bananas are seldom used except as a dessert, and the total production would be quite low were it not for the overseas demand. Local people grow far more *plantains* which are similar to, but bigger than bananas, and can be fried, baked, boiled, or ground into a flour. Strangely, very few people outside the tropics use plantains, although this may change.

(Top) Today the companies own their own ships, seaports, loading facilities, storage sheds, plantations, and other industries that at first sight appear to have nothing much to do with bananas. For example, United Brands owns a roofing material plant (for plantation houses and the general market), cattle ranches (to use the reserve land they hold), and so on.

(Bottom left) Banana plantations are established on areas that have been cleared of tropical rain forests. Banana plants are cultivated about 6 m apart. Plantations are carefully supervised and the plants are sprayed against fungal and insect diseases.
The banana plantations were seriously damaged in the 1920's and 1930's by *sigatoka* or Panama disease, whose spores infect the soil long after the banana plants have been killed off. It was only after World War II that new sigatoka-resistant varieties were developed, permitting the companies to replant their old banana lands. In the meantime, they had developed new areas in Colombia and Ecuador, far beyond their original base in Central America.

(Bottom right) Bananas are harvested by hand. They are then inspected while still green and packed into plastic bags for export. Modern banana boats transport the bananas to foreign markets as quickly as possible.

The banana trade in Europe and North America is largely in the hands of two or three companies. The largest of these is United Brands of Boston, which handles over seventy percent of all the bananas eaten in the United States and Canada. The company was formed by American investors who built the railroads in Central America and were given huge grants of land in part payment.

Questions
1. Why might it be difficult for independent banana growers to sell their fruit?
2. Why are bananas picked before they are yellow?
3. Examine the labels on banana bunches in your local food store to see which countries they come from.

Coffee

Coffee is one of the most popular drinks in the world, having spread from its original habitat in Ethiopia through the Turkish Empire and into Europe. Coffee consumption is still rising, as the taste for coffee "captures" more and more people. Unfortunately for the Brazilians, who are the world's most important coffee producers, world production of coffee is also rising very quickly. This results in world overproduction and falling prices, and the coffee growers have a hard time making a living. However, this problem is especially bad in Columbia, where many of the coffee growers own only a few hectares. The much bigger planters in Brazil, Guatemala, and Costa Rica can survive periods of lower prices.

Coffee must be picked by hand, which means that a lot of labour is needed at certain times of year. Even though wages paid to coffee harvesters are extremely low, for example, as little as seventy-five cents *a day* in Guatemala, the cost of labour can ruin a small coffee grower in times of low prices.

Most of the profit is made in processing and retailing coffee. This means that for every dollar we pay for coffee in a store, only about five cents go to the people who actually grew the coffee. The rest goes to the people who shipped it, powdered it, bottled it, and sold it.

Coffee accounts for more than one-third of Brazil's exports, and the industry provides employment for over six million Brazilians. Over forty percent of the world's coffee exports are shipped from such Brazilian ports as Santos and Rio de Janeiro.

In addition to changing market prices, the coffee plantation owners face the problems of diseases which attack plants, especially the *coffee rust* which appeared in Brazil for the first time in 1970, and unusual weather conditions during flowering, picking, and drying periods.

The future of coffee growing in South America depends upon two possibilities: (a) that the coffee-producing countries will get together to agree on how much to produce, and (b) that more of the actual coffee processing will take place in South America instead of in North America and Europe.

A special problem that affects coffee producers, but not banana, rubber, cocoa, or sugar producers, is the difficulty of forecasting changes in taste. There is quite a difference in taste and aroma between different varieties of coffee, and increasing numbers of consumers are learning to tell them apart. A coffee preference in, say, 1976

(Top) Coffee is picked by hand. Each red, cherry-like fruit contains two small, kidney-shaped beans. The shrubs are pruned each year so that no plant is over 4.5 m in height, which makes picking easier. Coffee grows best on well-drained mountain slopes. Frost is an enemy because it kills the blossoms and damages the berries. Therefore location and altitude limit are important. Cold night air drains down into valleys and hence the reason why coffee shrubs are grown on the hill slopes. Plantations in Colombia are generally small, approximately 3 to 4 ha, and are known as *incas*. Brazilian plantations, known as *fazendas*, reach 20 000 to 28 000 ha in size.

(Bottom) The coffee beans are dried in the sun and then placed in drum-shaped "bark" machines to remove the dried outer covering of the beans. They are then bagged and exported, as no further processing takes place in South America. The most popular variety, which grows well in Brazil, is known as *arabica*.

need not be the same as in 1979, so that the growers have to guess which varieties to plant and which varieties to uproot.

Sugar Cane

Sugar is the oldest commercial crop in South America, and was the main reason for the African slave trade. Work in the sugar fields and in the sugar mills is hard. Although sugar is a kind of giant grass, it needs a lot of energy and muscle to swing a machete or cutting knife to fell the cane. During the harvest season, this work usually goes on from dawn to dusk, for a total of 12 to 14 h of cutting. As with coffee picking, wages are very poor, and there is often no work for the cane cutters to do during the rest of the year. In Mexico and other countries, the cane fields are fired before cutting begins, as this makes cutting easier and drives out the snakes, thus eliminating the danger of bites. Unfortunately, firing reduces the juice content by as much as twenty percent.

In contrast to coffee, which thrives best on well-drained, cooler slopes in the mountains, sugar grows well in the hot flatlands along the coasts and in river valleys. The biggest sugar-producing areas today are around Tucuman (Argentina), in the Cauca Valley (Colombia), and in the Guyanese coastlands. In the past, Brazil and the West Indian islands were the main producing areas, but these declined in importance when slavery was abolished.

Like coffee, sugar prices can change dramatically from year to year. In 1974, for example, sugar prices reached an all time high, but by 1975 overproduction had driven prices down to such low levels that many producers faced bankruptcy.

Cocoa

Cocoa (often called cacao) trees thrive best in humid, hot conditions, and in this sense are more truly jungle crops than any other major export crop except, perhaps, rubber. Cocoa trees are usually grown *under* taller forest trees, since they cannot tolerate direct sunlight. Because of the even temperatures in which they grow and the high humidity, fungal infections often destroy the cocoa pods.

The cane is fed into a shredding machine, and is then repeatedly crushed to extract the juice. This is channeled into huge vats where the crystallization process takes place. Dark brown slab sugar is the result of this state, and several more processes must take place to obtain pure white sugar crystals. The pulpy, wooden residue, known as *bagasse,* is made into newsprint.

The most important cocoa-producing region in the world is in West Africa, but South American countries, such as Brazil, Venezuela, and Colombia, still export sizeable quantities. Because it is a risky crop to grow, the larger companies and investors try to keep out of the production of cocoa, leaving it to smaller farmers.

Interestingly, cocoa is a native plant of the Americas, and is used as a beverage by most Amerindian peoples from Mexico to Brazil. They drink it in its unsweetened form.

Cotton

Recently South American farmers in the drier regions have been steadily capturing a larger share of the world cotton market. This plant prefers a fairly dry climate, but is very demanding on soil nutrients. Several varieties of cotton plant and cotton "trees" are native to the Americas.

Most varieties of cotton grown in South America and the Caribbean are long-staple varieties. For example, *gossypium brasiliense* has fibres up to seven centimetres long. Very fine long-stapled cotton fetches high prices from textile manufacturers. The most famous areas for cotton in Latin America are the Peruvian oases along the Pacific coast, northeast Brazil, and the drier Caribbean islands such as Montserrat and Antigua (which now produce very little cotton). The areas of most rapid expansion are in Mexico and Nicaragua.

A close substitute for very short-stapled cotton, used for filling and pulping, is *kapok*, which comes from the seed pods of the stately Ceiba trees that are planted for shade in village squares all over tropical South America. Sometimes the trade refers to very short-stapled cotton as kapok, but this is botanically incorrect.

Rubber

The Amazon Basin was once the major rubber-producing region of the world. The

The production of cotton in dry northeastern Brazil is made possible by irrigation water obtained from the São Francisco River.

rubber tree, *hevea brasiliensis,* is tall and slender like many forest trees, and has been tapped for its latex for centuries by the Amerindians of the Amazon. There are other trees and shrubs throughout the world that yield similar forms of latex, but none are so prolific as the Brazilian rubber tree.

The discovery by Charles Goodyear, in 1839, of the vulcanization process that could turn rubber latex into a strong, durable, and resilient material, meant that rubber prices sky-rocketed at the turn of the century. Merchants flocked to the Amazon Basin and rounded up Amerindian and poor Brazilian workers to work in the jungle. Often an armed guard was stationed by the river, the only means of transportation, to make sure that no one returned unless he had gathered his "quota" of rubber latex. The successful merchants built palatial homes for themselves in Manaus and Iquitos, the two rubber capitals of the Amazon.

Eventually, rubber seeds were smuggled out of the Amazon — at great risk, for the Brazilian government had imposed the death penalty for anyone trying to take out rubber seeds or rubber plants. The seedlings were carefully nurtured in Kew Gardens, in England, and were then transported to Malaya, where huge rubber plantations were established and captured the world market. Dutch planters did the same in Java and Sumatra, and French plantations appeared in Cambodia and Vietnam . Thus, Brazil lost its monopoly, since the cost of extracting rubber from wild trees, even when near-slave labour was used, was much higher than collection from well-ordered planta-tions. The rubber boom collapsed, and Manaus and Iquitos both sank into an obscurity from which they are only now beginning to recover.

Questions
1. What is a monopoly? Why would having a monopoly probably mean that you would become very rich?
2. Why do you think the Brazilian govern-ment imposed the death penalty on people smuggling out rubber seeds and plants?
3. Which popular alcoholic drink is made from sugar cane juice?
4. Why do you think sugar production declined in the West Indies when slavery was abolished?
5. Why would even, high temperatures and high humidity encourage fungus infections in trees?

The Southern Cattle Lands

As Europe's population expanded rapidly during the nineteenth century Industrial

A herd of cattle on the Matto Grosso in Brazil.

209

Revolution, foodstuffs had to be imported from all over the world. Investors, mainly from England, poured money into cattle ranches in three main regions:

(a) Western Canada and the Western United States.

(b) Australia.

(c) Argentina, Uruguay, and parts of Paraguay and Brazil.

The cattle, usually of the same varieties found in European temperate climates, such as the Hereford, were shipped back live to Europe, and often arrived in poor condition.

The discovery of methods of refrigerating cargoes at sea was a major revolution, and cattle ranching flourished rapidly in the 1870's and 1880's. The Pampas of Argentina was criss-crossed with railways built to bring out the cattle and wheat, and huge stockyards appeared in Buenos Aires, Montevideo, Paysandu, and other smaller ports.

Further north, the European cattle breeds did not thrive because of the higher temperatures, but in recent years there has been a tremendous improvement due to cross breeding with tropical breeds. This is leading to South America's second cattle revolution, as huge areas of tropical forest are being cleared for ranches in such countries as Panama, Colombia, Bolivia, and Paraguay.

The Pampas of Argentina

This vast grassland region of Argentina, about the same size as the Canadian Prairies, extends south of the Rio de la Plata and is considered the heartland of the country.

The early Indians named this region *la pampa* or plain. On these vast, flat grassland plains they once hunted the llama-like guanaco and the ostrich-like rhea.

The cowboys of the Pampas are known as *gauchos*. They round up cattle, brand them, and drive them to the railway centres for transportation to the large meat-packing centres such as Buenos Aires and Bahia Blanca. Like the cowboy, the gaucho's role is rapidly changing in this age of mechanization. Dressed in his traditional baggy trousers, spurred boots and round black hat, the gaucho is a legendary figure of the Pampas. Instead of a lasso the gaucho used a *bolas* made of long leather thongs with heavy balls on each end to trip up a runaway cow.

Sheep are also reared on the Pampas. They are able to graze on the short, tougher grasses towards the drier interior. Sheep are also reared on the scanty pastures of the Patagonian semi-desert to the south of the Pampas. The sheep in the picture have been rounded up into pens and are ready for dipping. Dipping implies immersing the whole sheep in a liquid disinfectant to kill off parasites.

The first Spanish settlers used the plains to rear horses and to breed mules, which were the best beast of burden on the rough, mountainous tracks of the Andes.

As already stated, cattle were later introduced, and the invention of refrigeration made it possible to ship beef to all parts of the world. Alfalfa grass was cultivated to supplement the drier natural pampas grasses.

Vast ranches or *estancias* — some being 50 to 65 km² in area — occupy much of the Pampas. These estancias are generally run by managers, and are, in reality, communities, often with their own school, church, and post office. The labourers live on the estate, and may rent land and grow crops such as wheat, corn, and flax for themselves and for their landlord. In recent years laws have been passed to break down these estates by forcing the owners to will the land to be divided equally among his children. Also, the desire of the small farmers to own their land is creating the need for land reform.

Roads in the Pampas are few because in wet weather they become muddy and water-logged, while during dry, warm periods they are dusty. Railways, however, are effective, and lines radiate across the Pampas from Buenos Aires.

A road across the Pampas.

INDUSTRY AND RESOURCES

Industry

Although South America is rich in natural resources, it has, like Africa, long been notorious for its lack of industries. The guano deposits, for example, were mined in Peru and Chile, but were made into fertilizer in Europe; iron ore was mined in Brazil and Venezuela, but was made into steel in North America and Europe; rubber was exported, again to be turned into manufactured rubber goods in North America and Europe; even coffee and cocoa were exported in the form of dried beans, to be processed elsewhere.

Machinery and equipment, such as sugar milling machinery, was made in Europe and imported, often at great cost. Even simple consumer goods such as shirts and dinner plates were imported rather than manufactured locally, despite the fact that South America produced cotton and had good deposits of clay.

As soon as the South Americans won their independence from Europe, however, industry began to develop very rapidly, as the old colonial laws forbidding the establishment of competing industries were abolished. Cities such as Buenos Aires, São Paulo, Rio de Janeiro, and Santiago began to mushroom and attract skilled industrial workers from Europe.

To understand South American industries and their problems, it is useful to divide them into four categories:
1. The processing industries.
2. The consumer goods industries.
3. The capital goods industries.
4. The service industries.

The Processing Industries

From the days of the first plantations, it was necessary to carry out some processing in Latin America. For example, sugar cane would deteriorate if shipped in its raw state.

Santiago is the political, cultural, and industrial capital of Chile. Located in the Central Valley, the city's industries are based largely on the Mediterranean-type agriculture of the region, and include, fruit canning, wine making, flour milling, and meat packing. Power plants built at the foot of the Andes convert the water from the snow-fed rivers into hydro-electricity for the factories. The city today is a mixture of colonial-style Spanish buildings, modern concrete skyscrapers, and crowded low-income housing areas. A busy railway line links Santiago with the nearby port of Valparaiso.

Instead, the cane was crushed and boiled to make molasses which was shipped in barrels to Europe and North America.

These and a few other kinds of processing were permitted because the products would spoil during shipment; they were, therefore, not subject to the old colonial laws restricting industry.

A second reason for processing products before shipment was to save shipping space. Although it is easy to ship crude ore from a mine, it is costly and cumbersome because of the vast amount of useless rock which contains the ore. It is more profitable to crush and refine the ore and mould it into ingots for shipment. This was done with silver in Mexico, Peru, and Bolivia. Silver ingots from the great mines of Potosi (Bolivia) were shipped through Argentina to the ships waiting in the estuary that came to be known as the Rio de la Plata (River Plate), which should be translated as Silver River.

(Top) São Paulo, in Brazil, is one of the world's fastest growing cities . With a population of six million, it is Brazil's largest city and is second only to Buenos Aires in Latin America. It is South America's leading industrial centre and half of Brazil's total industrial production comes from São Paulo's 34 000 factories. They produce textiles, chemical and pharmaceutical products. São Paulo's car industry is the largest in Latin America. The nearby port of Santos serves both as an outlet for this andustrial centre and as Brazil's major coffee port. São Paulo attracts about a quarter of a million people from the poorer, rural areas of Brazil each year, and as a result there are severe housing problems.

(Bottom) Buenos Aires is not only the largest city in Argentina but is also the largest in the Southern Hemisphere. It contains about a quarter of the people of Argentina, and is named after the patron saint of Spanish sailors — Santa Maria de los Buenos Aires or St. Mary of the Good Airs (Breezes). Located at the mouth of the Rio de la Plata, the port serves the whole of Argentina. The city's industries are, in the main, related to the processing of agricultural products — flour milling, canning and freezing meat, and leather manufacturing. The fine natural harbour is well protected but, due to the silt carried down by the river, constant dredging is necessary to keep the navigation channels open to large oceangoing ships.

Much of the profit, however, occurs during the processing stages; this is true of most minerals and crops. For this reason a conflict has developed between the South American countries and the manufacturing countries of North America and Europe. Each side in the conflict wants most, if not all, of the processing to be done in its own country, to provide employment for its workers and taxes for its government.

Independence has meant that the South American countries can insist on more processing being done in South America, although it usually means a long battle with the exporting company. For example, in Bolivia tin was not smelted locally until the 1960's.

Consumer Goods Industries

In most countries of South America, Africa, and Asia many consumer goods are still imported. These include sports equipment, canned foods, cars, footwear, and furniture. Most countries, however, do manufacture some consumer goods, such as matches, pots and pans, shirts, and books, for local use. The larger South American countries, for example, Brazil, Argentina, and Peru, are becoming more highly industrialized and are finding markets for their goods all over South America and in North America and Europe. They are trying to establish markets for traditional South American manufactures and foodstuffs which, up to the present, very few people in North America or in Europe have learned to enjoy. These include avocados and guavas, and even less familiar tropical fruits such as *maracuya* and *guarana*. These fruits and their juices are now being canned for export, and may find foreign markets because people are continually looking for interesting new kinds of food.

Capital Goods Industries

Capital goods are those that will be used to manufacture other goods, or to provide

These "balls" of rubber have been made from the latex by the rubber-tappers in the forest. It represents only *partial* processing because the rubber is still not ready for industrial use, and is done to make shipping easier.

services, for example, transport. Latin American industry is extremely weak in the capital goods *sector;* very few plants exist that produce trucks, engines, electric motors, copper wire, ships, drills, pumps, and so on. There is even a shortage of plants producing the *basic components* for capital goods industries, such as steel plates, rods, plastics, and glass.

Questions
1. Make sure you know the meaning of the following terms, as they are used in the text: end products, capacity, sector, basic components, limited range, and consumer goods.
2. In a delicatessen or a supermarket, try to find examples of unusual foodstuffs. Check which come from South America.
3. Are all Canadian materials processed before being exported?

One of the main reasons for the lack of capital goods industries in South America is that no one country, except perhaps Brazil and Argentina, is big enough to have sufficient demand within its borders for any one product, such as deisel locomotives or electric planing machines. Thus, unless the factory can sell its goods to other Latin American countries or on the world market, it will not be able to work at anything like full *capacity*.

Service Industries

These industries employ such people as hotel and restaurant workers, storekeepers, bus drivers, cleaners, and maintenance personnel.

The service industry sector is very large in South America, and visitors often remark on the number of people trying to sell things, working as servants, shining shoes, and so on. These are usually the only jobs available, and most of the workers get very low rates of pay.

The two most important service industries, both closely intertwined, are commerce and transportation.

Supermarkets have sprung up throughout the continent, and some of the bigger cities have shopping centres and malls that rival any in North America. Nonetheless, markets are still very popular, partly because of their noise and colour, and partly because prices are usually lower, at least for people who know how to bargain.

The ambition of successful market traders is to become *wholesalers,* concentrating on supplying smaller dealers. To do this, they will travel to isolated villages to buy produce, or send a representative, and will offer goods on credit to sellers smaller than themselves.

Back-packing, canoes, mules, horses, donkeys, bicycles, trucks, and buses are all

Street vendors are very common in Latin American cities. They obtain their goods from either a wholesaler or a big storekeeper, and spend all day seeking out customers. It is a depressing way to make a living, but the only one available to many people.

216

used to get locally produced goods to market. Often the distances are great, and a trip to market may take twenty-four hours.

Even in the richer countries of Venezuela, Brazil, and Argentina, good secondary roads are a rarity. Heavy rains can completely isolate villages and even fairly large towns for weeks at a time. In the unusually heavy rains of 1974, for example, every Bolivian city was cut off from all its neighbours at one time or another during the rainy season. The few bridges are often washed out, and dry stream beds can become impassable during rainstorms.

Whenever a road or a bridge is damaged, the peasants experience heavy losses. Food runs short in the town, supplies of gasoline and kerosene run low, and prices can sky-rocket. This is partly because few South American towns, and almost no villages, have adequate storage space, let alone refrigerated storage space.

International trade in South America is at a much lower level than it is in Europe. For example, there is only one road from Bolivia to Paraguay. It is often closed in the rainy season, and it is many hundreds of kilometres from Bolivia to the nearest Paraguayan market. There is only one main road and a few dirt tracks between Colombia and Ecuador. The first highway link between Venezuela and Brazil was only opened in 1974 and is still in poor shape.

> *Questions*
> Study the map on page 218.
> 1. How many direct road and rail links are there between Argentina and Chile, and between Argentina and Paraguay?
> 2. How many road and rail links are there between Brazil and Guyana?
> 3. How many road and rail links are there between Peru and its neighbours, Ecuador, Chile, Bolivia, Brazil, and Colombia?

Page 216

(Top) The regular fruit and vegetable market in Otovalo, Ecuador. The Otovalo Indians wear very distinctive dress, and are among the wealthiest Indians in South America.

(Bottom) Transportation in the Andes is faced with many obstacles. Here a bridge has collapsed under the excess weight of the two vehicles that can be seen in the river. Washouts from flooding are more common.

Railway links are important in Brazil.

TRANSPORTATION

—— Railways

—— Roads

☆ Major Airports

A crowded bus is a common means of transportation throughout South America.

Most "international" trade in South America is carried on between people who live near to the borders, where they can walk across or paddle a canoe. A lot of this trade is illegal, and small-scale smuggling is so common that authorities have declared certain border areas as "free zones", giving up the attempt to impose customs control between them.

In transportation, as in industry and in peasant farming, South America generally suffers from a severe lack of capital. New, and more modern means of transportation are needed in many of the smaller, poorer countries. Dilapidated trucks, buses with faulty brakes, roads full of potholes, and ancient steam trains are picturesque for tourists, but are a menace to the South Americans who must use them.

In contrast, Brazil has forged ahead with an ambitious highway building project in the Amazon Basin, and most of its trucks, trains, buses, and coastal vessels are in good condition. Argentina has many kilometres of fine hard-topped highways, reaching right down to Tierra del Fuego.

Resources

The mineral resources of South America are still only partially developed and include vast reserves of iron ore, oil and natural gas, copper ore, nitrates, some gold and silver, and such precious stones as emeralds and diamonds.

Four regions of major interest are (a) the oil fields of Venezuela, (b) the copper ore regions of the high Andes, (c) the iron ore deposits of Brazil, Venezuela, and Chile, and (d) the nitrate producing area of Chile.

The Oil Fields of Venezuela

Venezuela is one of the "oil rich" countries of the world. Bordering the Caribbean Sea, it is about one-tenth of the area of Canada. The early Spaniards, seeing the Indian huts supported by stilts on the shores of shallow

Lake Maracaibo, called the region Venezuela, meaning "Little Venice".

Oil was first discovered to the east of the vast lake by the Shell Oil Company in 1914. Now fifty percent of the oil of Venezuela is produced by the Creole Oil Corporation, a branch of the Standard Oil Corporation which is known in Canada as Exxon and Esso. Other leading companies are Gulf Oil, Texaco, and Royal Dutch Shell.

Until 1970 these foreign companies were allowed to extract and refine oil in exchange for paying the Venezuelan government about fifty percent of the profits. However, in that year the government began to nationalize the oil industry and will take about eight-five to ninety percent of all profits gained from new fields as they are developed. New legislation in 1974 means that the foreign companies will soon have to leave Venezuela altogether.

> *Questions*
> 1. What neighbouring country also has good oil resources?
> 2. What type of drilling will be necessary off the Orinoco delta?
> 3. How is the oil transported to export terminals for shipment to foreign markets?

Today, oil fields cover some 25×10^6 ha and produce over 600 000 m³ of crude oil per day. Much of it is used in Eastern Canada.

Page 221

Hundreds of derricks rise from the water of Lake Maracaibo, some as far as 4.8 km offshore. British, American, and Dutch companies have developed these oil fields and have made Venezuela one of the largest oil exporting countries in the world. Before commercial drilling was started around the lake, the surrounding land had to be drained of malaria-infested swamps and the area was developed to provide homes and facilities for the workers. The Venezuelan government has used much of its oil revenues to build highways and to improve educational and health services. The natural gas provides heat and energy for several towns and cities.

Figure 5.13 Oil fields of Venezuela. Note the oil fields now in production, the tar fields from which oil might be extracted in the future, and fields to be drilled in the immediate future.

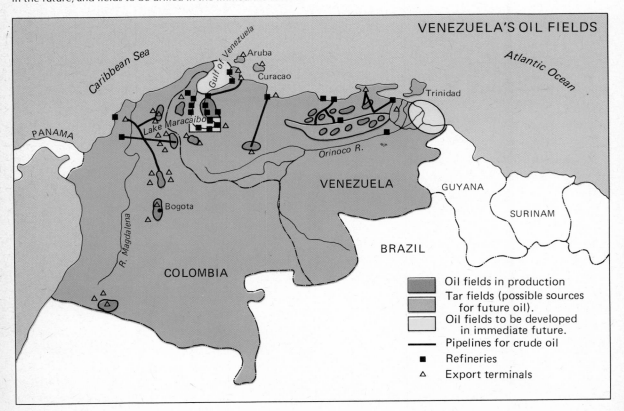

The Copper Ore Regions of the High Andes

Most of the old silver mines, such as those located at Cerro de Pasco in Peru, at an altitude of 4267 m in the Andes, became exhausted and were sold in the early 1900's to American mining corporations. However, instead of silver, the corporations mined these regions for copper, zinc, and lead.

The richest copper beds are located in Chile, mainly at higher altitudes. They extend through the Atacama Desert, in Northern Chile, to El Teniente, just south of Santiago. Although most of the ore is of low-grade quality, modern mining methods and the high market price of copper make mining profitable.

Copper bars make up nearly seventy percent of Chile's exports. The Andean copper mines in Peru, Bolivia, and Chile were owned and controlled by American corporations until a few years ago. First Bolivia (1952), then Chile (1971), and finally Peru (1973), nationalized their copper mining industry.

About half of Chile's copper supply is mined at Chuquicamata. This mine, more than 3 km long and 0.8 km wide, is located at an elevation of 3048 m, 209 km northeast of the port of Antofagasta. Mining is carried out by the open-pit method whereby giant, steam-powered mechanical shovels scoop up the iron ore for transportation to smelting furnaces such as this one. 1 t of ore produces about 15 kg of copper. The copper ingots are transported by rail to Antofagasta for refining.

The Iron Ore Deposits of Brazil, Venezuela, and Chile

Brazil, the largest country in South America and nearly as large as the United States in area, is sometimes referred to as the "Tropical Giant". This vast country has yet to fully develop her mineral resources. Indeed, the total extent of her mineral deposits is not yet known, for the vast interior has not been completely explored, but it is believed that her mineral wealth is great. Brazil, however, does lack coal and has to import nearly ninety percent of the coke needed for her iron and steel industries.

It is estimated that Brazil's known iron ore deposits exceed 40×10^6 t, and her reserves are second only to those of the U.S.S.R. However, the shipment of this ore makes up less than six percent of her total export figures. This is because coffee and other agricultural products command a higher export value, and also because the iron-importing nations of Western Europe, Japan, and North America still obtain most of their ore requirements from other sources. One of the main reasons for building the new roads into the Amazon Basin is to make it possible to bring out the iron ore in the near future. In addition, Brazil is developing her own iron and steel industry.

The hub of the mining industry is around Belo Horizonte, in the state of Minas Gerais. The ore is smelted into steel in such neighbouring centres as São Paulo, Volta Redonda, as well as at Belo Horizonte and Salvador.

Although Venezuela has much smaller iron ore reserves than Brazil, it exports much more because of its proximity to its major market, the United States.

The iron and steel works at Volta Redonda. Some of the iron and steel produced is used in car production and some in construction. Extensive plans exist to increase Brazil's production of automobiles. By 1980 it expects to produce one million a year for home sales. The apartment blocks in the foreground are steelworker's homes.

Chile was at one time the leading exporter of iron ore in Latin America, but several mines are now exhausted. Those still in production export to Japan and the United States.

The Nitrate Producing Area of Chile

The Atacama Desert of northern Chile, which extends some 966 km from north to south, is one of the most arid, inhospitable, and deserted regions of the world. Although lacking in water and vegetation, this northern part of Chile holds a wide variety of mineral deposits, including iron ore, zinc, silver, manganese, sulphur, and nitrates. Sodium nitrate, or Chile saltpeter, is found in beds varying in thickness from a few

centimetres to several metres near the coastal mountain ranges. It is believed that the nitrates originated in lakes and marshes which once occupied the valley floor adjoining the mountains. The dry climate has helped to preserve these layered deposits. One of these layers, known as *caliche*, is a gray, rock-like substance consisting of sodium chloride (common salt), sodium nitrate (saltpeter), and iodine salts.

Sodium nitrate was found to be an excellent fertilizer and an essential ingredient in the manufacture of explosives. Thus, a thriving industry developed and nitrates were shipped to European countries and especially to Germany. For a time, Chile was the world's major supplier.

The outbreak of World War I in 1914 increased the demand for Chile's natural salt for explosives. However, the problems of

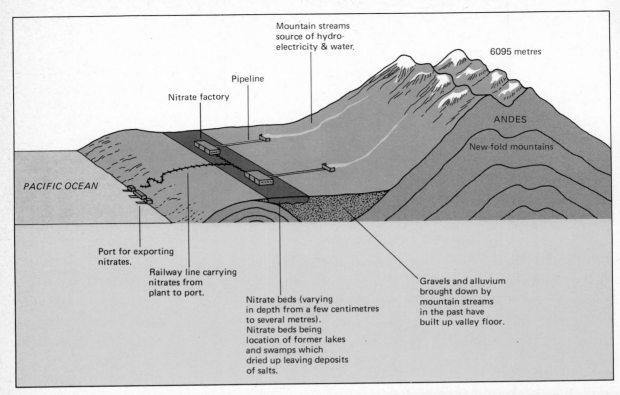

Mountain streams source of hydro-electricity & water.

Pipeline

Nitrate factory

6095 metres

ANDES

New-fold mountains

PACIFIC OCEAN

Port for exporting nitrates.

Railway line carrying nitrates from plant to port.

Nitrate beds (varying in depth from a few centimetres to several metres). Nitrate beds being location of former lakes and swamps which dried up leaving deposits of salts.

Gravels and alluvium brought down by mountain streams in the past have built up valley floor.

shipping in wartime led to the discovery of a process to produce nitrates by extracting nitrogen from the air by electrolysis. As a result, Chilean nitrates fell in price and the boom was over.

By 1930 the Chilean nitrate industry looked as if it would never recover. However, the industry was replanned and more importance was given to such by-products as iodine, potash, salt, and sodium sulphate. Today, Chile produces seventy-five percent of the world's supply of iodine. Nitrates are still exported from Iquique and Antofagasta, but in much smaller quantities than before World War I (1914-1918).

Questions

1. What is meant by the "nationalization of an industry"? Why do countries take such action? What steps are necessary to nationalize an industry?
2. Why is copper of such importance? What are its present-day uses?
3. What is the difference between guano and Chilean nitrates?
4. Why are Brazil's mineral resources not fully developed?
5. Why did World War I provide a spur to inventors seeking an alternative source of saltpetre?
6. The workers in an iodine plant must wear protective clothing. Can you find out why?

(Top) Figure 5.14 A diagrammatic section across northern Chile to show the origin and location of the sodium nitrate deposits, and the sources of water power.

(Bottom) Two workers in an iodine extraction plant. The nitrate is conveyed to such plants in small trucks pulled by powerful electrical locomotives. The rock-like nitrate is crushed and powdered and then the iodine is extracted by chemical processes.

TOURISM

Almost every country in the world is encouraging tourists because of the vast amounts of foreign currency that they bring in. With modern means of transportation, people are travelling more than ever before and many visit places that were once considered remote and difficult to reach.

Tourists visit various countries for some of the following reasons:

(a) to relax and enjoy the sun in a warm climate or to indulge in such sports as swimming, water-skiing, scuba diving, and fishing;

(b) to ski in the mountains during the winter months;

(c) to visit historical places and buildings and to learn to appreciate different forms of art;

(d) to meet the people and to see local festivals and customs;

(e) for the fun of buying locally-made products.

International tourism to South America has already passed through three main stages:

1. The days when only a handful of wealthy or very adventurous Europeans and North Americans travelled to visit exotic and unusual places.

2. The advent of the cruise ships, which stop at such ports-of-call as Port of Spain (Trinidad), Port-au-Prince (Haiti), La Guaira (Venezuela), and Rio de Janeiro (Brazil). For a few hours, thousands of visitors disgorge into the town, and are sold city tours, souvenirs and "duty-free bargains".

3. The great stampede to find the sun. Cheaper air fares have made it possible for millions of North Americans and some Europeans to reach the Caribbean and South America for short holidays to soak up the sun, mainly in winter.

Already, new kinds of tourism are appearing that may change the tourist map of South America and the Caribbean. These include *special interest* travel, where the

A popular tourist attraction near Quito, Ecuador, is this monument which is located on the Equator. Visitors like to straddle the line on the road representing the Equator. Locate Quito on your atlas map. Which two hemispheres would the tourist be standing in if they straddled the marked line?

now a good investment for tourist companies.

Increasingly, tourists are beginning to fan out from the main tourist centres to explore every town or village, by renting a car. Soon Latin American tourism may resemble that of Europe, where almost everywhere has some tourist interest.

Tourists visit South America for a variety of reasons.
(Bottom) Handmade items of pottery and metal are popular with tourists. These copper masks are on sale in a store in Cuzco, Peru.
Page 227
(Top) Tourists enjoy the glorious sunshine on a beach in Rio de Janeiro.
(Bottom left) The Gold Museum, in Bogota, Colombia, displays a fascinating collection of treasures from the ancient civilizations of South America.
(Bottom right) There are many beautifully decorated churches for the tourist to visit.

tourist is looking for something different — not just the sun, a beach, and a hotel. He may be interested in seeing tropical fish, trekking through the jungle for a few days, taking a boat trip up the Amazon, photographing plants and animals, or enjoying the experience of living in an isolated village and meeting the people.

The Colombian government has even bought an old stern-wheeler, that was once used for passengers and cargo on the Magdalena River, in order to redecorate it for use as a tourist boat. In Manaus, there are several of the old Mississippi stern-wheelers for sale; they spent their last working years on the tributaries of the Amazon, and are

PRESENT PROBLEMS AND FUTURE PROSPECTS

Some of the major problems faced by South American countries today include:
(a) a lack of cooperation and unity;
(b) an inability to pay long-standing debts;
(c) social conflicts;
(d) illiteracy;
(e) military rule;
(f) regional imbalances;
(g) territorial and frontier claims;
(h) movement of peoples from the rural areas to the large urban centres and the ensuing sprawling slum areas;
(i) overpopulation;
(j) the future of the Amerindians.

Cooperation and Unity

There have always been Latin Americans who have dreamed of unity — one country within which everyone would be a Latin American citizen rather than a Panamanian, a Bolivian, or a Paraguayan. During Bolivar's struggle against Spain in Colombia and Venezuela, volunteers came from Cuba, Santo Domingo, Mexico, and many other countries, for they saw the Independence Wars as one big struggle to create an independent Latin America. Similarly, the Argentinian volunteers, under San Martin, did not think twice about scaling the Andes and liberating Chile.

In spite of this feeling, there have been numerous bitter wars between Latin American countries, most of them over territory. Examples are: The War of the Triple Alliance, Paraguay versus Brazil, Argentina, and Uruguay (1865-1870); and the Chaco War (1932-1935), when Paraguay fought against Bolivia.

By the 1940's, each of the Latin American countries seemed to live in a world of its own. There was very little travel between Latin American countries, even neighbours, and very little trade. Most trade was with North America and Europe, to the extent that a few areas, for example, Yucatan in Mexico, even considered becoming part of the United States.

After World War II, however, governments began to feel that it was dangerous to be too reliant on one powerful country, and that it might be a good idea to build links with their neighbours.

The United Nations, which rapidly grew to include African and Asian countries, encouraged this feeling and created an Economic Commission for Latin America, ECLA.

ECLA, in turn, began to encourage the creation of Common Markets in both South and Central America. The Latin American Free Trade Area, LAFTA, grew up in the 1960's, and led to a great increase of trade between South American member countries; from 299 million dollars in 1961 to 635 million dollars in 1965.

Even as late as the 1960's, over ninety percent of all trade between Latin American countries was carried on by sea. As the road and rail links between countries are poor, and most seaports are in poor condition, it was usually cheaper to buy goods from outside South America than from other South American countries.

One of the most exciting developments has been the near-completion of the Pan American Highway, stretching from Mexico City to Buenos Aires, which today has only one small gap, in the jungles of southern Panama and northern Colombia. The Inter-American Development Bank, created in 1959, has lent money for highway construction to many governments, so that today far more trade is by road. Already, huge trucks run from Buenos Aires to Lima and Quito, from Rio de Janeiro to Santiago, and from Mexico City to Panama.

A major problem that has contributed to Latin America's poverty has been the low prices received for its raw materials and agricultural produce, and the high prices paid for imported goods. To solve this problem, a new sort of unity is being forged. Both Venezuela and Ecuador joined the Organization of Petroleum Exporting Countries, OPEC, which in 1973 raised the price of oil exports throughout the world. In this way they are linked with Indonesia, Iran, Libya, and other powerful oil exporters, and are already enjoying much higher incomes as a result. Support from other OPEC members has meant that Venezuela could nationalize its oil, thus keeping even more of the oil profits for its own needs.

Debts

Every Latin American country is chronically in debt to bankers and governments in North America and Europe, and has been since the nineteenth century. As early as 1901, Brazil's creditors met in Paris to *consolidate* that country's debts, and to impose conditions on Brazil in exchange for *refinancing* the debt. Yet, by 1974, Brazil's foreign debt had reached the staggering total of U.S. 20 000 000 000 dollars. In the 1960's it was realized that Latin America, as a whole, was losing more money each year through *servicing* its debts than it was gaining in foreign aid and in foreign private investment. In other words, Latin America, in spite of its poverty, was actually helping to finance growth and development in the rich countries of Europe and North America. To understand this simple fact is to understand one of the main reasons for poverty in South America.

Social Conflicts

There is a terrible gap in South America between rich and poor that is sharper than anywhere in North America. On the one hand a few long-established creole families, joined by a few successful businessmen and

The contrasts between rich and poor can be seen in the homes shown in these two photographs.
(Left)   Large houses in the Spanish colonial style in Salta, Argentina.

(Right)   An Indian dwelling in Colombia.

industrialists from among the more recent immigrants, control almost all the good farmland, industries, trucks, boats, and forests. On the other are the millions of poor peasants, agricultural workers, factory workers, drivers, miners, and fishermen. In the richer countries of Argentina, Brazil, and Venezuela rather more of the working people manage to live and eat better, but they are still comparatively poor by North American standards.

Past revolts and present trade union actions are slowly improving wages and working conditions generally.

Illiteracy

One of the worst effects of illiteracy is that the peasant farmers often find it difficult to keep accounts, and so they often operate needlessly at a loss. Another is that it is difficult to learn new skills without being able to read. Most Latin American countries do not allow people to vote unless they are literate, which means that the poorest people have had no say in government decisions. This is doubly unfortunate, because they are the ones who most need help. However, schools are now being built for children and adults, and many factories have their own training programs.

The Military in Latin America

The history of military involvement in Latin American governments is long and intense. Very few countries have not had a military government, and even they are not sure of the future. The reason, as with so many forms of violent political change, lies in the social conflicts that have plagued the continent. Not all military dictatorship are similar. Although many military governments have defended the wealthy families against the poor, a few have championed the poor, have attempted to protect the rights of the native peoples, and have introduced reforms.

Perhaps the most unfortunate aspect of military governments is that they usually feel it is necessary to spend more money on weapons than the country can really afford. Compared to Africa, South America is heavily armed.

Peruvian military parade in Iquitos. The military government of Peru has carried out a land reform, attempted to protect Amerindian tribes in the Amazon, and nationalized the big Cerro de Pasco mining company.

Regional Imbalances

Not only are there contrasts between rich and poor people, but there are also contrasts between rich and poor regions. Most of the wealth in Latin America is concentrated into a few places. Usually these are the capital cities, their immediate *hinterland,* and the main ports. Thus, in Ecuador only Quito and Guayaquil are really prosperous, while the smaller towns such as Ibarra, Esmeraldas, and Riobamba seem to be half asleep and much poorer. Almost all the factories and offices are clustered in Quito or Guayaquil, as are the banks, wholesalers, and universities.

Some geographers would describe Quito and Guayaquil as the *core* of Ecuador, while the rest of the country would be called the *periphery.* In countries such as Uruguay and Paraguay the core would simply be the capital city and a small nearby area.

This kind of concentration produces *regional imbalance,* and the likelihood that the core will continue to grow richer at the expense of the periphery. This in turn could produce new social tensions.

To solve this kind of imbalance, several countries have tried to invest money in the periphery, and to create what are called *growth points* away from the capital city. Brazil went even further, and built an entirely new capital city — Brasilia — several hundred kilometres in the interior, away from the old core area of Rio de Janeiro and São Paulo.

(Top) Quito, the capital of Ecuador.

(Bottom) Brasilia, the capital of Brazil, was deliberately built in the backlands to encourage development in Brazil's vast interior. Already the city is linked by road with Belem, at the mouth of the Amazon, and Cuiaba, near Bolivia. So far, very little industry has been attracted to Brasilia, and many top government officials commute to the coast by jet. Perhaps Brasilia is still a dream of the future.

232

Territorial and Frontier Claims

A great fear on the part of many South American governments is that if their lands in the Amazon Basin are not more densely populated, Brazil will gradually move in and eventually take over these parts of their national territories. These governments call the infiltration of Brazilian goods, people, and capital *penetracion pacifica,* or peaceful penetration. In order to establish a "national presence" in the Amazon Basin, they have encouraged settlers, and have also allocated lands to ex-soldiers. In the military settlements, there is usually a military doctor, an army-run school and store, and the inhabitants include some serving soldiers as well as many more who are still in the army reserve corps. Both Paraguay and Uruguay are also worried about *penetracion pacifica* along their northern borders.

The Migration to the Cities

South America is changing rapidly. All over the continent people are demanding a better life, and old social structures are crumbling. One of the greatest social pressures leading to change is *urbanization.* Every year hundreds of thousands of peasant farmers are moving into the towns and cities seeking jobs. They are driven from the countryside by poor prices for their crops, by disasters, and poor wages. If they are often faced with the same kind of problems in the cities, there is still always the hope of a steady factory job, an office job, or at least a better future for their children. There are more schools and health facilities, and there is always a promise of a possible better standard of living.

This sudden growth of Latin American cities has meant the appearance of poor

Page 232

(Top) People moving to the cities cannot afford to buy ready-made clothes and so buy from a seamstress or tailor.
(Bottom) It does not require much capital to provide amusements. This woman feeds her family from an operation worth about $50.

Slum housing in La Oroya, Peru.

housing conditions. Older homes in the city centre tend to be subdivided into small apartments, which are soon overcrowded. The worst slum conditions exist, therefore, right at the heart of some of the most beautiful cities in the world. At the same time, thousands of poor huts are thrown up around the city and on vacant lots, just as in Africa and Asia. The water supply is no longer sufficient for all the urban dwellers; electricity and sewage networks become overloaded; buses become overcrowded; and prices rise.

Overpopulation

Overpopulation and food shortages are world-wide problems. Many countries today, including those in South America, cannot adequately support their population, and face alarming rates of population increase.

The Future of the Amerindians

South America's Indian population has long been discriminated against, and is in general much poorer than any other section of society. Their lands have, over time, been whittled away, and their languages have been ignored. Like other peasants, they have

Page 234

A crowded urban tram.

(Top) In the past, people had large families because extra children meant extra hands to work on the farm. Also, as child mortality rates were high, having seven or eight children would mean that perhaps two or three would survive to help their parents as they became too old to work. The tradition of having large families is changing, as people move to the cities, as child mortality declines, and as birth control techniques spread. The present rapid rate of population increase in South America may soon "flatten out", but for a few years to come South American countries will have to grapple with the problem of population increase.

(Bottom) Amerindian communities in South America are no longer willing to be a tourist attraction while losing their lands and dignity. Today they are demanding better treatment, fairness before the law, and protection of their lands. This photograph shows Indians outside the Ministry of Social Assistance in Lima, Peru.

been denied identity cards (without which it is impossible to travel or to obtain a regular job in a city) unless they are literate in Spanish. Medical and educational facilities in Indian areas have usually been very poor.

Some of the demands raised at the 1971 Shipibo-Cunibo Indian Conference in the Amazon give a good idea of the problems faced by South America's first inhabitants.

Today, the Amerindian population is demanding fair treatment and recognition of its rights. National conferences of Indian leaders have taken place in Colombia, Peru, and Ecuador. In 1974 the first all-American Amerindian conference took place, with delegates attending from as far away as Canada.

Prospects

Looking ahead, for the next ten or twenty years we can predict many changes in South America — new kinds of government, social reforms, and a change in South America's place in international affairs.

South America will also gradually change its image as a producer of minerals and agricultural products, and will begin to control more and more of its own wealth. The terrible conflict between rich and poor will, in some regions, begin to disappear, while in others it will remain as a slumbering volcano. In many areas, such as architecture, music, and social welfare, South American countries will continue to give a lead to the rest of the world, which, in its turn, must learn to understand this complex, vibrant, and constantly changing continent.

6. ANTARCTICA – THE LONELIEST LAND

INTRODUCTION

The Antarctic Continent, which is about 13 200 000 km² in area, is by far the loneliest, coldest, and most isolated of all the landmasses of the world. It has been aptly called "the South Tip of the World", because not only is it situated at the South Pole, but also its interior ice- and snow-covered plateau reaches heights of 2740 to 3660 m above sea level. Present-day Antarctica gives some indication of the conditions that prevailed in the Northern Hemisphere during the Ice Ages of the past. Antarctica is truly a bleak, barren ice desert, and has been described as a "continental refrigerator". It is no wonder that it was the last of the world's seven continents to be explored.

> "No trees or bushes grow there and the continent sustains a minimum of life – sea birds, seals, a few insects and plants. It is neither hospitable nor inviting to men who have battled their way into it against cruel odds...
>
> It is a land almost entirely covered with snow, yet very little snow falls. Blizzards are like sandstorms, and consist mostly of loose snow being blown about by violent winds, which often nip across the plateaus at more than 100 miles [167 km] per hour. The constant winds sculpture and cut the snow into many shapes. One common type of formation called *sastrugi*, resembles giant sand ripples on a beach."
>
> From: *Antarctica* Eklund and Beckman

From: Eklund and Beckman, *Antarctica*, Holt, Rinehart and Winston, Inc., New York, 1963.

Snow-covered peaks at Hope Bay in Grahamland.

238

Although Antarctica was first explored comparatively recently, this vast landmass was named by the ancient Greeks as *antarktikos* meaning "opposite to the Bear". The Greeks only assumed that there was land in this region — a landmass which they thought had to exist to give the world its balance. As the known-world of the ancient Greeks was small and their study of the stars was confined to the northern constellations — particularly the Great Bear, which was used for bearings for navigational purposes — the region to the far south was naturally the very opposite, i.e. the "antarktikos".

It was Captain Cook, the British navigator, who first sailed into Antarctic waters. Little did he realize, during his voyages between 1772-1775, that he was within 240 km of what is known today as Queen Maud Land. His accounts of his journeys, however, lured hunters to the region in search of seals.

The first recorded landing on the mainland of Antarctica was made by an American sealing expedition led by Captains Davis and Burdick in 1821. Between 1839 and 1843 James Ross led a British expeditions which sailed around the continent and forced a passage through the pack ice in the sea which was later to bear his name.

From then on, several countries sent ships to explore the waters and coastal areas of this forbidding continent. In 1901-1904 a British team, led by Captain Scott, penetrated some 400 km inland, and this expedition was followed by Shackleton who journeyed to within 156 km of the South Pole. Shackleton discovered nearly 800 km of mountain ranges flanking the Ross Ice Shelf.

In 1912 Captain Scott returned, determined to reach the South Pole. He reached the Pole only to find that the Norwegian flag had been placed there a few weeks earlier by the explorer, Roald Amundsen. Bitterly disappointed and exhausted, Scott and the four members of his party started on their return journey but perished before they could reach their ship. In a diary found later near his frozen body, Scott had written, "Great God! This is an awful place and terrible enough for us to have laboured to it without the reward of priority."

In 1929 Admiral Byrd of the U.S. Navy flew over the South Pole and in 1934 he manned a small weather research station. Here is an extract from one of his reports:

> "Cold does queer things. At 50° below zero [-45°C] a flashlight dies out in your hand. At -55° [-48°C] kerosene will freeze, and the flame will dry up on the wick, at -60° [-51°C] rubber turns brittle. . . Below -60° cold will find the last microscopic touch of oil in an instrument and stop it dead. If there is the slightest breeze, you can hear your breath freeze as it floats away, making a sound like that of Chinese fire crackers. . ."

THE PHYSICAL ENVIRONMENT

The most valuable information about Antarctica was collected during the International Geophysical Year (IGY) of 1957-58. Scientific bases were established by various countries to study the continent's weather, land structure, and meagre plant and animal life.

Questions
Study the map on page 240 and answer the following:
1. At the intersection of which lines of latitude and longitude is the South Pole located?
2. List the countries which claim parts of Antarctica.
3. Which countries have overlapping territorial claims?
4. Name the two big ice shelves.
5. Name the three oceans that merge to form the Antarctic Ocean.
6. With the aid of reference books, find out how the South Pole differs from the South Magnetic Pole.

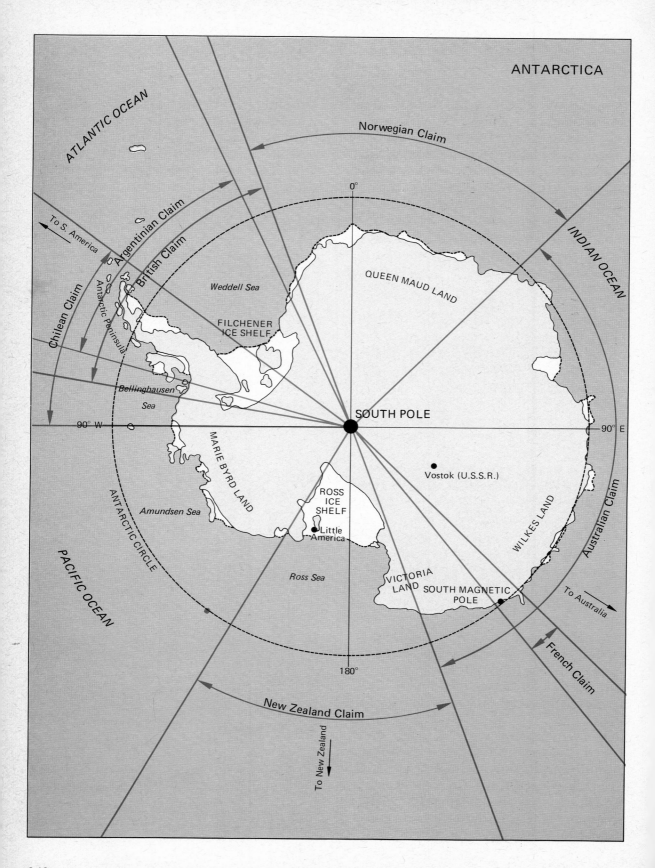

ANTARCTICA

ATLANTIC OCEAN

Norwegian Claim

0°

INDIAN OCEAN

To S. America

Argentinian Claim

British Claim

Chilean Claim

Antarctic Peninsula

Weddell Sea

QUEEN MAUD LAND

FILCHENER
ICE SHELF

90° W

Bellinghausen
Sea

SOUTH POLE

90° E

ANTARCTIC CIRCLE

MARIE BYRD LAND

Amundsen Sea

Vostok (U.S.S.R.)

ROSS
ICE
SHELF

Little
America

WILKES LAND

Australian Claim

PACIFIC OCEAN

Ross Sea

VICTORIA
LAND

SOUTH MAGNETIC
POLE

To Australia

French Claim

180°

New Zealand Claim

To New Zealand

The Erebus, an active volcano on Ross Island.

Page 240

Figure 6.1 Map showing the position of Antarctica and the territorial claims of other countries. The U.S.A. has no claims and does not recognize the claims of other countries.

Antarctica is really an enormous icecap which has developed, increased in depth over the years, and covered the true landmass beneath it. This vast dome of ice, which covers ninety-nine percent of the continent, varies in thickness from a few hundred metres to over 4 km. The tops of the highest mountain peaks are visible through this icecap during the summer months. Such peaks known as *nanatucks,* appear as small, dark islands in the sea of ice and snow.

It is estimated that some 29 000 000 km³ of ice cover Antarctica and, in a descriptive sense, this is enough to cover the entire North American continent with glacial ice over 1.5 km deep.

Extending from the continent, and in reality a part of the icecap, are large floating ice shelves. These shelves are numerous and are located around the coast. The largest is the Ross Ice Shelf — roughly the size of Alaska. Because of underwater action, the edges of these towering ice shelves break off to form icebergs.

Of the huge glaciers that cover extensive areas of the interior of the continent, the most maqnificent and awe-inspiring is the Beardmore Glacier. Beyond it is a bleak, monotonous ice plateau which stretches for 1600 km towards the South Pole. Both Scott and Shackleton had to conquer the Beard-more Glacier before journeying across this windswept plateau. Scott described the region as follows:

"We see only a few miles of ruffled snow, bounded by a vague, wavy horizon, but we know that beyond that horizon are hundreds and even thousands of miles which can offer no change to the weary eye. . . One knows there is neither tree, nor shrub, nor any living thing, not even inanimate rocks. . . nothing but this limitless expanse of snow. It has been so for countless years, and it will be so for countless more. And we, little human insects, have started to crawl over this awful desert. . . Could anything be more terrible than this silent windswept immensity. . .?"

(Top) Figure 6.2 Simple diagrammatic cross section of Antarctica to show the icecap extending over the rock structure of the continent. The thickness of the icecap varies considerably — from a few hundred metres to 4 km. The *average* thickness is believed to be about 1830 m. Nearly ninety percent of the world's ice is found in this South Polar region, and it is estimated that it has taken some 15 000 years to build up this thickness of ice sheet.

(Bottom) Figure 6.3 Diagram showing the formation of icebergs. What causes the ice "cliffs" to break away to form icebergs? What is a crevass? Icebergs form from portions dislodged from ice shelves or from glaciers which border a coastal area.

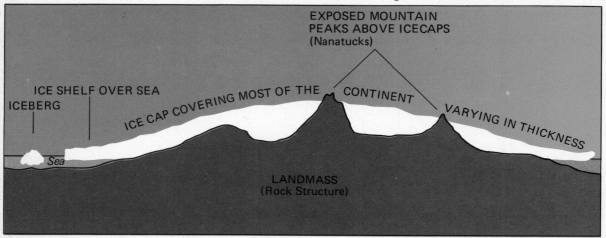

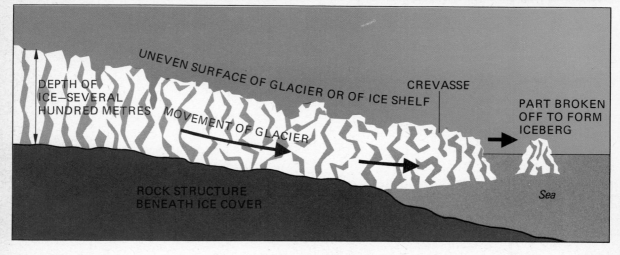

The climate of Antarctica is probably one of the least attractive in the world. During the dreary winter months of darkness (April to September), when the sun never appears above the horizon, temperatures may drop to − 73°C. Blizzards are frequent and winds may reach a force of 160 km/h. Much of the Southern Ocean freezes during these winter months, forming thick layers of pack ice that stretch hundreds of kilometres from the coast. During severe winters the area of pack ice is almost as large as the continent itself.

Questions
1. What is common to all the temperatures?
2. Where is the coldest part of the continent?
3. What happens to the temperatures as one moves towards the interior?

Figure 6.4 The average temperature patterns of Antarctica. The lines on a map which link up places with the same temperature at the same time or with the same average temperature over a period of time (as indicated here) are known as isotherms. Note: Locate Vostok Weather Station (U.S.S.R.). The coldest temperature ever recorded on earth was noted at this station in August (winter), 1960, when the thermometer reading was -88°C.

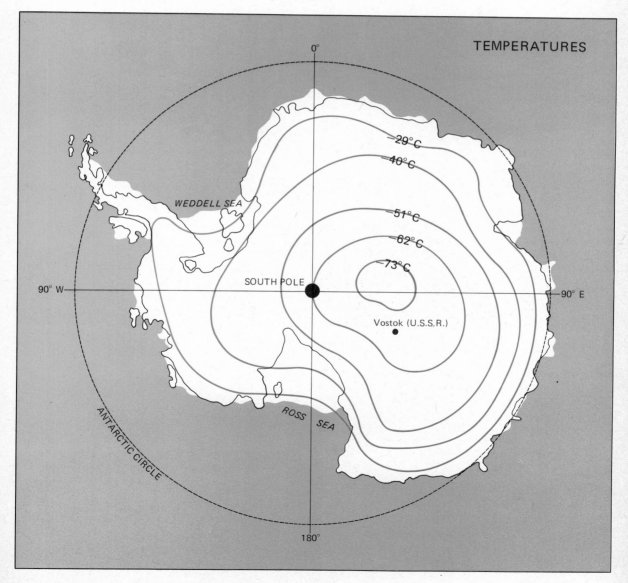

244

Because of the extremely cold climate and the lack of soils, Antarctica supports the minimum of vegetation. The plant life consists of particles of mosses and lichens and an occasional area where primitive microscopic organisms belonging to the algae family thrive. Incidentally, germs or bacteria are rarely found in the region.

The questions might now be asked: What use is Antarctica to man? Why are nations interested in this isolated, inhospitable continent? It was once thought that there might be reserves of gold, diamonds, and coal in the rocks beneath the icecap. However, to date, only a little coal of poor quality has been discovered. Some scientists have considered the continent as a future natural "refrigerator" for the world's surplus food supplies. Weathermen have studied conditions over Antarctica and have found that certain atmospheric conditions there affect the weather in Australia and New Zealand. Further studies will help to understand the weather conditions in these Pacific countries.

ANTARCTICA TODAY

Antarctica today is really a research centre. Many nations have their scientific laboratories on the continent — U.S.A., U.S.S.R., United Kingdom, Argentina, Chile, New Zealand, France, Belgium, etc. The stations are modern and well equipped. Areas of research include geology, biology, meteorology, and the effects of such a climate and such a region on man and materials. The researchers hope that they may get new insights into man's ability to live in the future on planets in outer space.

The Antarctic Treaty of 1961, signed by several nations, allows for the use of the continent for peaceful purposes and for the benefit of mankind. Furthermore, the Treaty encouraged the exchange of personnel, information, and research, and although no nation was asked to give up its territories, each agreed to allow the others complete freedom of operation anywhere on the continent. Nuclear testing and the use of the continent for the disposal of radioactive wastes was forbidden.

The science laboratories of Antarctica are already providing interesting and much needed information, and it is hoped that the spirit in which the Treaty was signed in 1961 will continue so that all nations will benefit.

(Top) The animal population consists mainly of birds. The best known bird of Antarctica is the penguin. The largest of the penguin family is the Emperor Penguin (shown here), which, when grown, has a mass of 36 to 41 kg. Other birds include the snow petrel, the tern, and the skua. The skua, or the "eagle of the Antarctic", has a wing span of 1.37 m. It preys on the chicks and eggs of penguins.

(Bottom) The seas around Antarctica abound with "plankton" — minute, single-celled organisms which provide food for small shrimp-like animals known collectively as "krill". Krill, in turn, is the basic food of whales. Hence the presence of whales in the seas around Antarctica, which attracts the whaling ships and the whaling industry. Whaling is the only industry of the region. The "catch" is processed into foods, oils, and fertilizers. The whale population of the world is decreasing and efforts are being made by certain nations, notably Canada, to shorten the hunting season and to reduce the number to be caught each year. There is also a large seal population. Shown here is a Weddell Seal.

PHOTO CREDITS

Front Cover:
PAT SHEA, Geographical Visual Aids, Wiarton, Ontario

Back Cover:
E.A. SULLIVAN (Top left); **BRAZILIAN CONSULATE, TORONTO** (Top right, Centre right); **M. MACDONALD** (Centre left); **NEW ZEALAND GOVERNMENT TOURIST OFFICE** (Bottom).

AFRIQUE PHOTO 120 (Bottom), 121 (Top); **AIR AFRIQUE** 145 (Bottom left); **AMERICAN AIRLINES** 184; **THE AMERICAN MUSEUM OF NATURAL HISTORY** 186; **AUSTRALIAN DEPARTMENT OF INFORMATION** 36 (Top left), 38 (Top right), 43; **AUSTRALIAN INFORMATION SERVICE** 17 (Left), 19, 21 (Centre left, Top centre right, Bottom centre right), 24, 36 (Top right, Bottom left), 38 (Top left), 42, 44, 45, 51 (Top right, Centre left and right), 54, 57, 58, 62 (Top, Bottom left), 63; **AUSTRALIAN NEWS AND INFORMATION BUREAU** 49 (Top left and right), 51 (Bottom), 61, 62 (Bottom right); **ARNOLDS BALINS** 21 (Bottom right); **BENGUELA RAILWAY CO.** 98, 152 (Bottom); **BRAZILIAN CONSULATE, TORONTO** 160, 177, 189 (Top), 191 (Bottom), 199 (Bottom), 213 (Top), 217, 227 (Top and Bottom right), 231 (Bottom); **BRITISH AIRWAYS** 9, 114 (Centre left); **P. CITRON** 49 (Bottom), 227 (Bottom left), 229 (Right); **D.H. COLLINS** 181 (Top); **COMMONWEALTH INSTITUTE** 99 (Bottom left), 133, 149 (Top left), 155 (Bottom); **IAN CUNNISON** 131, 132 (Top left and right); **DE WYS INC.** 12 (Left), 105 (Top), 156; **CAROL DONOHUE** 71, 75, 77 (Centre), 80 (Top right); **F.A.O. PHOTO, ITALY** 181 (Bottom left), 206 (Bottom), 208, 210; **GHANA INFORMATION SERVICES** 134, 141, 147; **RAPHO GUILLAMETTE** 89 (Left), 155 (Top); **RICHARD HARRINGTON** 4 (Right), 35, 36 (Bottom right), 112 (Left), 114 (Bottom right), 179, 203, 237, 245 (Bottom); **HOA-QUI** 93, 100 (Bottom right), 152 (Top); **CLIFFORD JANOFF** 129 (Bottom), 148, 152 (Centre); **DAVID JONES** 101, 136 (Top right), 139, 150 (Bottom), 201 (Bottom), 204 (Top), 235 (Top); **KEYSTONE** 158; **VICTOR LAST, Geographical Visual Aids, Wiarton, Ontario.** 144; **LEHNERT AND LANDROCK** 149 (Bottom); **JOHN LUCKHURST** 201 (Top), 233, 235 (Bottom), 232; **M. MACDONALD** 88; **MAGNUM PHOTOS** 100 (Top left); **L. MASON** 178, 231 (Top); **BRIAN McDERMOT** 129 (Top); **TOMISLAV MILINUSIC** 161, 195 (Right), 196, 198, 230; **MILLER SERVICES** 89 (Right), 123, 238; **DR. RICHARD P. MOMSEN** 4 (Left), 164, 168, 183, 195 (Left), 199 (Top), 214, 215, 216 (top), 234; **NASA** 173; **NEW ZEALAND GOVERNMENT TOURIST OFFICE** 68-69 (Top left, centre, and right, Bottom left and right), 73 (Top), 74 (Left), 77 (Top and Bottom), 79 (Left, Bottom right); **NEW ZEALAND HIGH COMMISSION, OTTAWA** 74 (Right), 86; **NEW ZEALAND INFORMATION SERVICE** 78, 79; **NEW ZEALAND MEAT PRODUCERS BOARD** 73 (Bottom); **NIGERIAN FEDERAL MINISTRY OF INFORMATION** 150 (Top); **O.A.S.** 194, 224; **JACK OLDHAM** 135; **PICTORIAL PRESS** 146 (Left), 153; **POPPERFOTO** 103, 104 (Right), 105 (Bottom), 114 (Top left and right), 120 (Top), 127 (Left), 136 (Bottom), 149 (Top right), 169 (Bottom), 175, 181 (Bottom right), 204 (Bottom left), 206 (Top), 211 (Top), 223; **RADIUS PHOTO SERVICE, Calgary** 169 (Top), 176, 191 (Top), 209, 211 (Bottom), 212, 213 (Bottom), 221, 241, 245 (Top); **REX FEATURES** 100 (Bottom left); **ROYAL GEOGRAPHICAL SOCIETY** 91, 114 (Bottom left); **RST INTERNATIONAL METALS LTD.** 146 (Right); **VALERIE SEATON** 120 (Centre), 132 (Bottom); **PAT SHEA, Geographical Visual Aids, Wiarton, Ontario.** 1, 16, 17 (Right), 21 (Bottom left), 23, 29, 31, 33, 41, 64, 68-69 (Bottom centre), 83; **SHELL INTERNATIONAL PETROLEUM CO. LTD.** 102 (Top left and right), 104 (Left), 119; **MISS N. STRICKLAND** 185; **E.A. SULLIVAN** 21 (Top); **PAUL THOMAS** 163, 166, 187, 207, 216 (Bottom), 219, 222, 226; **UNESCO** 12 (Right), 99 (Top left and right, Bottom right), 100 (Top right), 102 (Bottom), 112 (Right), 117 (Top), 121 (Bottom), 124, 127 (Right), 159; **UNITED BRANDS CO.** 204 (Bottom right); **ROBIN J.S. WHITE** 165, 189 (Bottom), 229 (Left); **GEOFFREY WILLIAMS** 136 (Top left), 137, 145 (Top and Bottom right).

ACKNOWLEDGMENTS

Sketch on page 172 is by William Papas.
Page 172 From: *Drought,* Andrew Salkey, Oxford University Press, London, 1966, page 53.

Page 90: Figure 4.1 redrawn from J. Desmond Clark, ed., *Proceedings of the Third Pan-African Congress on Prehistory,* Chatto and Windus, London, 1957, page 103.
Page 90: Figure 4.2 redrawn from Jan Vansina, *Kingdoms of the Savanna,* The University of Wisconsin Press, Madison ® 1966 by the Regents of the University of Wisconsin, page 39.
Page 93: Figure 4.4 redrawn from Basil Davidson, *A History of West Africa 1000-1800,* Longmans, London, 1965, and from Basil Davidson, *East and Central Africa to the late Nineteenth Century,* Longmans, London, 1967.

INDEX

TABLE OF MEASURES			
		1 m²	= 1.196 square yards
			= 10.764 square feet
1 m	= 1.093 yards	1 km²	= 0.386 square mile
	= 3.281 feet	1 ha	= 2.471 acres
	= 39.370 inches	1 m³	= 28.377 bushels
1 km	= 0.621 mile	1 t	= 1.1 ton